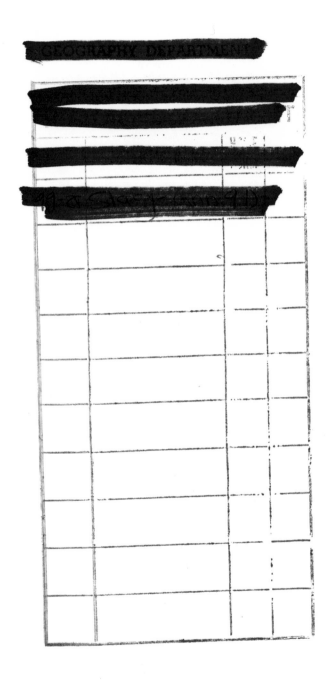

PERSPECTIVES

CANADIAN

GEOGRAPHY

About the cover: The bridge on the cover is an artist's view of the Confederation Bridge connecting New Brunswick with Prince Edward Island. The bridge represents both a bridge to our past—the first conference leading to Confederation in 1867 was held in Charlottetown, PEI, September 1864—and a link to our future, as illustrated by the view of the Earth from space. For more about the bridge, see section 3.5, page 106.

Photo: Courtesy of Fuji Graphic Systems Canada, Inc. Designed by Elliot Sinclair Communications and VISU*TronX*.

PERSPECTIVES

CANADIAN

GEOGRAPHY

WAYNE ANDREW • **GRAHAM DRAPER**

IRWIN
PUBLISHING

Toronto, Canada

Canadian Cataloguing in Publication Data
Draper, Graham A
  Perspectives : Canadian geography

Includes index.
ISBN 0-7725-2757-1

1. Canada – Geography. I. Andrew, Wayne. II. Title.

FC75.D72 1999   917.1   C99-931073-9
F1011.3.D72 1999

Design and artwork: VISU*TronX* Services
Irwin Editorial: Norma Pettit, Tim Johnston, Susan Berger, Linda Taylor, Heather Murray, Lisa Brant, Martin Ahermaa, Colborne Communications

The authors and publisher would like to thank the following reviewers for their insights and suggestions.
Kristen Barbour, Teacher, Ottawa, Ottawa-Carleton District School Board
Keith Lickers, Field Officer, Toronto, Aboriginal Reviewer
Dan Robinson, Teacher, Welland, District School Board of Niagara
Andrea Saunders, Teacher, Toronto, Toronto Catholic District School Board
Pamela Schwartzberg, Coordinator, Learning for a Sustainable Future, Toronto
Poul Von Bulow, Teacher, Mississauga, Peel District School Board

We acknowledge the financial support of the Government of Canada through the Book Publishing Industry Development Program (BPIDP) for our publishing activities.

Published by
Irwin Publishing
325 Humber College Blvd.
Toronto, ON M9W 7C3

Printed and bound in Canada
2 3 4   03 02 01 00 99

This book is manufactured by Transcontinental Printing, using environmentally safe soy-based inks on 60lb. Pristine Opaque, a paper containing 50% recovered material, including 20% postconsumer waste.

CONTENTS

TO THE STUDENTS

Perspectives: Canadian Geography is a book that explores the geography of Canada, an extraordinary thing to attempt in just one volume. As the second largest country in the world, home to over 30 million people whose ethnic roots span the globe, this country is far too big to fit such a small package. And so, we–the authors–have not tried to include everything in this book. Instead, we have tried to draw an outline of this country–in a sense, to make a sketch map of the place–to help you to see how the pieces fit together. We are counting on you to fill in the details through your own investigations, both in this course and as you go through life.

In drawing the "sketch map" of Canada we have organized our ideas around five strands or themes.

Methods of Geographic Inquiry: At its core, Geography is about exploring and investigating the world. Tools to help us do this include mapping, interpreting a variety of graphic sources of information, and applying Geographic Information Systems (GIS). The skills to use these tools are an important part of this book.

Space and Systems: Geographers work to understand the space that is the surface of the Earth and the natural and human systems that operate upon it. An understanding of these two types of systems and how they are interconnected will shape many of your activities.

Human-Environment Interactions: People affect the natural environment, and the natural environment influences people. To really know our country, we must recognize these interactions and try to understand their consequences through research and investigation.

Global Connections: An important part of understanding Canada is to recognize its role in the world setting. Many of the problems and issues facing Canadians now, and in the future, are ultimately international issues and must be approached from that perspective. Geography is uniquely equipped to help you understand Canada's global connections.

Understanding and Managing Change: We will be better equipped to face the future if we understand the process of change and how we can use change to create better futures. Geography approaches change from local, regional, national, and international perspectives and explores ideas that can help to improve relationships between people and their physical environment.

These strands will help you to organize the great many ideas that are presented in this book, and those that you will encounter in other settings.

Perspectives has special features that will help you understand the topics. Each content **topic** is covered in two- to four-page sections that have been clearly numbered. The sections begin with a listing of the **Major Concepts** covered in the topic. Special ways of presenting information, such as **Fact Files**, **Case Studies** and **Definitions**, are used to point out interesting or important details. Terms in **bold type** are defined in the Glossary. Wherever possible, information and ideas are shown in visual ways to make using the book more appealing. **Questions and Activities** are provided with each topic to help you check your understanding of the ideas and to encourage you to apply your new understandings. Each units ends with a **Changing Perspectives** section. These sections include questions or activities that ask you to speculate about future developments. They also include suggestions for skills that you will find useful in your studies. The **Appendices** at the end of the book includes a physical and political map of Canada and illustrations of commonly used topographical maps symbols. You will want to refer to both frequently. As well, the Appendices contains six additional statistical tables of information on Canada's ecozones.

Good luck with your geographic studies and developing your perspectives of Canada!

Wayne Andrew

Graham Draper

UNIT 1 CANADA'S NATURAL ENVIRONMENT

Physical systems that contribute to Canada's geographic differences are the subject for this unit. The interaction of physical systems produces regional patterns that we see as ecozones.

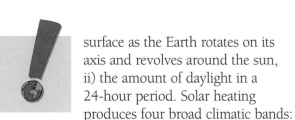

GLOBAL ENVIRONMENTS

Major Concepts
- Solar heating
- Climatic bands
- Natural regions

The amount of solar energy received at different areas of the Earth's surface plays an important role in creating the Earth's distinctive environments. Two factors help determine how much **solar radiation** is received to heat the surface: i) the angle of the sun's rays to the surface as the Earth rotates on its axis and revolves around the sun, ii) the amount of daylight in a 24-hour period. Solar heating produces four broad climatic bands:

- **tropical** conditions are found within 15° of latitude of the equator where the climate is always moist and hot;
- **desert** conditions are found in broken bands roughly centred on the Tropics of Cancer and Capricorn where the descending air is dry;
- in **temperate** areas, generally between 30° and 60° of latitude, the weather is mild and changeable;
- cold and dry **polar** climates exist at high latitudes where the heat of the sun is far less strong than elsewhere on Earth.

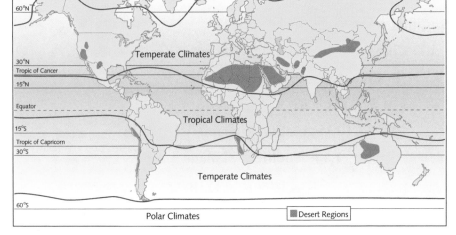

Figure 1.1.a The broad pattern of climates on Earth

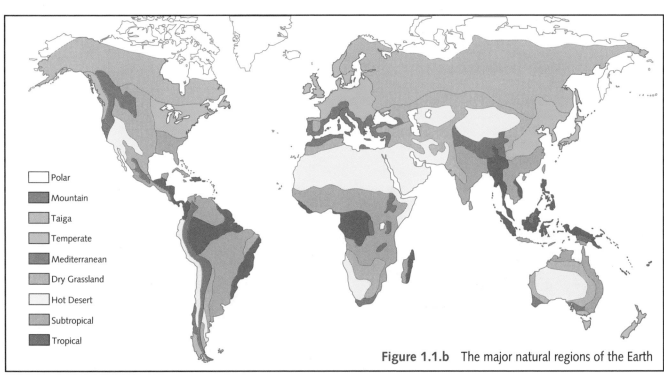

- Polar
- Mountain
- Taiga
- Temperate
- Mediterranean
- Dry Grassland
- Hot Desert
- Subtropical
- Tropical

Figure 1.1.b The major natural regions of the Earth

Region	Temperature	Precipitation	Vegetation
Polar	extreme cold year round	little precipitation	mosses or lichen, or no vegetation
Mountain	temperatures vary with elevation	tremendous variation	vegetation varies with altitude
Taiga	long, cold winters and short, warm summers	little precipitation	coniferous forests
Temperate	cool winters and warm to hot summers	moist, with the moisture coming throughout the year	deciduous forests
Mediterranean	hot summers and mild winters	dry summers and moist winters	open woodland and shrubs
Dry Grassland	hot summers and cold winters	sparse rainfall, mostly in summer	grasses
Hot Desert	hot days and cool nights	little rainfall	cacti and other drought-adapted plants
Subtropical	hot summers, mild winters	marked wet and dry seasons	lush forests
Tropical	hot temperatures year round	heavy precipitation, no dry season	tropical evergreen forests

Figure 1.1.c Characteristics of the Earth's natural regions

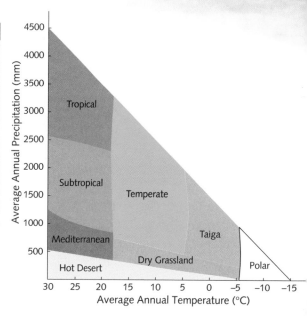

Figure 1.1.d A theoretical classification of environments

QUESTIONS & ACTIVITIES

1. In Figure 1.1.a, the four broad climate bands circle the Earth in lines parallel to the equator. Explain why this is the case. (You may want to look at Figure 1.7.b on page 21.)

2. a) Suppose you were able to walk across North America from the Beaufort Sea to the Gulf of Mexico. (Use an atlas to locate these two bodies of water.) Using Figure 1.1.b, produce an organizer to show, in order, the environments that you would encounter in your walk.

   b) Complete a similar organizer as though you walked across Africa from the Mediterranean Sea to the Cape of Good Hope. Create a list for the crossing of Asia from the Laptev Sea to the Bay of Bengal.

   c) What similarities are there in your three lists of environments? What are the differences?

   d) Suggest some reason to explain why there are differences in the lists of environments.

3. Examine the names for the regions shown in Figures 1.1.b and 1.1.c. These are commonly used names for classifying natural regions. Justify the use of these names.

4. a) Look at the triangular chart in Figure 1.1.d. Why are temperature and precipitation appropriate **variables** to use when studying the physical conditions of regions on Earth?

   b) In several sentences, put into words the main ideas that this chart illustrates.

5. In North America (including Central America), the land is used in this way:

arable and crop land	13 %
grazing land	16 %
forest land	32 %
other land	39 %

   a) Make a pie graph of this information.

   b) Decide which of the environmental regions discussed on these pages would be most associated with each type of land use.

6. Research and identify an example of vegetation from each of the environments identified in Figures 1.1.b and 1.1.c. Sketch the vegetation example, or photocopy the picture, or scan and print it. Organize the examples in a comparison chart with the following headings: Region, Vegetation Example, General Location Where Example Is Found.

ECOZONES OF CANADA

Major Concepts

- Ecozones
- Characteristics of ecozones
- Multi-faceted regions

Canada's immense size and broad physical diversity make it very hard to investigate the whole of the country. One way of simplifying conditions, to make studying them more manageable, is to break the physical environment into zones with the same characteristics. These regions can then be used as a basis of investigation. This book uses the concept of **"ecozones"** for the study of the environment.

Ecozones are not based on a single physical characteristic, such as landforms, but on combinations of characteristics: landforms, climate characteristics, soils and vegetation, wildlife, and patterns of human activity. They are **multi-faceted** regions. Fifteen ecozones have been defined in Canada. Because of the size of the land, each one of these ecozones has considerable variation. Ecozones have been broken into smaller divisions, each with fewer variations in characteristics than the larger ecozone.

Canada has 15 ecozones

- that have been divided into 47 **ecoprovinces**
- that are further subdivided into 177 **ecoregions**
- that can be broken into 5395 **ecodistricts**.

There are also 5 maritime ecozones around Canada.

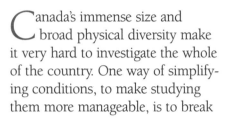

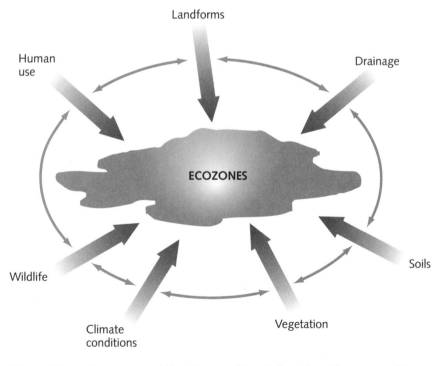

Figure 1.2.a Ecozones are defined by a variety of physical and human conditions. Using ecozones to study the land helps us understand the interconnections among natural and human systems and to see that humans are an essential part of the Earth's **ecosystem**, rather than separate from it.

Words that are based on landform features:
Cordillera
Plain
Shield

Words that are based on climate characteristics:
Arctic
Maritime

Words that are based on vegetation:
Tundra
Mixed-wood
Montane
Prairie
Taiga
Boreal

Words that are based on geographic location:
Northern Pacific
Southern Hudson Bay
Atlantic

Figure 1.2.b Terms used in ecozone names

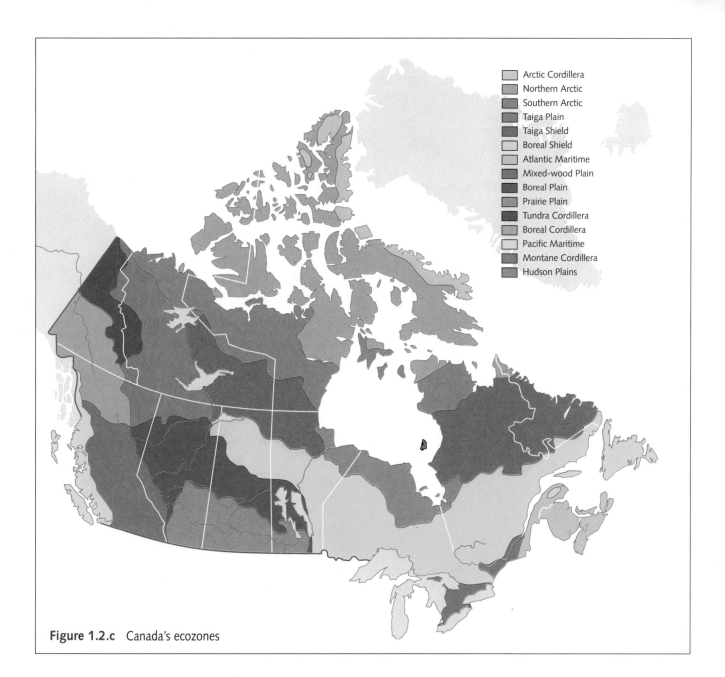

Figure 1.2.c Canada's ecozones

Legend:
- Arctic Cordillera
- Northern Arctic
- Southern Arctic
- Taiga Plain
- Taiga Shield
- Boreal Shield
- Atlantic Maritime
- Mixed-wood Plain
- Boreal Plain
- Prairie Plain
- Tundra Cordillera
- Boreal Cordillera
- Pacific Maritime
- Montane Cordillera
- Hudson Plains

ECOZONE	LANDFORMS	VEGETATION	CLIMATE
Arctic Cordillera	Mountainous highlands	Non-vegetated; some shrub/herb arctic tundra	Extremely cold, dry arctic
Northern Arctic	Plains and hills	Herb-lichen arctic tundra	Very cold, dry arctic
Southern Arctic	Plains; some interior hills	Shrub/herb/heath arctic tundra	Cold, dry arctic
Taiga Plain	Plains; some foothills	Open woodland; shrub lands and wetlands	Cold, semi-arid subarctic to moist boreal
Taiga Shield	Plains; some interior hills	Open woodlands; some arctic tundra and lichen heath	Moist, cold boreal to cold, semi-arid, subarctic
Boreal Shield	Plains; some interior hills	Conifer and broadleaf boreal stands	Cold, moist boreal
Atlantic Maritime	Hills and coastal plains	Mixed broadleaf and conifer stands	Cool, wet temperate maritime
Mixed-wood Plain	Plains; some interior hills	Mixed broadleaf and conifer stands	Cool to mild boreal
Boreal Plain	Plains; some foothills	Conifer and broadleaf boreal stands	Moderately cold, moist boreal
Prairie Plain	Plains; some foothills	Short and mixed grasslands; aspen parkland	Cool, semi-arid
Tundra Cordillera	Mountainous highlands	Alpine and arctic tundra	Cold, semi-arid, subarctic
Boreal Cordillera	Mountainous highlands; some hills and plains	Boreal; some alpine tundra and open woodland	Moderately cold, moist montane
Pacific Maritime	Mountainous highlands; some coastal plains	Coastal, western and mountain hemlock	Very wet, mild, temperate maritime
Montane Cordillera	Mountainous highlands and interior plains	Mixed vegetation; conifer stands to sage-brush fields	Moderately cold, moist montane to arid
Hudson Plains	Plains	Wetlands, arctic tundra and some conifer stands	Cold, semi-arid subarctic and cold boreal

Figure 1.2.d The physical characteristics of Canada's ecozones

Figure 1.2.e A protected wetland area on Lake Scugog, Ontario, in the Mixed-wood Ecozone.

Figure 1.2.f Looking from the Boreal Plain Ecozone just west of Rocky Mountain House, Alberta, to the Montane Cordillera Ecozone

QUESTIONS & ACTIVITIES

1. Draw a bar graph to show the number of ecozones, ecoprovinces, ecoregions, and ecodistricts in Canada.
2. Explain why the use of multi-faceted regions such as ecozones is more helpful in understanding the physical environment of Canada than regions defined by only one characteristic.
3. Figure 1.2.b lists various terms that are used in the names of the ecozones. Using dictionaries and other reference sources, including the glossary in this book, write definitions in your own words for:
   taiga
   cordillera
   boreal
   prairie
   maritime
   montane
   Add to the list any other terms used in the ecozone names that you cannot define easily.
4. a) Using the map in Figure 1.2.c, describe the overall geographic pattern of the 15 ecozones in Canada.
   b) Here are some possible factors that might be important in creating the geographic pattern of ecozones. Which three do you think are most important? Write a paragraph defending your choices.

   the Atlantic Ocean
   the flat interior plains
   distance north of the equator
   the Pacific Ocean
   the western mountains
   the Great Lakes

5. Figure 1.2.d lists some physical characteristics of each of the ecozones. For you personally, which ecozone is most appealing as a place to live? Which one is least appealing? Give reasons for your choices.
6. Environment Canada maintains Internet sites and produces other materials to inform Canadians about ecozones. Access this information and determine the ecoprovince that you live in. List typical examples of landforms, vegetation, and wildlife found in the area. Prepare a report that includes a map and your lists of examples.
7. Compare the characteristics of ecozones. Using two notebook pages, put these headings at the top of the pages: Ecozone, Landforms, Climate, Soils, Vegetation, Wildlife, Human Activity. In the left-hand column, list the 15 ecozones. As you work through this unit, add information to your chart. Use descriptive words and diagrams as well as statistics. Sketches and diagrams should be used where appropriate.

LANDFORMS IN CANADA

Major Concepts

- Landforms
- Topographic maps
- Contour lines

Many of the popular images of Canada have to do with its **landforms**, from the towering peaks of the Rockies to the level plains of Saskatchewan to the highlands of Cape Breton. While these landforms help to shape our national identity, they also help to shape the ecozones of the country.

Canada's landforms can be grouped into three main types. The Canadian **Shield** takes up about one-half of the country's total area, and underlies the rest of the continent, acting like a foundation for the other areas. These ancient rocks are some of the oldest found on Earth. To the south, west and north of the Shield, pressing up against it, are somewhat younger, flat-lying **plains**. The sedimentary rocks of the plains were deposited in shallow seas during Precambrian times.

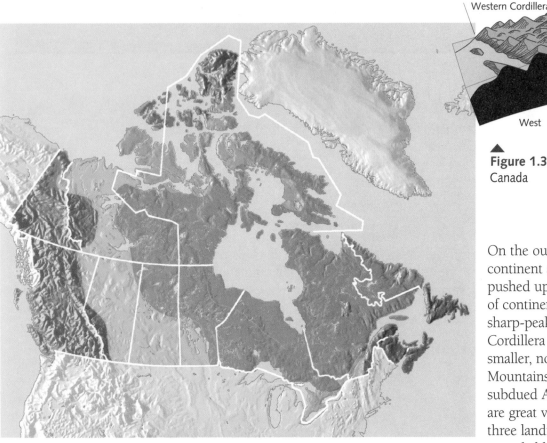

Figure 1.3.b A cross-section of Canada

On the outside edges of the continent are **mountains** pushed up by the movements of continental plates. The high, sharp-peaked mountains of the Cordillera are in contrast to the smaller, northern Innuitian Mountains and the older, more subdued Appalachians. There are great variations within these three landform types, leading to remarkably diverse environments within the country.

Western Cordillera	Canadian Shield
Interior Plains	Appalachian Mountains
Innuitian Mountains	Great Lakes-St. Lawrence Lowlands
Hudson Bay Lowlands	Arctic Lowlands

Figure 1.3.a The shape of the land in Canada

Figure 1.3.c A typical scene from the Interior Plains

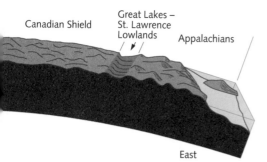

Canadian Shield

Great Lakes –
St. Lawrence
Lowlands   Appalachians

East

Figure 1.3.d The main landform types in Canada

1.3 continues ▶

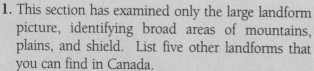

QUESTIONS & ACTIVITIES

1. This section has examined only the large landform picture, identifying broad areas of mountains, plains, and shield. List five other landforms that you can find in Canada.
2. Suppose, like Terry Fox, you decided to run across Canada, from St. John's, Newfoundland, to Victoria, British Columbia. Using Figure 1.3.a, identify those parts of your journey that would be most difficult and demanding, and those parts that would be easiest.
3. What does the presence of Hudson Bay tell you about the shape of the surface of the Canadian Shield?
4. The cross-section of Canada in Figure 1.3.b shows the location of some of the continent's landform regions.
   a) Which region is the oldest?
   b) Which region was formed most recently?
   c) Which region can be described as composed of worn and rounded mountains?
   d) Which region is composed of flat-lying layers superimposed one on the other?
   e) In which region do you live?
5. What is the surface of the land like in each of the three landform areas identified in Figure 1.3.d?
6. Figures 1.3.e, 1.3.g, and 1.3.i on the next pages are portions of topographic maps showing three different landform types. Answer the following questions for each map, using the topographic map information below the maps and the list of topographic map symbols in the Appendices for help when necessary.
   a) What is the scale? What is the contour interval?
   b) What are the highest and lowest elevations on the map?
   c) What landforms are shown in this area?
   d) In what ways have human activities been influenced by the landforms?
   e) What landform type is shown by this map? Give reasons for your answer.
7. Construct a cross-section of the Bow River valley near Lake Louise following the directions in Figure 1.3.j.

1.3 cont'd

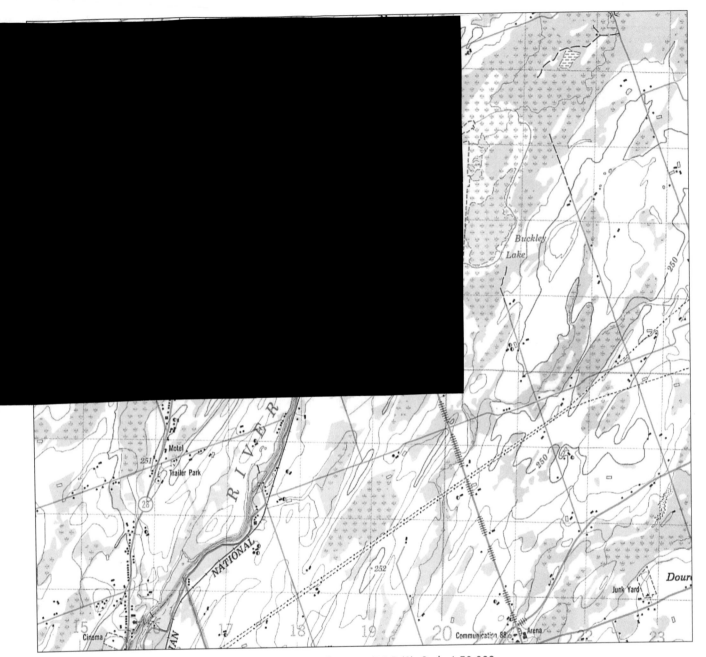

Figure 1.3.e North of Peterborough, Ontario, topographic map (31 D/8). Scale 1:50 000

The **map scale** gives the relationship between the size of actual features on the Earth's surface and the same features as shown on a map. Scales are usually expressed in three ways:

i. a fraction or ratio, such as 1:50 000. This ratio means that 1 cm on the map represents 50 000 cm on the ground.

ii. a statement scale, such as 1 cm to 0.5 km, which means that 1 cm on the map represents 0.5 km on the ground

iii. a line scale, like this:

500   0   500   1000   2000 meters

Scale

Figure 1.3.f Map scales

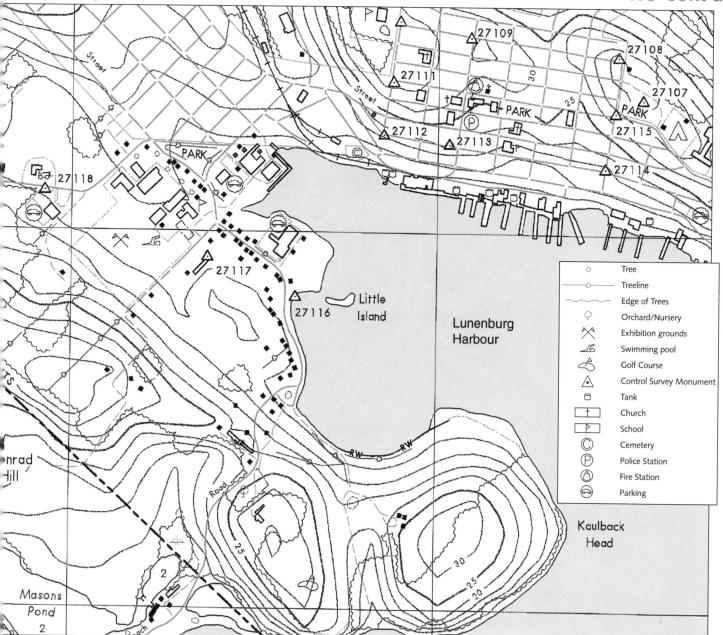

Figure 1.3.g A portion of a Lunenburg, Nova Scotia, topographic map (21 A/8 Sheet 10 44 3500 64 300). Scale: 1:10 000

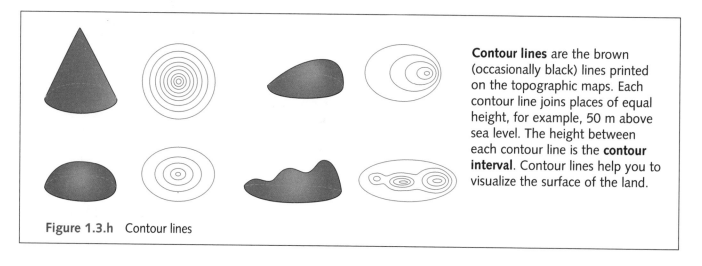

Contour lines are the brown (occasionally black) lines printed on the topographic maps. Each contour line joins places of equal height, for example, 50 m above sea level. The height between each contour line is the **contour interval**. Contour lines help you to visualize the surface of the land.

Figure 1.3.h Contour lines

Figure 1.3.i A portion of a Lake Louise, Alberta, topographic map (82 N/8). Scale 1:50 000

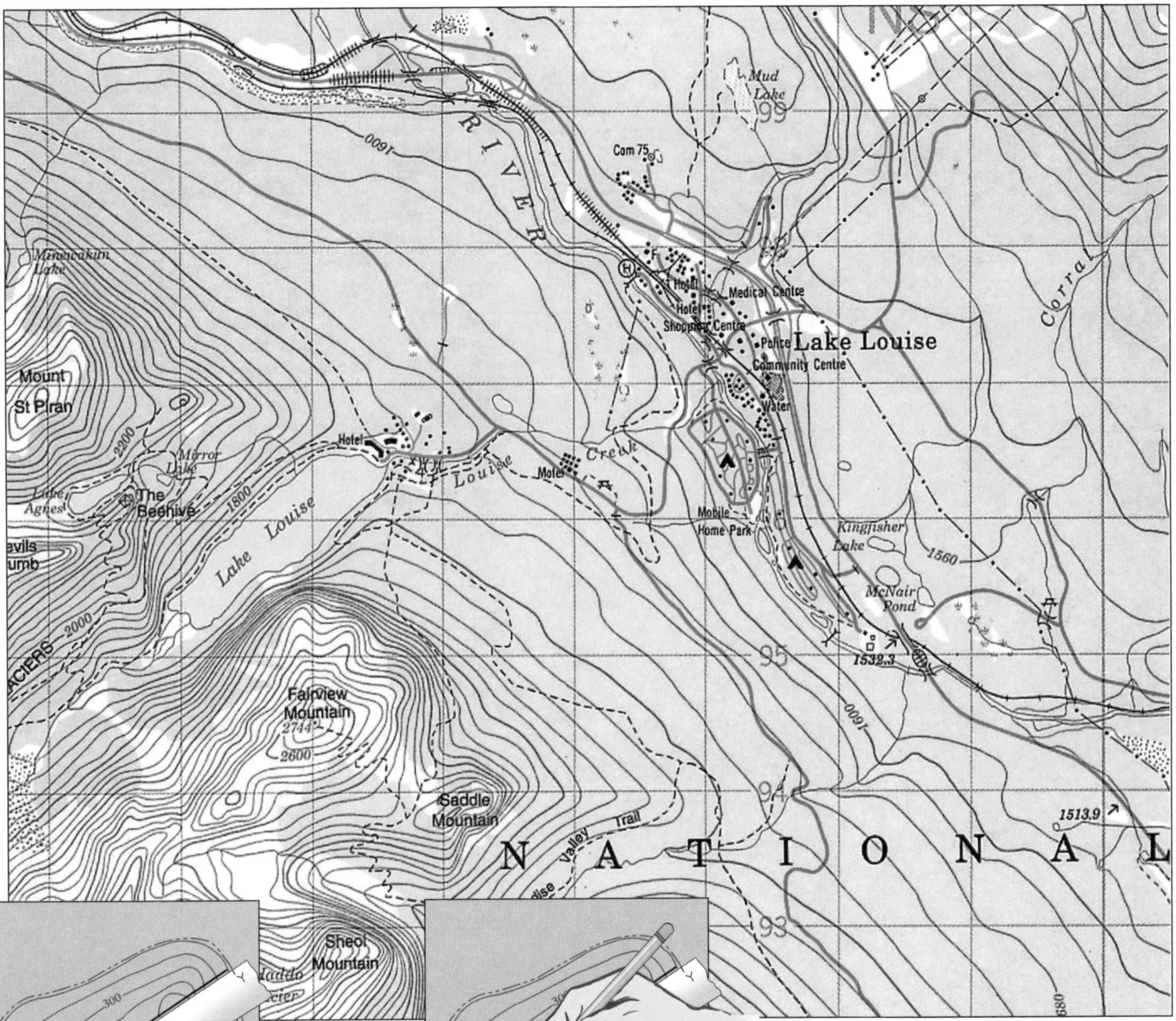

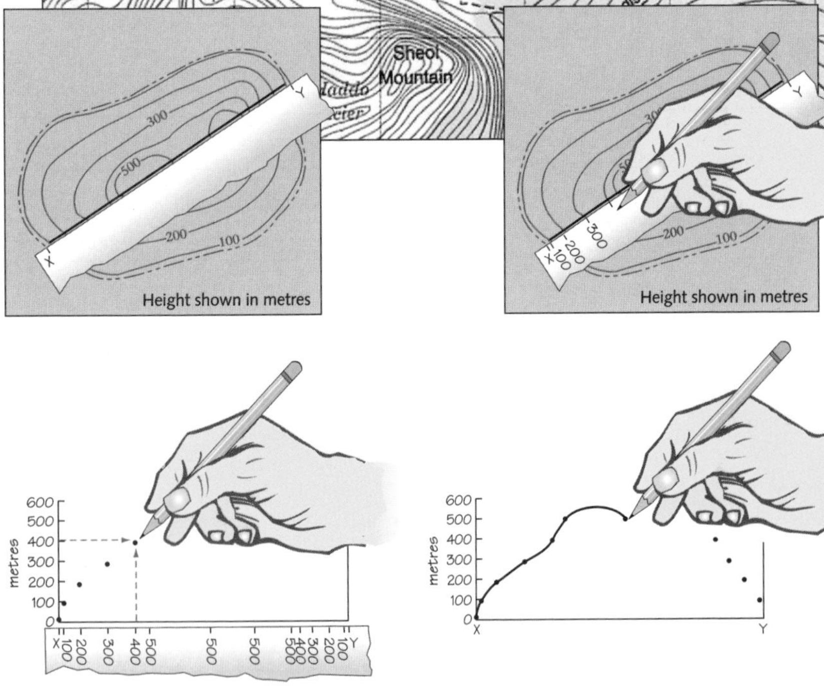

Height shown in metres

Height shown in metres

Figure 1.3.j Drawing cross-sections

A **cross-section** shows the relief of the land as though a huge knife had cut the land so that the heights were exposed from the side.

1) Lay a straight-edged piece of paper along Figure 1.3.i where you want the cross-section to be.
2) Tick off and label where each contour line touches your paper.
3) Move your paper to the bottom of a frame the same width as your cross-section, with appropriate heights marked on the vertical axis. Plot dots at the correct elevations.
4) Join the dots.

BUILDING THE LAND

Major Concepts
- Plate tectonics (continental drift)
- Earth's convection flows
- Geologic time

The surface of the land that we now see in Canada has been constructed over a very long time by global **tectonic forces**. **Plate tectonics** are the forces that move the six major separate **plates** (large slabs of crustal rock) that make up the Earth's crust. Plate tectonics, earlier known as **continental drift** has been particularly important in building the landforms of North America.

Convection within the Earth's **mantle** (the denser, slowly moving rock below the Earth's crust) brings flows of hot, less-dense materials upwards towards the **lithosphere**, the crust. These materials begin to cool and flow sideways as colder rock is brought down into the mantle to replace them. Places on the surface above the rising magma—the melted or molten rock—are zones where the plates are moving apart (Figure 1.4.b). The Mid-Atlantic Ridge (Figure 1.4.c) is one such area. Here the magma is creating new ocean floor as the plates separate. Those places where surface materials are being pulled into the mantle are zones where plates are colliding. The friction that is created as one plate is pulled below another melts the rock, forming volcanoes (Figure 1.4.e) and causing earthquakes. Other times when plates collide they crumple up along their leading edges, helping to create mountains. The edges of the plates are areas of great instability in the Earth's crust.

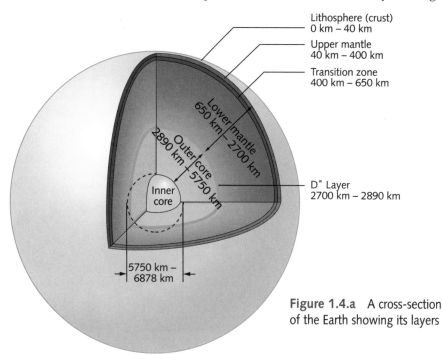

Lithosphere (crust)
0 km – 40 km

Upper mantle
40 km – 400 km

Transition zone
400 km – 650 km

Lower mantle
650 km – 2700 km

Outer core
2890 km – 5750 km

Inner core

D" Layer
2700 km – 2890 km

5750 km –
6878 km

Figure 1.4.a A cross-section of the Earth showing its layers

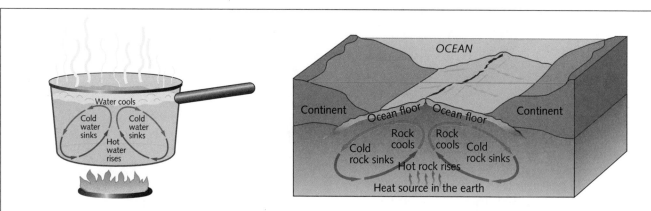

Figure 1.4.b Convection currents provide the "power" that moves the continental plates about on the Earth's surface.

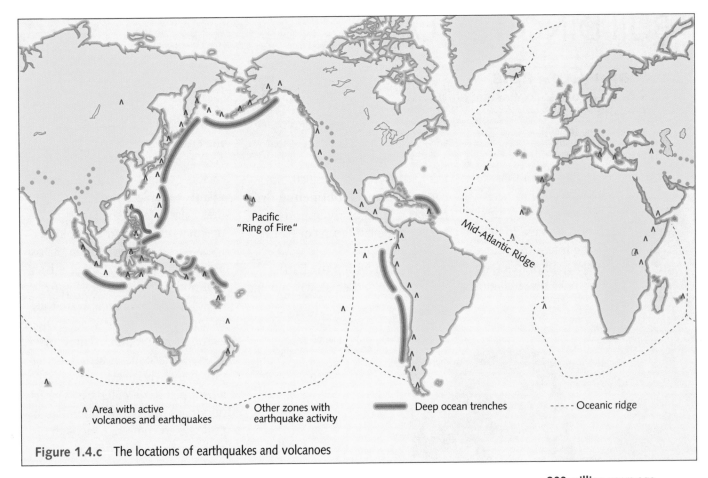

Figure 1.4.c The locations of earthquakes and volcanoes

Legend:
∧ Area with active volcanoes and earthquakes
• Other zones with earthquake activity
▬ Deep ocean trenches
- - - - Oceanic ridge

Map labels: Pacific "Ring of Fire", Mid-Atlantic Ridge

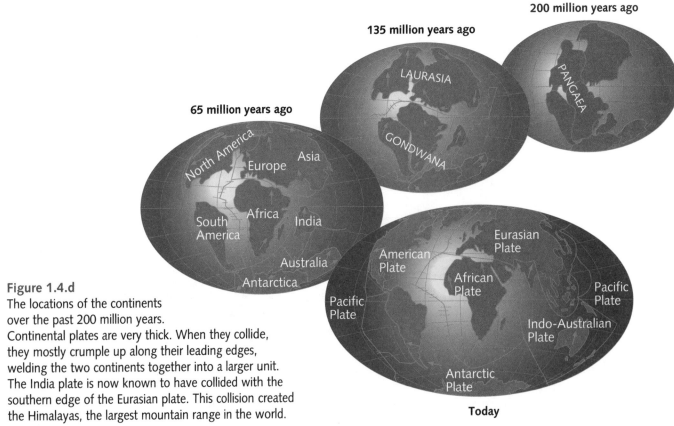

Figure 1.4.d
The locations of the continents over the past 200 million years.
Continental plates are very thick. When they collide, they mostly crumple up along their leading edges, welding the two continents together into a larger unit. The India plate is now known to have collided with the southern edge of the Eurasian plate. This collision created the Himalayas, the largest mountain range in the world.

Globe labels:
200 million years ago — PANGAEA
135 million years ago — LAURASIA, GONDWANA
65 million years ago — North America, Europe, Asia, Africa, India, South America, Australia, Antarctica
Today — American Plate, Eurasian Plate, African Plate, Pacific Plate, Indo-Australian Plate, Antarctic Plate

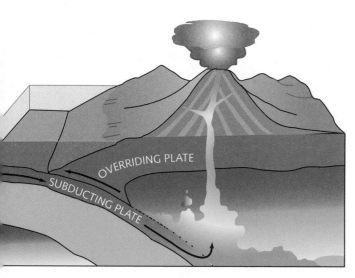

Figure 1.4.e This is a **subduction zone**, a place where one plate slides below another, creating volcanoes on the surface.

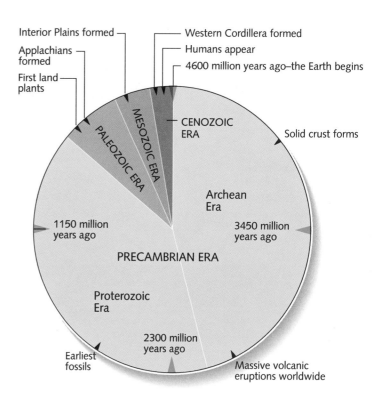

Figure 1.4.f The geological age of the Earth

QUESTIONS & ACTIVITIES

1. List the parts of the Earth's interior from the centre to the crust.
2. In your own words, explain how continental plates are moved around on the Earth's surface.
3. Use the information in Figures 1.4.b and 1.4.e to explain why there are chains of mountains on the west side of Canada.
4. The edges of the Pacific Ocean have been dubbed the "Ring of Fire." Is this an appropriate label? Give reasons for your answer.
5. The west side of Canada has seen a great deal of tectonic activity over the past 100 million years, including mountain building, volcanoes, and earthquakes. Using Figure 1.4.c, explain why the east side of the continent has not had the same instability.
6. There are two types of collision zones between plates—when a continental plate meets an oceanic plate (such as the west side of North America) and when two continents collide. Figure 1.4.d shows that two continents collided to the north of India.
   a) Which plates are colliding?
   b) In what directions are the plates moving?
   c) What features are created by this collision?
7. Based on Figure 1.4.d, what changes will take place in the locations of the continents over the next 50 million years or so?
8. Examine Figure 1.4.f. For each of the four eras, list:
   a) the length of time in millions of years
   b) significant geological events
   c) significant life forms that emerged
9. Suppose you had a friend in another part of the world who had never heard of continental drift or plate tectonics. Write a one-page letter to your friend summarizing these ideas.

SHAPING THE LAND: WATER AND ICE

Major Concepts

- Weathering
- Erosion by water
- Glaciation

While plate tectonic activity was building the landforms of the continent, other forces were wearing away at the surface. Running water and moving ice have been important processes in shaping the landforms of Canada.

Water is a principal agent in **weathering**. Weathering breaks rocks down into smaller pieces. It does this in two ways:

- mechanically, as when water freezes in a crack, expands and puts pressure on the rock; and
- chemically, as when water dissolves some of the chemicals in rock.

The small, weathered pieces of rock are able to be carried more easily by moving water, ice, or wind, a process called **erosion**.

Glaciation

Glaciation has left a visible impression on the landscape of Canada. Geologically speaking the last glacial

Canada Centre for Remote Sensing, Natural Resources Canada

Figure 1.5.b This Landsat image shows sediments being flushed into the Strait of Georgia by the Fraser River. Metropolitan Vancouver occupies much of the delta that has built up at the mouth of the river.

period occurred very recently, and landforms are still well defined. **Glaciers** are created when more snow falls in a winter than can be melted during the following summer. As snow builds up or accumulates, the increasing mass causes the lower layers to change into ice. When the mass of ice and snow becomes thick enough, gravity pulls the frozen mass downwards or outwards. Glaciers have two distinct zones: the **zone of accumulation** where the amount of snow added is more than the amount melted, and the **zone of ablation**, where melting is taking place. Glaciers flow from the accumulation zone to the ablation zone.

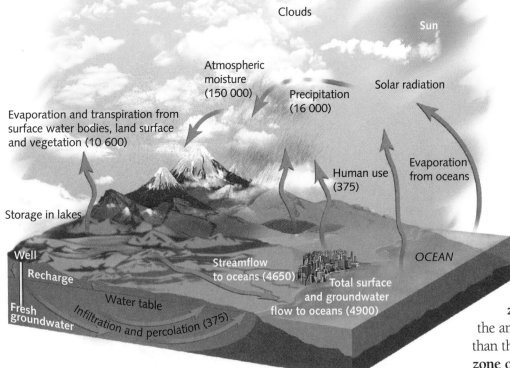

Clouds

Sun

Atmospheric moisture (150 000)

Precipitation (16 000)

Solar radiation

Evaporation and transpiration from surface water bodies, land surface and vegetation (10 600)

Human use (375)

Evaporation from oceans

Storage in lakes

Well

Recharge

Streamflow to oceans (4650)

OCEAN

Water table

Total surface and groundwater flow to oceans (4900)

Fresh groundwater

Infiltration and percolation (375)

Figure 1.5.a The **hydrologic cycle** illustrates the processes that allow water to be used as weathering and erosion mechanisms. The volumes are those calculated for the United States in millions of cubic metres of water per day.

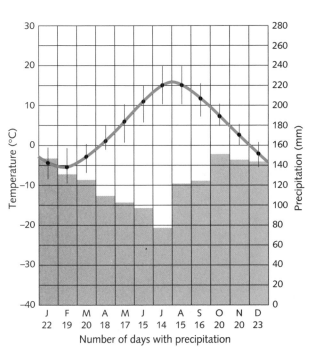

Figure 1.6.d A climate graph for St. John's, Newfoundland

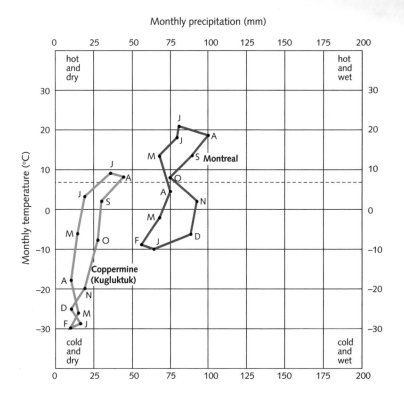

Figure 1.6.e A **hythergraph** showing Monteal, Quebec, and Coppermine (Kugluktuk), Nunavut

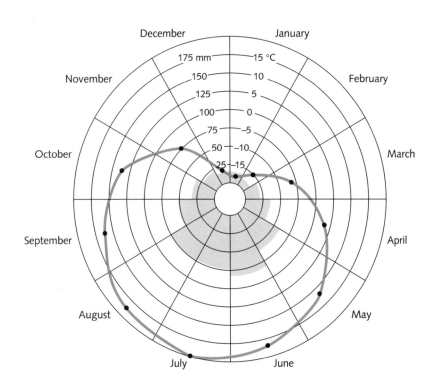

Figure 1.6.f A circular climate graph for Winnipeg, Manitoba

Toronto	J	F	M	A	M	J	J	A	S	O	N	D
Daily Max. Temp. (°C)	–3	–2	4	12	18	24	27	26	21	14	7	0
Daily Min. Temp. (°C)	–11	–11	–5	1	6	11	14	13	9	4	–1	–7
Daily Mean Temp. (°C)	–7	–6	–1	6	12	17	21	20	15	9	3	–4
Precipitation (mm)	46	46	57	64	66	69	77	84	74	63	70	66
Measurable Prec. (days)	14	12	13	12	11	11	10	11	10	12	13	15
Vancouver	J	F	M	A	M	J	J	A	S	O	N	D
Daily Max. Temp. (°C)	6	8	10	13	16	19	22	22	18	14	9	6
Daily Min. Temp. (°C)	0	1	3	5	8	11	13	13	10	6	3	1
Daily Mean Temp. (°C)	3	5	6	9	12	15	17	17	14	10	6	4
Precipitation (mm)	150	124	109	75	62	46	36	38	64	115	170	179
Measurable Prec. (days)	19	16	16	13	12	10	7	7	9	15	19	21

Figure 1.6.g Climate data for Vancouver, British Columbia, and Toronto, Ontario

Figure 1.6.h Most North Americans have become adept at dealing with our climate.

QUESTIONS & ACTIVITIES

1. Compare the climate characteristics of four different parts of the country using a comparison chart. The areas to compare are: Vancouver Island, Baffin Island, southern Ontario, and the island of Newfoundland. Record January and July average temperatures and total annual precipitation.

2. a) Write a description of the patterns of temperatures in Canada.

   b) Describe the precipitation pattern.

3. a) Using the climate data in Figure 1.6.g, construct a climate graph for Toronto, a circular climate graph for Vancouver, and a hythergraph that shows both locations.

   b) Which type of graph did you find easiest to construct? Why?

   c) Which type of graph displays the climate patterns most effectively? Explain your answer.

4. In your opinion, which part of Canada has the best climate? Give reasons for your choice by comparing its climate to other places in Canada. Write a one-page report giving your opinion and your evidence.

5. Environment Canada maintains an Internet site that includes detailed climate data for many places in Canada at http://www.cmc.ec.gc.ca/climate/normals. Access the climate data for your community or a community in Canada that interests you. Construct a graph that shows the climate patterns in this community.

CLIMATE SYSTEMS: GLOBAL FACTORS

Major Concepts

- Latitude as a climate factor
- Global wind systems
- Ocean currents

Energy from the sun drives the processes that create climate. The sun heats the Earth's surface and its atmosphere, but the unequal heating of the Earth's surface means that some parts of the world are hotter than others. This unequal heating sets into motion global wind systems and ocean currents that carry heat across the globe. The climate that Canada experiences is caused by its northern location, the air masses that cross the land, and the ocean currents that move past our three coastlines.

Figure 1.7.a Weather systems can produce dramatic scenes like this ice-coated landscape.

FILE

FACT

	Latitude Zone	Temperature (°C)	Cloud Cover (%)
North of 0°	80–90	−23.6	62
	70–80	−15.9	66
	60–70	−7.2	65
	50–60	0.5	60
	40–50	7.5	53
	30–40	14.0	46
	20–30	20.4	43
	10–20	25.4	47
	0–10	25.5	52
South of 0°	0–10	24.8	52
	10–20	23.3	48
	20–30	18.8	48
	30–40	13.5	54
	40–50	8.7	66
	50–60	1.2	72
	60–70	−11.0	76
	70–80	−29.5	65
	80–90	−47.9	54

The average temperature and percentage cloud cover for each ten degrees of latitude

Equal Amount of Solar Energy

Figure 1.7.b Solar energy in the polar regions is utilized much less than at the equator because of the slanted surface of the Earth. The slanted surface causes the energy to be spread over larger areas.

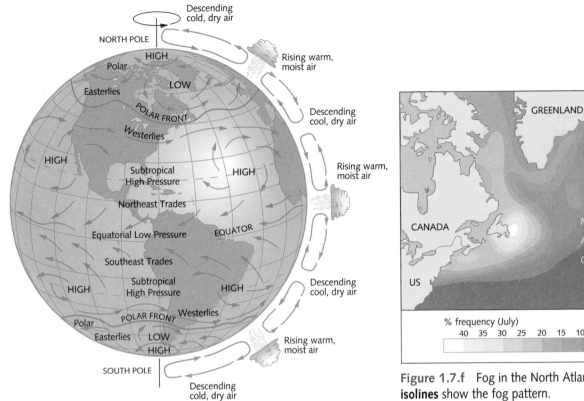

Figure 1.7.c The global winds

Figure 1.7.f Fog in the North Atlantic Ocean. The **isolines** show the fog pattern.

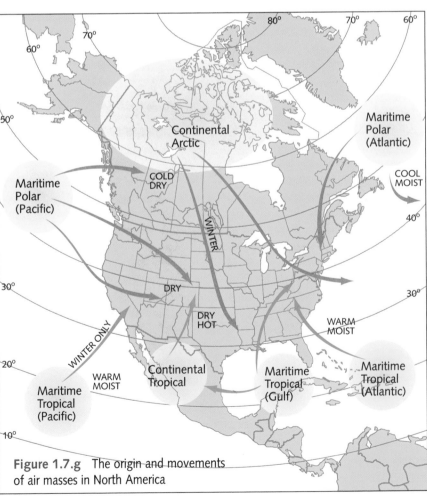

Figure 1.7.d Winds blowing across water produce dramatic forces.

Air Mass	Conditions	Temperature
Continental Arctic	• very cold, dry	–40°C
Maritime Polar	• cool, moist	4°C
Continental Tropical	• warm, dry	24°C
Maritime Tropical	• warm, moist	24°C

Figure 1.7.e The air masses of North America

Figure 1.7.g The origin and movements of air masses in North America

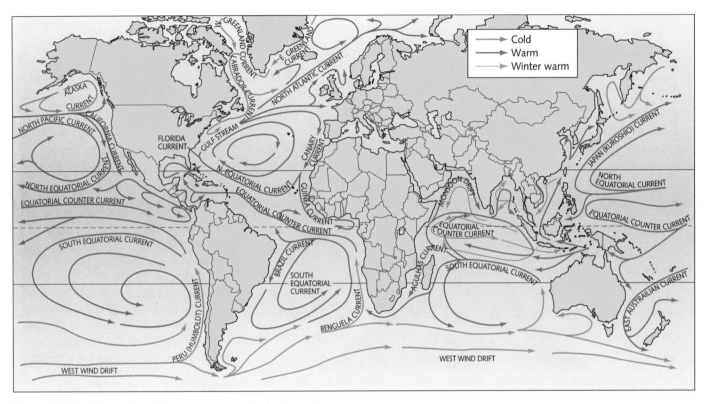

Figure 1.7.h The main surface ocean currents of the world

QUESTIONS & ACTIVITIES

1. Explain why temperatures are much warmer in the equatorial zone than at the poles.

2. Examine the data in the Fact File. Suggest explanations for the following observations:
   a) the 80°S-90°S zone is much colder than the 80°N-90°N zone,
   b) the lowest amounts of cloud cover are between 20° and 30°.

3. a) Using Figure 1.7.c, identify the climate conditions associated with rising air. Identify the climate conditions associated with descending air.
   b) Generally, in which direction are winds blowing between 0° and 30°, both north and south of the equator? between 30° and 60°?
   c) List the winds that affect the climates of North America.

   d) Which of these winds would be considered the **prevailing** (most common) winds?

4. a) In Figures 1.7.e and 1.7.g, you will notice that the names of the air masses have to do with where they originate. Why do you suppose this is so?
   b) Explain how the origin of an air mass affects the climate of other locations, such as when a Continental Arctic air mass affects southern Canada.

5. Figure 1.7.h shows the global pattern of ocean currents. What factors do you suppose help to create this pattern?

6. a) Use Figure 1.7.f to identify the foggiest part of the east coast of Canada.
   b) Why is this area so foggy? (Hint: look at the pattern of ocean currents in this area in Figure 1.7.h.)

CLIMATE SYSTEMS: LOCAL FACTORS

Major Concepts

- Elevation as a climate factor
- Mountain climates
- Influence of lakes and oceans

In Climate Controls: Global Factors, we saw how the unequal distribution of the sun's energy is instrumental in setting up a global wind system and a global pattern of ocean currents. While wind systems and ocean currents help shape the overall climate of a place, local conditions also influence the climate patterns. This section will deal with how physical conditons, particularly mountains, cause wide variations in climate, often over a short distance. Nearby water bodies also cause local climate variations. This type of climate control is influential in a country like Canada with many large lakes and three oceans for margins.

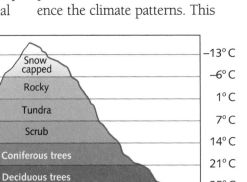

Figure 1.8.a The effect of **altitude** on climate. Mountains influence climate much the same as latitude influences climate. The higher up you go, whether in latitude or in altitude, the colder the climate is. As altitude increases, the air is less acted on by the pull of gravity and air pressure is reduced, leading to expansion of the air mass. This expansion results in cooling: in dry air at a rate of 1°C for every 100 m of altitude, and in moist air at a rate of 0.6°C/100 m.

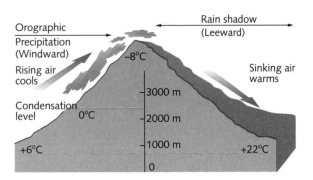

Figure 1.8.b A mountain barrier often creates a rain shadow on its leeward side (side away from the wind).

DEFINITIONS

Orographic (relief) precipitation—precipitation caused by rapid condensation in moist air that cools as it rises up the side of a mountain

Rain shadow—As air starts to sink down on the leeward side of a mountain barrier, the air becomes warmer and can hold more moisture. As well, the air lost moisture in the form of precipitation as it rose up and over the mountain. Low precipitation regions on the leeward side of a mountain barrier are called rain-shadow regions.

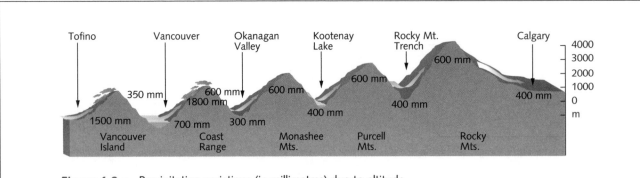

Figure 1.8.c Precipitation variations (in millimetres) due to altitude

Impact of nearby water bodies on climate

Large water bodies have two effects on nearby land.

Moisture

Water bodies are sources of moisture. Onshore winds and breezes carry the moisture over the land, making the climates there more moist.

Moderation

Water bodies make the climate of the land more moderate. Because of the mixing that takes place between the colder deep water and the warmer surface water, water bodies heat up much less quickly than the land in summer and cool down more slowly in winter. The water bodies then influence the climate of the land by making it cooler in summer and warmer in winter.

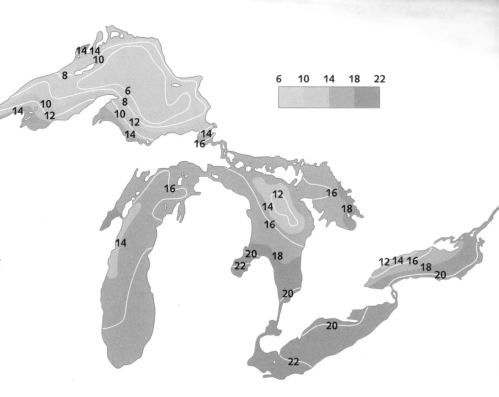

Figure 1.8.d Surface temperatures on the Great Lakes in July

QUESTIONS & ACTIVITIES ?

1. a) In your own words, explain how altitude affects climate.
   b) In what parts of Canada would altitude be a significant climate control?
2. Refer to Figure 1.8.b.
   a) What is **condensation**?
   b) Why does condensation occur on the windward side of a mountain?
   c) Why do you think the leeward side of a mountain is said to be a rain shadow?
3. Figure 1.8.c shows the changes in altitude in the western mountains, and the differences in precipitation. Explain why the precipitation is heavier on the Coast Range than on the Rocky Mountains.
4. a) Using Figure 1.8.d, list the Great Lakes in order of temperature, from warmest to coolest.
   b) Besides latitude, what are other factors that might influence the surface temperatures of the lakes?
   c) In what ways do the Great Lakes affect the climate of the areas nearby?

d) With the prevailing westerly winds in this area, where will the impact of the lakes be most pronounced?
5. What parts of Canada have the most rainfall? On an outline map of Canada, draw a vertical bar graph for each of the following places to show the number of days that rainfall is received. Locate the bottom of the bar as close as possible to the location of the place. The scale for the bars is 1 cm = 10 days of rain.

Vancouver, British Columbia	156 days
Edmonton, Alberta	70
Regina, Saskatchewan	59
Winnipeg, Manitoba	72
Toronto, Ontario	99
Montreal, Quebec	114
Saint John, New Brunswick	124
Halifax, Nova Scotia	125
Charlottetown, Prince Edward Is.	124
St. John's, Newfoundland	156

SOILS

Major Concepts

- Components of soil
- Soil formation factors
- Leaching

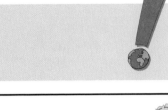

Without soil, much of the life on Earth could not exist. Soil is a complex mixture of particles that have come from weathered rocks, living and dead organisms, water, and air (Figure 1.9.d). The factors that affect the development of soils are:

- the parent rock or original rock; this material determines the size of the grains that give the soil its texture and its basic chemical properties;
- plants and animals that recycle nutrients and add organic material to the soil;

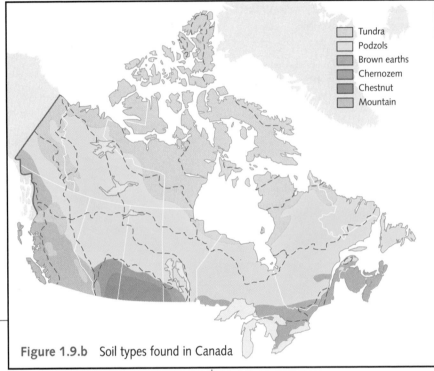

Tundra
Podzols
Brown earths
Chernozem
Chestnut
Mountain

Figure 1.9.b Soil types found in Canada

The "O" horizon is a thin layer of humus (dead leaves and other organic matter)

The "A" horizon is topsoil, dark and rich in humus

The "B" horizon is subsoil, poorer in humus, but rich in minerals from the topsoil

The "C" horizon is unfertile, weathered rock fragments

The "D" horizon is unfertile, solid bedrock

Figure 1.9.a A generalized soil profile. A **soil profile** is a vertical section from the surface of the ground to the bedrock. In a well-developed soil profile there are five layers or horizons. However, the size and number of the horizons vary with the type of soil and the conditions under which it developed.

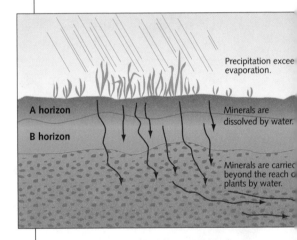

Precipitation excee evaporation.

A horizon

B horizon

Minerals are dissolved by water.

Minerals are carrie beyond the reach o plants by water.

Figure 1.9.c The process of leaching removes minerals from the soils. Water from precipitaiton dissolves the minerals and washes them through the layers.

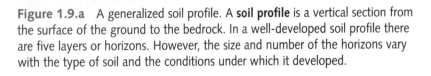

| | Inorganic Material | | | Organic Material | | |
| pebbles | sand and gravel | silt and clay | water | air | nutrients | leaves, humus, insects, etc. |

Figure 1.9.d The components of soil

	Soil Type	Chief Natural Vegetation	Character of Soil	Major Land Uses
	Tundra	tundra	shallow, waterlogging frequent, slow organic decay	largely unused
	Podzols	coniferous forest (boreal)	thin acidic humus, A horizon often leached	forestry, general livestock farming where appropriate
	Brown earths	deciduous or mixed forests	rich in humus, slightly acidic	livestock farming, vegetables, field crops, potatoes
	Chernozem	tall grasslands	humus-rich A horizon, thick profile	grains, field crops
	Chestnut	short grasslands	humus-rich A horizon, thinner profile	wheat
	Mountain	wide variation due to relief	usually thin or non-existent because of steepness of slope, some pockets of good soil, such as river deltas	forestry and agriculture where conditions permit

Figure 1.9.e Characteristics of soil types in Canada

- climate, since heat and moisture are factors that help determine the rates at which the parent rock is weathered and organic materials decay;
- the slope of the land, because on a steep slope, materials are eroded quickly and soils are not able to build up. Soils pile up on flat land or in hollows;
- time determines the amount of soil built up.

Soils are classified according to the type of vegetation that they support.

QUESTIONS & ACTIVITIES

1. Explain why the first sentence of this unit is a true statement.
2. Define these terms using the text, the glossary or a dictionary:
   - weathering
   - parent rock
   - leaching
   - inorganic material
   - soil profile
3. a) Using Figure 1.9.a, explain why the fertility of soils is easily lost through overuse or erosion.
   b) Farmers and gardeners try to improve the fertility of their soils by adding animal manure or peat moss. In what ways do these materials improve soil?
4. a) Examine Figure 1.9.b. Describe the distribution of soil types in Canada.
   b) Make two points of comparison between the pattern of soil types and the vegetation patterns shown in Figure 1.10.a.
   c) Using the climate information in section 1.6, make two points of comparison between the pattern of soil types and climate patterns.
5. What causes leaching in soils? Where might it be a problem?
6. Figure 1.9.d shows the materials that make up soils. Explain why inorganic materials are necessary in soils. Why is air necessary in soils?
7. Suppose global warming raised the average temperature of Canada by several degrees. Does that mean that more of Canada will be able to support agriculture and food production? Explain your answer. using information about soils and soil formation.

VEGETATION CHARACTERISTICS

Major Concepts

- Natural vegetation
- Growing season
- Permafrost

"Natural vegetation" refers to the community of plants that existed in an area before the impact of humans. Without the influence of people, vegetation achieves a stability that allows it to remain largely unchanged for long periods of time. This occurs because the vegetation reaches a balance with the environment. The key environmental controls are heat, moisture, and minerals (available from the weathered bedrock).

Many parts of Canada no longer have completely natural vegetation. Humans have removed unwanted species, introduced new plant vari-

eties, and modified the natural environment in such ways that natural species have had to make significant adaptations. Except in

the most remote areas of Canada, most of the vegetation that we find today includes plant varieties shaped by human activities.

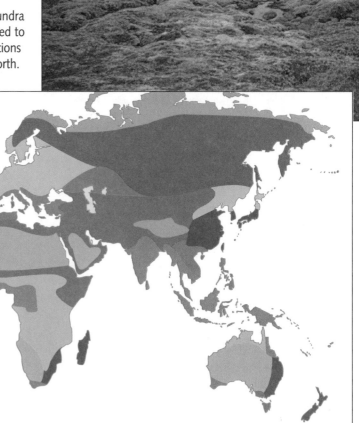

Figure 1.10.b Tundra vegetation is adapted to the cold, dry conditions of the Canadian North.

Tundra
Coniferous Forest
Temperate Rain Forest
Prairie
Deciduous Forest
Semi-Arid Scrub
Mediterranean
Evergreen Forest
Tropical Forest
Grassland
Steppe Grassland
Monsoon Forest
Savanna Grassland
Desert

Figure 1.10.a General natural vegetation regions of the world

WILDLIFE IN CANADA

E cosystem is a term used to describe a group of living organisms that, along with their environment, form a self-regulating system through which energy and materials are transferred. Any analysis of the natural environment must connect the role of wildlife to the function of their particular ecosystem. Wildlife, or fauna, plays a critical role in recycling nutrients and energy to keep the ecosystem functioning.

At the broadest level, all living organisms can be classified into one of two groups: **autotrophs** and **heterotrophs**. Autotrophs manufacture their own food. These are the green plants. Heterotrophs obtain their food from the autotrophs, either eating them directly (herbivores), eating other heterotrophs (carnivores), or attacking the dead

a Food Chain

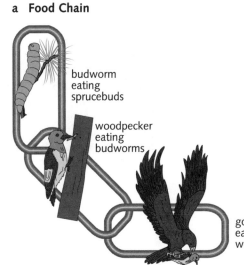

budworm eating sprucebuds

woodpecker eating budworms

goshawk eating woodpecker

b Food Pyramid

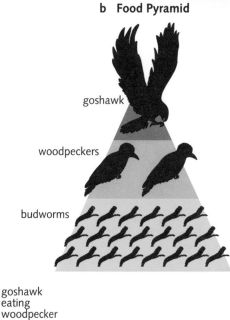

goshawk

woodpeckers

budworms

Figure 1.11.b A food chain and food pyramid

tissue of organisms (decomposers and scavengers). The sun's energy that the plants have captured is made available to all parts of the ecosystem by the work of fauna.

This set of relationships can be seen as a food web. Food webs are made up of a series of complex, interlocking food chains (Figure 1.11.b).

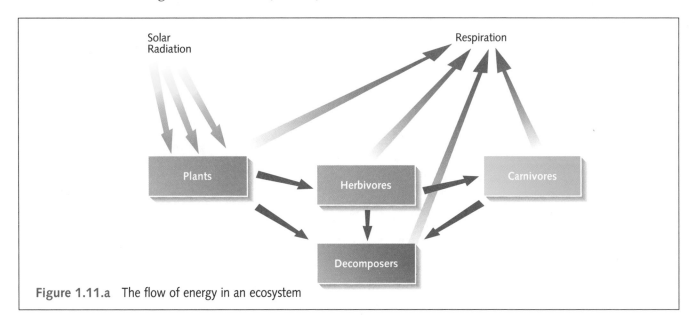

Solar Radiation

Respiration

Plants

Herbivores

Carnivores

Decomposers

Figure 1.11.a The flow of energy in an ecosystem

> *Changes and movements in the bird populations are not only the result of climatic changes but also of habitat changes, and those caused by the European settlers [1750–1850] are probably as great as any since the ice age. In many places, the face of the land has changed beyond all recognition.*

Richard Coomber,
The Living World of Canadian Birds

Figure 1.11.c The cougar is a carnivore near the top of the food chain.

Ecozone	Land Use Change				Hunting/ Trapping	Pollution[3]	Disease	Exotic Introductions[4]
	Agriculture	Forestry	Resource Development[1]	Other[2]				
Tundra Cordillera				●	●			
Boreal Cordillera			●		●			●
Pacific Maritime	●	●			●	●		●
Montane Cordillera	●	●	●		●			●
Boreal Plain	●	●	●	●	●	●		
Taiga Plain			●	●	●	●	●	
Prairie	●				●			●
Taiga Shield			●		●	●		
Boreal Shield		●	●		●	●		
Hudson Plains					●			
Mixed-wood Plain	●					●		●
Atlantic Maritime	●	●			●	●		●
Southern Arctic				●	●	●		●
Northern Arctic					●	●		
Arctic Cordillera			●		●	●		

[1] Includes larger dam construction, mining development
[2] Includes transportation corridors, seismic lines, power lines
[3] Includes oil, SO_2 gas, mine residues
[4] Includes consideration of birds and mammals only

Figure 1.11.d Current influences on Canadian wildlife

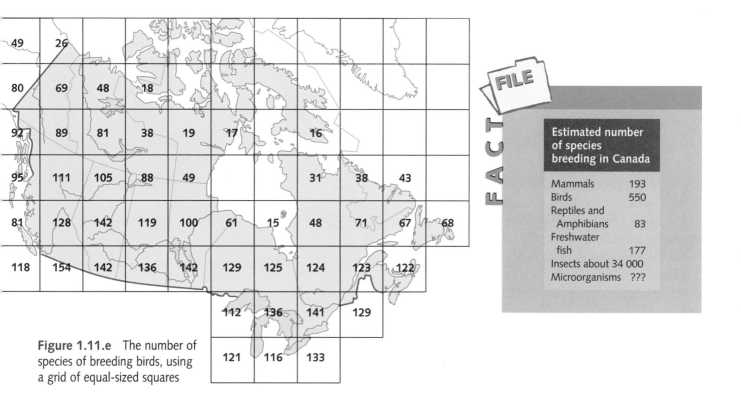

Figure 1.11.e The number of species of breeding birds, using a grid of equal-sized squares

FACT FILE

Estimated number of species breeding in Canada

Mammals	193
Birds	550
Reptiles and Amphibians	83
Freshwater fish	177
Insects about	34 000
Microorganisms	???

QUESTIONS & ACTIVITIES

1. Figure 1.11.a shows the energy cycle in nature. Suppose you were to remove, in turn, each of the four types of living organisms in the energy cycle. For each that is removed, explain what the impact would be on the energy cycle.

2. Why do the terms "food chain" and "food pyramid" seem to be appropriate for the relationships shown in Figure 1.11.b?

3. a) Notice in Figure 1.11.d the forces that are currently affecting wildlife in each of the ecozones. Explain why some ecozones, such as the Tundra Cordillera, have only a small number of forces while others, like the Boreal Plain, have many.

   b) In the future, which influences are likely to become more important? Which influences are likely to become less important? Explain your answers.

4. Estimates of the number of species breeding in Canada are given in the Fact File. For each category (except microorganisms) name two species and

indicate whether they are herbivores, carnivores, or decomposers.

5. a) Observe the pattern shown by the number of breeding species in Figure 1.11.e. Describe the pattern that you see in the map.

   b) What are some reasons that might account for this pattern?

   c) The far North is not included on the map. Based on the pattern that you have identified, how many species of birds do you suppose are breeding on Ellesmere Island in the high Arctic? Explain your answer.

6. Why is it important to identify and protect endangered species of wildlife in Canada and around the world?

7. What is Canada doing to protect species that are threatened by habitat loss, overhunting, pollution, and other events? Research this country's approach to protecting its wildlife and write a one-page report giving your findings.

DRAINAGE SYSTEMS

Major Concepts

- Runoff
- Drainage basins
- River flow

When rain falls or snow melts, water starts to run across the land. Some of it is used by plants, animals, or people. Some of it sinks into the ground and some of it evaporates. Surplus water on the surface starts to move into creeks and streams which flow into rivers. Rivers, generally, flow into lakes or oceans.

An area of land that supplies a river with its water is a called a **drainage basin**. Basins are separated by the high ground between individual river systems. In Canada, the Rocky Mountains are an important **drainage divide**, separating the rivers that flow west from those that flow north, east, and south.

Figure 1.12.b The parts of a drainage basin

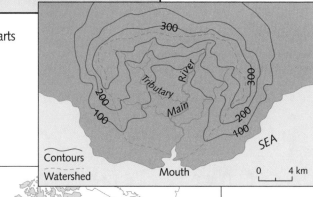

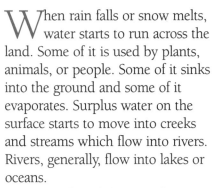

Continent	Precipitation rate	Evaporation rate	Runoff rate
Africa	20.8	16.6	4.2
Asia	32.1	19.2	12.8
Australia	6.4	4.4	2.0
Europe	7.2	4.2	3.0
North America	13.9	8.0	5.9
South America	29.4	19.0	10.4

Figure 1.12.a Water flow on the continents ('000 km³ of water per year)

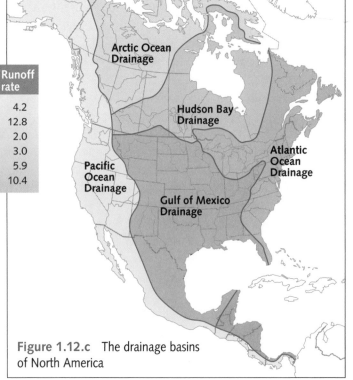

Figure 1.12.c The drainage basins of North America

FACT

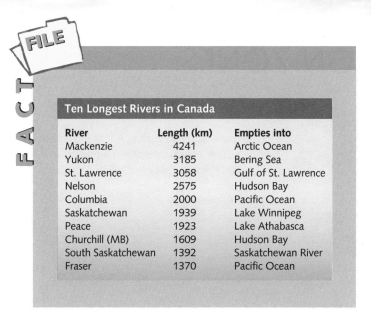

Ten Longest Rivers in Canada

River	Length (km)	Empties into
Mackenzie	4241	Arctic Ocean
Yukon	3185	Bering Sea
St. Lawrence	3058	Gulf of St. Lawrence
Nelson	2575	Hudson Bay
Columbia	2000	Pacific Ocean
Saskatchewan	1939	Lake Winnipeg
Peace	1923	Lake Athabasca
Churchill (MB)	1609	Hudson Bay
South Saskatchewan	1392	Saskatchewan River
Fraser	1370	Pacific Ocean

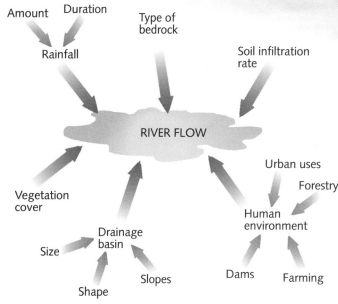

Figure 1.12.e Factors that will affect the volume of water in a river

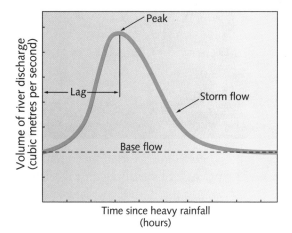

Figure 1.12.d A hypothetical flood hydrograph of a river. The **stream flow** (river flow or storm flow) of a river is the volume of water (e.g., the number of cubic metres per second) that flows by a given point along a river. The stream flow can vary with weather, the seasons, or other factors that affect water flow.

QUESTIONS & ACTIVITIES

1 **a)** List the drainage basins of North America.
  b) What determines the size and shape of the drainage basins?
  c) In which drainage basin is your community located? Describe your location in this drainage basin (such as near the mouth or on a tributary, etc.) using Figure 1.12.b as a guide.

2. On an outline map of Canada, label the ten longest rivers that are identified in the Fact File.

3. Examine the runoff rates for the continents given in Figure 1.12.a. What reasons can you suggest for the high runoff rates for Asia and South America? Why might Australia's rate be so low?

4. Figure 1.12.d shows how the volume of water in a river might change following a storm with heavy precipitation while Figure 1.12.e identifies some factors that affect the volume of a river. Select any three of the factors in Figure 1.12.e and produce a written explanation for how each would impact on stream flow. Be sure to offer explanations, not just a hypothesis, for the change in stream flow.

5. Using an atlas or a road map, determine the size and shape of the drainage basin for a small river in your part of the province or territory. Sketch a map to show the location of the river and its drainage basin, the approximate watershed line, the mouth of the river, and important communities. What are some threats or forces that potentially will change this river?

WETLANDS: TRANSITION ZONES

Major Concepts

- Transition zones
- Types of wetlands
- Succession of vegetation

Wetlands occupy the **transition zone** between permanently wet and generally dry environments. They have some characteristics of both wet and dry environments. These shared aspects mean that wetlands cannot be categorized solely as completely aquatic or terrestrial.

The presence of water for long periods of time gives wetlands their particular characteristics, especially high productivity and diversity.

Figure 1.13.b Succession of vegetation in a wetland. **Succession** is a process in which certain species of plants replace others.

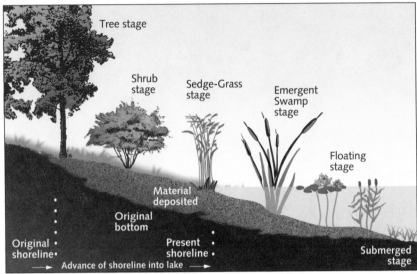

There is great variety in wetlands because of variations in water availability, the dominant plants, and location. Wetlands are found in Arctic tundra, prairie sloughs, along the shores of lakes and rivers, and on ocean coastlines. In Canada, the poor drainage because of the scouring of glaciers, has made the Canadian Shield an important wetland area.

Wetlands	Water Characteristics	Vegetation Characteristics
Marshes	sustained by water sources other than direct rainfall; have frequent flooding	dominated by reeds, rushes, sedges and grasses that grow partly in and partly out of the water
Swamps	saturated soils or flooding for most of the year	dominated by a single species of reed or grass, or are forested
Peatlands	soils are waterlogged due to high water table, slowing decomposition and allowing a build up of organic material	grasses, sedges and mosses that prefer acidic, poorly drained soils; trees grow in some peatlands
Floodplain Wetlands	water is supplied by the periodic flooding of rivers, such as at deltas	often support forests and thick grasses
Tidal Freshwater Swamps	regular inundations of tidal salt water into primarily fresh water areas	forests with the ability to grow in salty environments
Lakes	stable water level	reeds, sedges and grasses grow at the edges of the lakes where water levels are shallow
Estuaries	salt water environments where rivers empty into seas or oceans; the fresh water supplies nutrients and sediments	support a wide range of vegetation types depending on location and physical conditions
Artificial Wetlands	may include ponds, reservoirs, quarries, canals, aquaculture ponds, and so on	vegetation is often accidental to the intended use of the water body

Figure 1.13.a The forms of wetlands

FACT FILE

Wetlands in Canada
- Canada has 24% of all the world's wetlands.
- Fourteen percent of the country—127 million hectares—are classified as wetlands.
- Prairie wetlands support 50%-80% of the ducks in North America.
- Eighty percent of wetlands near major urban centres have been converted to agricultural or urban uses.

Photograph by Tim Hagen

Figure 1.13.c Wetlands at Long Point National Wildlife Area, on the shores of Lake Erie.

QUESTIONS & ACTIVITIES

1. a) Explain why wetlands are called transition zones.
   b) Transition zones occur in other contexts as well. In one or two sentences, point out how these places could also be considered transition zones:
      i. the foothills of the Rocky Mountains;
      ii. the suburbs of a large urban area;
      iii. a busy harbour.
2. Using Figure 1.13.a as an aid, brainstorm reasons for preserving wetlands. Brainstorm another list with reasons why wetlands should be developed into other uses. Based on your lists, are you for or against the development of Canada's wetlands?
3. a) According to Figure 1.13.b, what natural processes may cause wetlands to become smaller over time?

   b) What changes do you suppose will take place in the wildlife of a wetland as succession is taking place?
4. Examine Figure 1.13.c. Which letters in the photo refer to these characteristics of wetland areas?
   i.   standing water;
   ii. plants that grow partly in and partly out of water;
   iii. higher land that is not subject to standing water;
   iv. evidence of human uses of the wetlands.
5. In what ways might global warming affect wetland areas in Canada? Gather several sources of information on this topic and be prepared to share the details with your class members.

CONTINENTAL SHELVES

Major Concepts

- Continental shelves and continental slopes
- Origins of continental shelves
- Ocean depths

Continental shelves are part of the continents that are under water. Around all of the continents is a shallow margin of land beneath the water, averaging about 130 m in depth. The width of the continental shelves depends on the geologic activity that is happening there. Active margins are where two of the Earth's plates come together or are sliding past each other. On active margins the continental shelves are narrow and rugged, like the one on Canada's West Coast. On passive margins, where there is no nearby tectonic activity, the continental shelves are wide. Canada's eastern continental shelf is more than 300 km in width in some locations.

The continental shelves are important feeding and breeding areas for fish. Sunlight penetrates the shallow waters, providing the plants that thrive there with energy for **photosynthesis**. Also, nutrients are provided by the rivers that drain the land nearby. These conditions create environments that allow a tremendous variety of fish, plants, and animals to survive there.

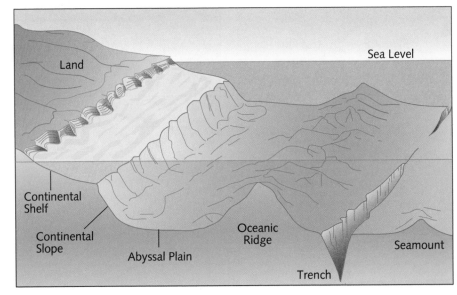

Figure 1.14.a The major geologic features of the ocean floor

The ocean depths drop off quickly from the continental shelf, in a sharp angle known as the **continental slope**. The continental slope plunges to the deep ocean bottom—the **Abyssal Plain**.

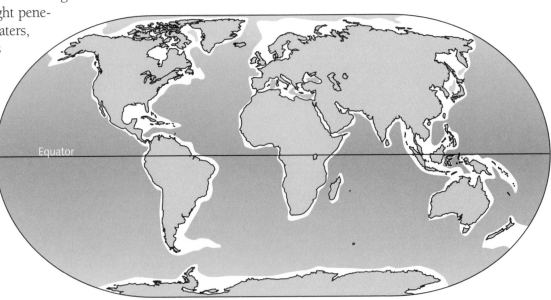

Figure 1.14.b The continental shelves are at the margins of all the continents

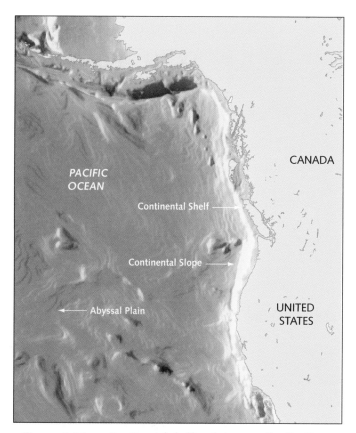

Figure 1.14.c Continental shelf and slope on the Pacific coast of Canada

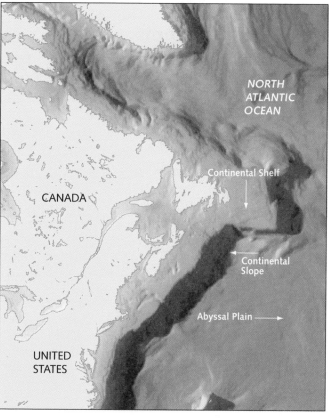

Figure 1.14.d Continental shelf and slope on the Atlantic coast of Canada

QUESTIONS & ACTIVITIES

1. Briefly explain how the width of continental shelves is directly related to plate tectonics.

2. Explain why "continental shelf" and "continental slope" are appropriate terms to use for these ocean features.

3. Use Figure 1.14.b for this exercise. Put a piece of clear plastic or tracing paper over the map of the world and trace the continents, *including the continental shelves*. Now cut out the continents of Africa and South America and fit them together like a jigsaw puzzle. Do these continental shapes fit closely enough to support the idea of plate tectonics or continental drift?

4. **a)** Describe the shape and width of the continental shelf on the Pacific coast of Canada.

   b) Describe the shape and width of the continental shelf on the Atlantic side of Canada.

   c) In what ways are these shelves the same? different?

5. **a)** How might the width of the continental shelves on Canada's coasts affect the economy on the different shores?

   b) How might the width of the shelves affect environmental concerns?

6. In your notebook, make a sketch to show the area of the East Coast of Canada. Include the Gulf of St. Lawrence, the continental shelf, and the continental slope. Shade and label your sketch.

THE NATURAL ENVIRONMENT IN ART AND LITERATURE

Major Concepts
- National identity
- National symbols
- Culture

The natural environment has been very important in shaping images that represent Canadian culture and identity. By simply looking at the symbols on our money we know that this is true. The importance of nature goes to the root of our national consciousness. It is the centre of what Canadians hold to be their true character. This character is expressed in a variety of forms, including in our art and literature. The figures that follow demonstrate how the natural environment, and its role in our national identity, has been expressed in words and images by Canadians.

Gift of Dr. and Mrs. J. Murray Spiers. McMichael Canadian Collection, 1969.20

Figure 1.15.b "Edge of the Forest" by Emily Carr, circa 1938. Oil on paper, 86.7 cm × 58.4 cm. Along with the Group of Seven painters, Carr presented Canada in a vibrant, colourful, new way.

PETER EMBERLEY

My name 'tis Pe-ter Em-ber-ley, as you may un-der-stand. I was born on Prince Ed-ward's Is-land near by the o-cean strand. In eigh-teen hun-dred and eigh-ty-four when the flo-wers were a bril-liant hue, I left my na-tive coun-ter-ie my for-tune to pur-sue.

2. I landed in New Brunswick in a lumbering counterie,
I hired to work in the lumber woods on the Sou-West Miramichi.
I hired to work in the lumber woods where they cut the tall spruce down,
While loading teams with yarded logs I received a deadly wound.

3. There's danger on the ocean where the waves roll mountains high,
There's danger on the battlefield where the angry bullets fly,
There's danger in the lumber woods, for death lurks sullen there,
And I have fell a victim into that monstrous snare.

4. I know my luck seems very hard since fate has proved severe,
But victor death is the worst can come and I have no more to fear.
And he'll allay those deadly pains and liberate me soon,
And I'll sleep the long and lonely sleep called slumber in the tomb.

5. Here's adieu to Prince Edward's Island, that garden in the seas,
No more I'll walk its flowery banks to enjoy a summer's breeze.
No more I'll view those gallant ships as they go swimming by
With their streamers floating on the breeze above the canvas high.

Collected and edited by Edith Fowke. First published by *The Penguin Book of Canadian Folk Songs*, Penguin Books Canada, 1973. Permission granted by The Writers' Union of Canada.

Northwest of Montreal, through a valley always in sight of the low mountains of the Laurentian Shield, the Ottawa River flows out of Protestant Ontario into Catholic Quebec. It comes down broad and ale-coloured and joins the Saint Lawrence, the two streams embrace the pan of Montreal Island, the Ottawa merges and loses itself, and the mainstream moves northeastward a thousand miles [1600 km] to the sea.

Nowhere has nature wasted herself as she has here. There is enough water in the Saint Lawrence alone to irrigate half of Europe, but the river pours right out of the continent into the sea. No amount of water can irrigate stones, and most of Quebec is solid rock. It is as though millions of years back in geologic time a sword had been plunged through the rock from the Atlantic to the Great Lakes and savagely wrenched out again, and the pure water of the continental reservoir, unmuddied and almost useless to farmers, drains untouchably away. In summer the cloud packs pass over it in soft, cumulus, pacific towers, endlessly forming and dissolving to make a welter of movement about the sun. In winter when there is no storm the sky is generally empty, blue and glittering over the ice and snow, and the sun stares out of it like a cyclops' eye.

All the narrow plain between the Saint Lawrence and the hills is worked hard. From the Ontario border down to the beginning of the estuary, the farmland runs in two delicate bands along the shores, with roads like a pair of village main streets a thousand miles long, each parallel to the river. All the good land was broken long ago, occupied and divided among seigneurs and their sons, and then among tenants and their sons. Bleak wooden fences separate each strip of farm from its neighbour, running straight as rules set at right angles to the river to form long narrow rectangles pointing inland. The ploughed land looks like the course of a gigantic and empty steeplechase where all motion has been frozen. Every inch of it is measured, and brooded over by notaries, and blessed by priests. …

Figure 1.15.a A portion of a traditional folk song of the Maritime provinces

Figure 1.15.c These are the first paragraphs of Hugh MacLennan's landmark novel *Two Solitudes* published in 1945

Figure 1.15.d A poem by Metis writer Marilyn Dumont, published in her book *A Really Good Brown Girl* in 1996

Not just a platform for my dance

this land is not
just a place to set my house my car my fence

this land is not
just a plot to bury my dead my seed

this land is
my tongue my eyes my mouth

this headstrong grass and relenting willow
these flat-footed fields and applauding leaves
these frank winds and electric sky

are my prayer
they are my medicine
and they become my song

this land is not
just a platform for my dance

Courtesy Roy Henry Vickers

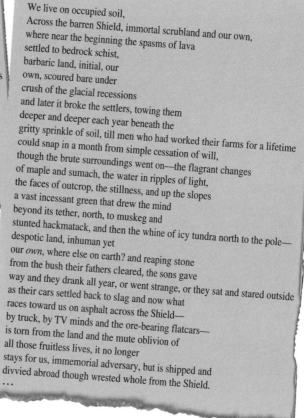

. . .
We live on occupied soil,
Across the barren Shield, immortal scrubland and our own,
where near the beginning the spasms of lava
settled to bedrock schist,
barbaric land, initial, our
own, scoured bare under
crush of the glacial recessions
and later it broke the settlers, towing them
deeper and deeper each year beneath the
gritty sprinkle of soil, till men who had worked their farms for a lifetime
could snap in a month from simple cessation of will,
though the brute surroundings went on—the flagrant changes
of maple and sumach, the water in ripples of light,
the faces of outcrop, the stillness, and up the slopes
a vast incessant green that drew the mind
beyond its tether, north, to muskeg and
stunted hackmatack, and then the whine of icy tundra north to the pole—
despotic land, inhuman yet
our *own*, where else on earth? and reaping stone
from the bush their fathers cleared, the sons gave
way and they drank all year, or went strange, or they sat and stared outside
as their cars settled back to slag and now what
races toward us on asphalt across the Shield—
by truck, by TV minds and the ore-bearing flatcars—
is torn from the land and the mute oblivion of
all those fruitless lives, it no longer
stays for us, immemorial adversary, but is shipped and
divvied abroad though wrested whole from the Shield.
. . .

▲
Figure 1.15.e An excerpt from Dennis Lee's poem "Civil Elegies"

Figure 1.15.f "The Elders Are Watching" by Native painter Roy Henry Vickers. Vickers' work brings the Aboriginal and non-Aboriginal worlds together. He invites the viewer to experience the peace of nature, a memory of ancestors, and a sense of how the past and the present can exist at the same time.

QUESTIONS & ACTIVITIES

1. For each of the six figures included on these pages, complete the following analysis:
   a) What part of Canada is, or seems to be, portrayed or described?
   b) What aspects of the physical environment appear to be dominant in the figure?
   c) Identify the images or features of the physical environment that are used in the figure.
   d) Does the figure show a positive or negative attitude towards the environment? Explain your answer.
   e) In what ways does the figure help to build on the popular symbols we connect to our national character?
   f) In your opinion, is this figure an accurate portrayal of the way Canadians of today view their physical environment? Explain your answer.

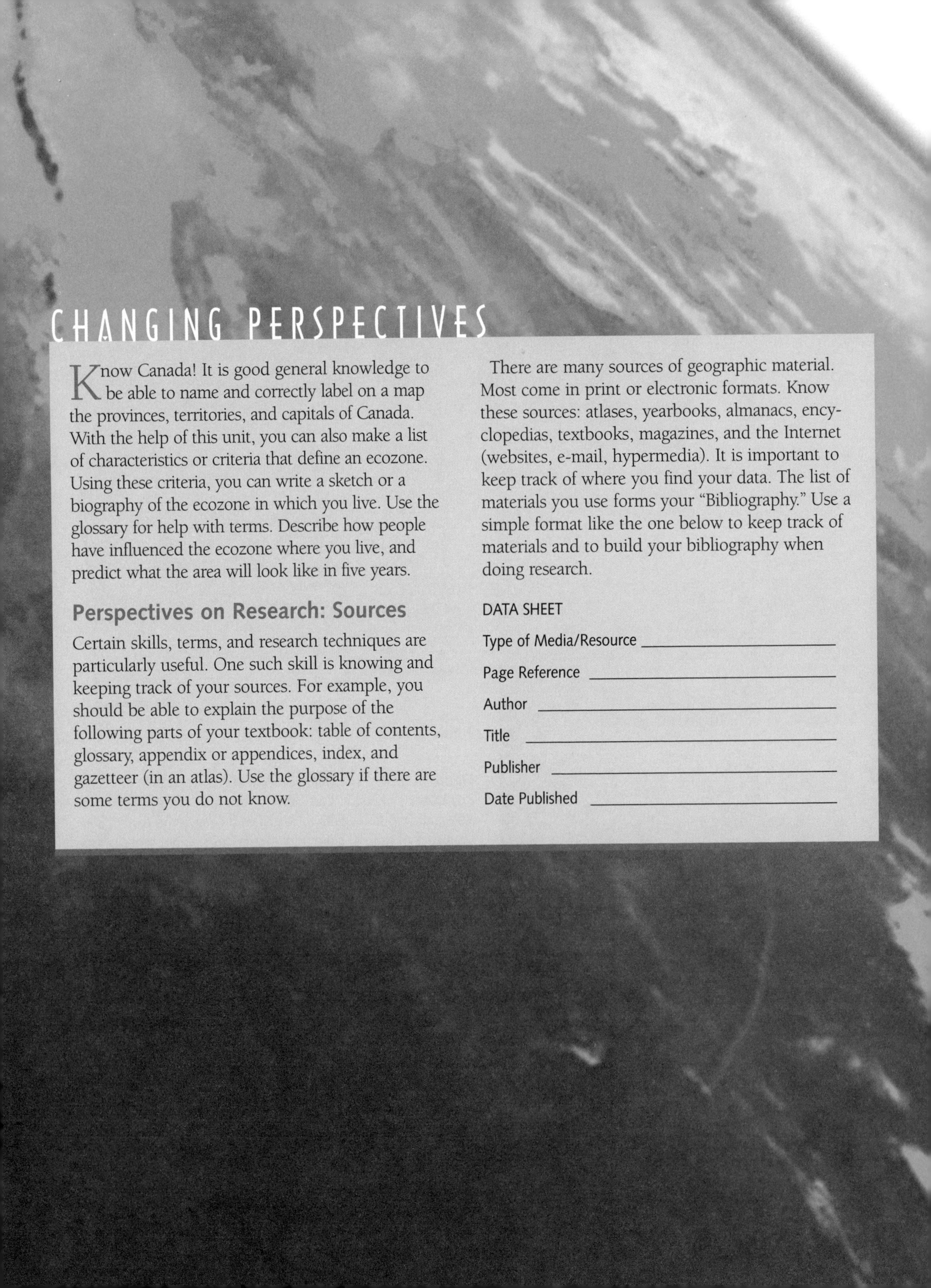

CHANGING PERSPECTIVES

Know Canada! It is good general knowledge to be able to name and correctly label on a map the provinces, territories, and capitals of Canada. With the help of this unit, you can also make a list of characteristics or criteria that define an ecozone. Using these criteria, you can write a sketch or a biography of the ecozone in which you live. Use the glossary for help with terms. Describe how people have influenced the ecozone where you live, and predict what the area will look like in five years.

Perspectives on Research: Sources

Certain skills, terms, and research techniques are particularly useful. One such skill is knowing and keeping track of your sources. For example, you should be able to explain the purpose of the following parts of your textbook: table of contents, glossary, appendix or appendices, index, and gazetteer (in an atlas). Use the glossary if there are some terms you do not know.

There are many sources of geographic material. Most come in print or electronic formats. Know these sources: atlases, yearbooks, almanacs, encyclopedias, textbooks, magazines, and the Internet (websites, e-mail, hypermedia). It is important to keep track of where you find your data. The list of materials you use forms your "Bibliography." Use a simple format like the one below to keep track of materials and to build your bibliography when doing research.

DATA SHEET

Type of Media/Resource _____

Page Reference _____

Author _____

Title _____

Publisher _____

Date Published _____

UNIT 2 OUR NATURAL RESOURCES

We have learned to use resources in our physical environment to meet our needs. This unit explores ways that our natural systems affect our use of resources.

2.1

ABORIGINAL PEOPLES AND THE ENVIRONMENT

Major Concepts
- Humans are part of the natural world
- Traditions are important
- Harmony is essential in life

"A traditionalist is one who gets up in the morning and goes outside to make an offering to the east. A traditionalist is one who applies the values of sharing and giving. A traditionalist is one who makes another offering as the sun goes down to the spirit world. That's **traditional**."
- *Floyd Red Crow Westerman, actor, activist, and singer on what it means to be a traditional Native*

"The tradition was the church. Service on Sunday morning, sing, kneel, pray, sermon—gone. That was tradition."
- *Susan Aglukark, Inuk singer, on whether she grew up with traditional Inuit practices*

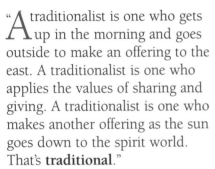

Photograph by Jim Allen

Figure 2.1.a Susan Aglukark

"Our hunters are our farmers. Gold and diamonds and minerals will come and go, but our wildlife will sustain us."
- *John Amagualik, Nunavut statesman*

"We believe animals have souls. My father taught me always to honour animals. They were sent down here to us, and if I did not honour them, I would have had bad luck hunting. I always cut their heads off, so that the creature can come to life again. As a boy, I learned to pour water into the mouth of every seal I killed because they grow thirsty from the salty sea."
- *Wesley Ekak, Inuit hunter*

Figure 2.1.b This illustration by Ken Suzana captures the importance that Aboriginal peoples place on harmony with the natural world.

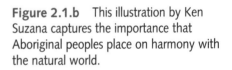

CASE STUDY   The Circle

The circle is a basic symbol of all traditional Aboriginal peoples. Aboriginal spirituality believes that all things are interrelated, interdependent members of the same family and that all should live together in harmony and respect. The circle reflects this belief in the equality of all beings and the constantly renewing rhythms of life. Black Elk, an Oglala Sioux, explains:

Everything an Indian does is in a circle,
because the power of the world
always works in circles,
and everything tries to be round
the sky is round,
and the earth is round like a ball,
and so are all the stars.
The wind, in its greatest power, whirls.
Birds make their nests in circles,
for their religion is the same as ours.
The sun comes forth and goes down again in a circle.
The moon does the same, and both are round.
Even the seasons for a great circle
in their changing,
and always come back again to where they were.
Human life is a circle
from childhood to childhood,
and so it is in everything where power moves.

People are an important natural resource. As part of our natural resources, Canada's **Aboriginal peoples** can teach their fellow Canadians many lessons. Just as Aboriginal peoples learn from the wisdom of their elders, everyone can learn from Native approaches to nature. In this first section on Canada's resources, we will examine some traditional Aboriginal philosophies that if practised could help keep the environment of Canada, and indeed the world, in balance.

Traditional Aboriginal peoples have a strong **spiritual** approach to life. In these beliefs, natural things such as animals, rocks, trees, and water, like humans, contain spirits, including the spirits of grandparents who have died. Aboriginal spiritual traditions entwined Aboriginal lives with the natural world and with the spirits of their ancestors.

The original inhabitants of Canada often led **nomadic** or **semi-nomadic** lives, moving in harmony with the seasons and food supplies. Fish runs, bird flyways, and animal migrations were critical elements of the food supply and survival. The understanding of these patterns was passed from generation to generation, from elder to child, primarily in story form, song, or ritual. The elders taught their peoples that they should respect animals and plant life and should kill only what they needed to clothe and feed themselves.

Many Aboriginal peoples in Canada today want to preserve or to return to traditional values and ways of life. People sharing the land with nature and wild animals in a harmonious and balanced way is an important part of that desire. This traditional value, with its emphasis on always considering how their actions today will affect future generations, may be the most important Aboriginal legacy in helping Canadians preserve open spaces and protect areas that are still natural.

Another Aboriginal **legacy** may be in the area of decision making. Many Aboriginal councils listen to all members of their particular group or band before they make decisions. Ideas do not always have to win or lose. Once all people have considered and discussed ideas or proposals, council members come to a consensus or general agreement based on the input they receive. The new territory of **Nunavut** is a forum for the Inuit government there to test these approaches in a modern context. In Nunavut politics, there are no political parties.

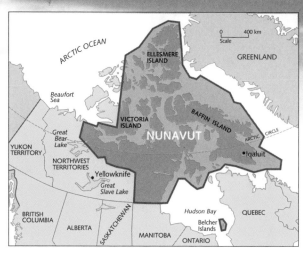

Figure 2.1.c   The new territory of Nunavut, April 1, 1999

People run for election as individuals, not as members of a political party. The elected members then vote for the member they want to lead the government.

There are other traditional Aboriginal values that may also prove useful in modern society. **Traditional status** was won by activities like being a skilled hunter who shared meat from his hunt with less fortunate families, calmness under pressure, and the ability to make good decisions for the family and the group. The great chiefs display these qualities.

It is from all these traits and values that a vision of harmony and peace between humans and their natural environment may emerge and a move to **environmental harmony** may grow. We should all remember that the elders are watching.

Figure 2.1.d   In 1998 Joe Crowshoe, 92, and his wife Josephine, 81, the last living ceremonial Elders of the Piegan Nation in southern Alberta, were awarded a National Aboriginal Achievement Award. Throughout their lives they worked to educate Aboriginal and non-Aboriginal people about Native culture, tradition and history and to promote a harmonious relationship between Aboriginal and non-Aboriginal peoples.

CASE STUDY   Elders Are Watching

The **Healing Rock** stands at the entrance to the Aboriginal burial ground on South Point at the fork where the Red and Assiniboine rivers meet in Winnipeg. It is beside the Oodena Celebration Circle, a site that is 3000 years old.

The Healing Rock was created by Natalie Rostad, a **Metis** artist who discovered the rocks near the Lake of the Woods. She has covered the rock with more than 100 paintings and symbols. As she did each painting and symbol, she prayed to the Creator, offering gifts of tobacco and wild flower seeds and waited for the rock to talk to her. Native spirituality holds that the rock contains the spirits of grand-mothers and grandfathers and that this wisdom of the **elders** gives guidance.

Natalie Rostad has been given many awards, including the Aboriginal Role Model award for Manitoba.

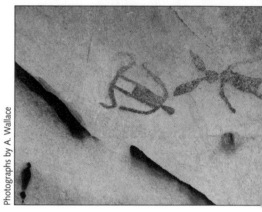

Photographs by A. Wallace

Figure 2.1.f Part of the Teaching Rock—Aboriginal rock carvings in Petroglyphs Provincial Park, Ontario. Found in 1954 at the east end of Stony Lake, these well-preserved symbols and figures tell a story of spiritual life.

Photograph by Louise Chernetz

Photogaph by Louise Chernetz

Figure 2.1.e Natalie Rostad and the Healing Rock

Close up of part of the Healing Rock

CASE STUDY An Elder

Johnny D. Charlie was a member of the Gwich'in Nation. He was born on December 24, 1930, at Rampart House on the Alaska/Yukon Territory border, and died on September 9, 1998, in Fort McPherson in the Northwest Territories.

Johnny was raised on the land and attended residential school in Aklavik. He hunted, fished, and trapped before working for Imperial Oil in the 1960s. Johnny was band councillor for many years before being elected Chief of the Tetlit Gwich'in of Fort McPherson, a position he held from 1975 until 1985.

Johnny was one of the founding members of the Porcupine Caribou Management Board and was an avid crusader for the protection of the Porcupine Caribou herd and its calving grounds, which are located in the Alaska National Wildlife Refuge on the north slope of Alaska.

Johnny's knowledge of the land and the caribou provided him with the desire and foresight to work so that future generations of Gwich'in and other harvesters can use the herd, undisturbed by political and economic pressures.

Johnny, and many others like him, lobbied the Canadian and American governments to provide adequate protection of the land where the caribou migrate. The Gwich'in still continue to lobby the governments and continue to carry on the work that Johnny started many years ago.

The struggle to protect the caribou herd is an example of an Elder using traditional knowledge to protect the Earth and its resources, and to ensure future generations can enjoy them as well.

Figure 2.1.g   Johnny Charlie

QUESTIONS & ACTIVITIES

1. a) What does "traditional" mean?
   b) Why do you think some people lost their traditional values?
2. a) Give one example that shows traditional values of Aboriginal peoples.
   b) How were traditions passed along?
3. a) Describe some of the spiritual beliefs of Aboriginal peoples and how these beliefs can bring harmony with the natural world.
   b) How did hunters make peace with their prey?
4. Describe four Aboriginal values and traditions that can help Canadians keep their society in balance with nature.

5. Write a paragraph to explain the concept of "The Elders are Watching."
6. Make a chart listing ways you think people can be considered natural resources.
7. Research the migration routes of the Porcupine herd of caribou in the Yukon.
   a) Create a map showing the caribou's travels.
   b) Use the migration of the caribou to explain why early Aboriginal peoples led nomadic lives.

POPULATION DISTRIBUTION OF ABORIGINAL PEOPLES

Major Concepts

- Aboriginal peoples are original inhabitants
- In Canada, Indian, Inuit, and Metis make up the Aboriginal peoples
- Aboriginal peoples, made up of over fifty cultural and language groups, are spread across Canada

Aboriginal peoples, or Native peoples, are **descendants** of the original inhabitants of a country. In Canada, three groups—Indians, Metis, and Inuit—make up the Aboriginal peoples. In the 1996 Census about 800 000 people— almost 3% of the Canadian population—reported they were one of these three groups.

Aboriginal peoples in Canada have diverse cultures, languages, and lifestyles. Their art, sports, literature, spirituality, and customs are part of the wealth of Canada's natural resources. Figure 2.2.a shows the distribution of Indian and Inuit peoples and their language groups at the time of European contact.

The Constitution Act, 1867, gave the federal government jurisdiction over "Indians and lands reserved for the Indians." In 1876 the government passed the *Indian Act*. Part of the *Act* implemented and extended a reserve system in which land was set aside, or

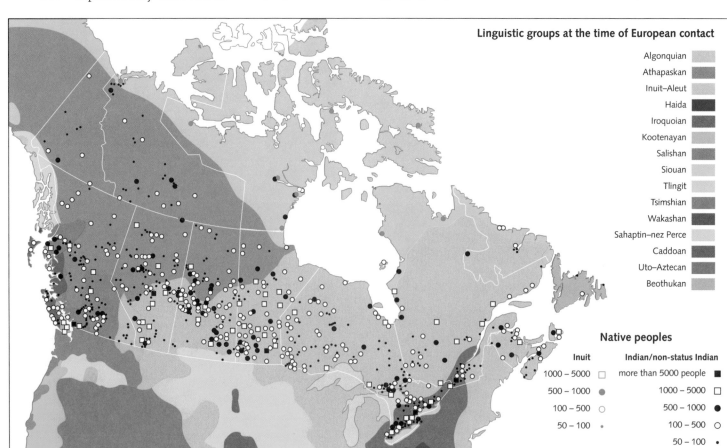

Figure 2.2.a Distribution of Canada's Aboriginal peoples and their languages at the time of European contact

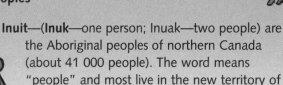

Some terms used in describing Canada's Aboriginal peoples

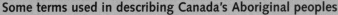

Aboriginal—someone descended from an original inhabitant—or *indigenous* inhabitant—of a country.

Indian—a person registered under the *Indian Act* (about 554 000 people).

First Nation—a term created in the 1990s used in place of "Indian band."

Status Indian—see "Registered" Indian.

Treaty Indian—a Status Indian who belongs to a band that signed a treaty with the Crown.

Registered Indian—a person who, under the *Indian Act*, is registered as an Indian or is entitled to be registered as an Indian. Status Indian and Registered Indian are interchangeable terms.

Metis—someone with mixed Indian and European ancestry (about 210 000 people). Metis have a unique status and culture separate from Indian, Inuit, or non-Aboriginal peoples.

Inuit—(**Inuk**—one person; **Inuak**—two people) are the Aboriginal peoples of northern Canada (about 41 000 people). The word means "people" and most live in the new territory of Nunavut, north of the tree line.

Indian Act—first passed in 1876 and revised with the Constitution Act of 1982 and amended in 1985. This amendment—called Bill C-31—removed such discriminatory practices as taking away Indian status from women when they married non-Indian men. Since 1985 over 100 000 individuals have regained their full status.

Band—a group of Indian people for whom lands have been set aside and money is held by the Crown. The band has a council and their head is the Chief. Today, Indian band has been replaced by First Nation.

reserved, for the use and occupancy of an Indian band. Today there are 2407 reserves, now referred to as First Nation communities, in Canada and just over 600 bands. Many reserves are extremely small. Indeed, some ranches in the West are bigger than ten or fifteen reserves put together. In all, fewer than 900 of the reserves are inhabited.

On average, Canadian Aboriginal peoples are about ten years younger than the general population of Canada. In Nunavut 40% of the population is fifteen years of age and under. As a result, large

	North American Indian*	Metis*	Inuit*
Canada	**554 290**	**210 190**	**41 080**
Newfoundland	5 430	4 685	4 265
Prince Edward Island	825	120	15
Nova Scotia	11 340	860	210
New Brunswick	9 180	975	120
Quebec	47 600	16 075	8 300
Ontario	118 830	22 790	1 300
Manitoba	82 990	46 195	360
Saskatchewan	75 205	36 535	190
Alberta	72 645	50 745	795
British Columbia	113 315	26 750	815
Yukon Territory	5 530	565	110
Northwest Territories	11 400	3 895	24 600

* Single and multiple responses have been combined.

Figure 2.2.b Distribution of the population who reported identifying with at least one Aboriginal group, by province and territory, 1996

numbers of Aboriginal young people will enter the work force in the next two decades. Many people have already left their communities, where unemployment is often high, to seek work in the cities in the south. About 30% of the Aboriginal population live in large cities. In both Regina and Saskatoon in Saskatchewan, over 7% of the city population is Aboriginal.

Figure 2.2.c Distribution of the population who reported identifying with at least one Aboriginal group by province and territory, as a percentage, 1996

	Total population	Total Aboriginal population	Aboriginal population as % of total population	Geographic distribution of Aboriginal population
				%
Canada	**28 528 125**	**799 010**	**2.8**	**100.0**
Newfoundland	547 160	14 205	2.6	1.8
Prince Edward Island	132 855	950	0.7	0.1
Nova Scotia	899 970	12 380	1.4	1.5
New Brunswick	729 630	10 250	1.4	1.3
Quebec	7 045 080	71 415	1.0	8.9
Ontario	10 642 790	141 525	1.3	17.7
Manitoba	1 100 295	128 685	11.7	16.1
Saskatchewan	976 615	111 245	11.4	13.9
Alberta	2 669 195	122 840	4.6	15.4
British Columbia	3 689 755	139 655	3.8	17.5
Yukon Territory	30 655	6 175	20.1	0.8
Northwest Territories	64 120	39 690	61.9	5.0

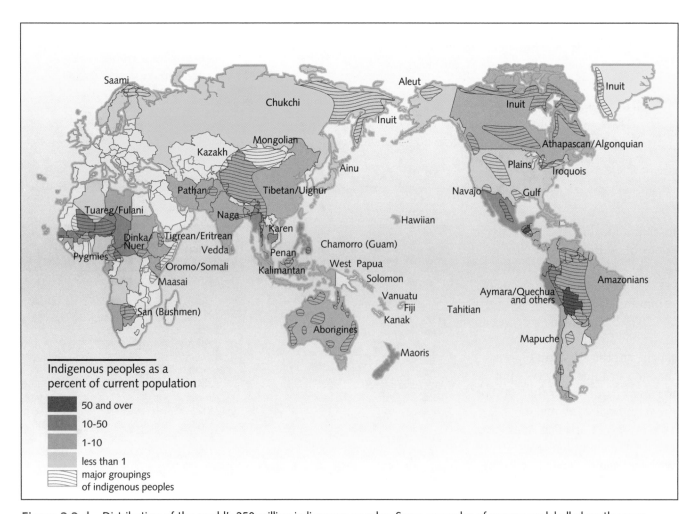

Figure 2.2.d   Distribution of the world's 250 million indigenous peoples. Some examples of groups are labelled on the map.

CMA	Total population	Total Aboriginal population	Aboriginal population as % of total population
Toronto	4 232 905	16 100	0.4
Winnipeg	660 055	45 750	6.9
Regina	191 480	13 605	7.1
Saskatoon	216 445	16 160	7.5
Calgary*	815 985	15 200	1.9
Edmonton	854 230	32 825	3.8
Vancouver*	1 813 935	31 140	1.7

Figure 2.2.e The population who reported identifying with at least one Aboriginal group, in selected **Census Metropolitan Areas**, 1996

*These CMAs (Census Metropolitan Areas) contain, within their boundaries, Indian reserves that were incompletely enumerated during the 1996 Census. Consequently, their counts of North American Indians are affected by this incomplete enumeration.

QUESTIONS & ACTIVITIES

1. Write definitions for the following terms in your own words: Aboriginal, Inuit, Inuk, Status Indian, Treaty Indian, Metis, First Nation, and chief.
2. Examine Figure 2.2.a.
   a) Aboriginal peoples living in northern Canada are among the few Aboriginal people to have maintained the everyday use of their traditional languages. Why do you think this is so?
   b) Why are Native peoples living on reserves more likely to be able to speak their aboriginal language than Native peoples living off the reserves?
3. Using the data in Figure 2.2.a, explain in your own words the distribution of Aboriginal peoples in the province of Quebec.
4. Use the data in Figure 2.2.b to create a pie graph illustrating the distribution of Aboriginal peoples in Canada by province and territory.
5. a) Use the data in Figure 2.2.c to create a bar graph showing the percentage distribution of Aboriginal peoples by province and territory. Put the provinces and territories along the horizontal axis and percentage population figures along the vertical axis.
   b) Shade in the column that represents your province or territory.
   c) With a partner or in small groups analyze what the results of your graph tell you about the distribution of Aboriginal peoples.

6. a) How does the relative age of Aboriginal peoples compare to that of non-Aboriginal Canadians? Create a graph to illustrate your answer.
   b) How might the difference in age present problems in the next two decades?
   c) Where do many Aboriginal peoples tend to go when they leave their reserves or homes in the North? Why?
   d) What cities have the largest Aboriginal populations? Suggest reasons that these cities have larger Aboriginal populations.
7. Find a map showing the distribution of Aboriginal peoples in Canada today.
   a) How is the pattern of population different from that in Figure 2.2.a?
   b) Research reasons for any changes.
8. Study Figure 2.2.d.
   a) Name three groups of indigenous peoples from around the world.
   b) What continent has the most indigenous people?
   c) Select a group and conduct a cultural study of the people. Include: location, history, customs, religion, housing, food, clothing, relationships with surrounding people, and the future of the group.

EARLY IMMIGRATION TO CANADA

Major Concepts

- Resources affect settlement patterns in Canada
- Boom and bust cycles
- People move to nations, from nations, and within nations

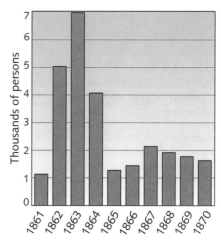

Figure 2.3.b Population of Caribou, 1861–1870, showing the boom and bust cycle

Canada's resources have attracted people since the earliest times. Native peoples on the Prairies followed the buffalo as their main resource. European fishermen from Scandinavia, Spain, Portugal, England, and France fished for cod on the Grand Banks off Newfoundland. Their voyages sparked a wave of explorers to this New World to seek resources and riches.

Canada's variety of resources have created many bursts of population growth and movement. Often these "boom" times were followed by rapid declines in population when the resource ran out or the market for the resource disappeared. These cycles are often called "**boom and bust cycles.**" The "**Gold Rushes**" in the Klondike and in the Caribou Country are examples of huge migrations of gold-seekers creating an instant demand for towns and

services. These boom times were quickly followed by crashes—busts—when the depletion of the resource led to desertion, abandonment and decay of these sites.

Some resource development led to permanent population growth. In Ontario, lumber companies opened huge parcels of land. At first these companies cut down trees for masts for sailing ships. Later, they cut trees for wood for sawn lumber. Loggers built access roads northward through large tracts of forests. Pioneers looking for new homes soon followed. British soldiers were given tracts of land as retirement packages to encourage them to settle in the cut-over lands. Settlers from Ireland where a potato famine was impoverishing people were recruited to come to Canada. Dr. Thomas Barnardo took a different approach. He found orphans in England in the

late 1800s and brought these youngsters, known as "**Barnardo children,**" to help work the lands.

In Quebec, similar growth occurred as immigrants from France followed the successful coureurs de bois to settle the regions of the St. Lawrence.

The railway played a large role in the migration patterns of Canada. A key factor in the Confederation of Canada was the promise of a railway to join the two coasts. A wave of

Figure 2.3.a "Buffalo Herd Grazing" by George Caitlin. First Nations peoples hunted only enough buffalo to supply them with necessary food, clothing, and shelter.

Figure 2.3.c Between 1869 and 1885 approximately 15 000 Chinese immigrants were encouraged to come to Canada specifically to work as cheap labour on the western portion of the transcontinental railway.

Figure 2.3.d Sod house around 1900. Early settlers on the Prairies built their first homes out of sod, the only construction material readily available.

settlers came to the west in the 1870s and 80s, following the rail tracks into new territories. From 1900 to 1910 another wave came from Europe to settle the opening Prairies. The grasslands became known as the "bread basket" of Canada. Many settlers came to the West to take part in the growing wheat industry. Migration to Canada came to an abrupt end as the Great Depression and drought settled in for ten years in the 30s, followed by six years of the Second World War. Large-scale immigration did not start again until the early 1950s.

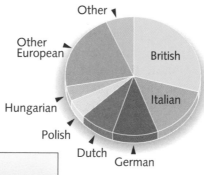

Figure 2.3.f Origin of immigrants to Canada, 1951

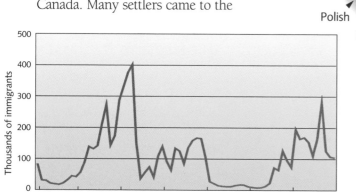

Figure 2.3.e Immigration to Canada, 1890–1960

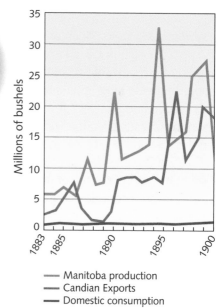

— Manitoba production
— Candian Exports
— Domestic consumption

Figure 2.3.g Manitoba wheat production

QUESTIONS & ACTIVITIES ❓

1. What is a "boom and bust" cycle?
2. Write a definition for gold rush, crash, and bread basket.
3. Look at Figure 2.3.b. What caused the rise in Caribou's population around 1863? What caused the population to drop by 1870?
4. Study Figure 2.3.e. Explain the reasons for the peaks in 1911 and 1951 and the flat line in the 1930s and early 1940s.
5. What are the countries of origin of the four largest sectors in Figure 2.3.f?
6. Examine Figure 2.3.g.
   a) Explain why the production peaks rise from 1885 to 1900.
   b) What changes in transportation happened to allow exports of wheat to rise while domestic or Canadian consumption stayed at the same level?
7. From 1880 to 1905, Canada lost population. New arrivals and people already here were leaving as fast as they could for the United States. Investigate and report on this early "brain" and "brawn" drain from Canada.
8. Research the development of different strains of wheat and of farm implements used in the late 1800s. What new technologies allowed farming in the Prairies to expand so rapidly?

FISHING ON THE EAST COAST

Major Concepts

- Fishing in Atlantic Canada
- Economic activities on the Grand Banks
- Importance of offshore fishing limits

Canada is a world leader as a fishing nation. However, our fish stock is under severe pressure. The world's population needs the rich protein that fish can provide and Canada exports much of its harvest. The fish in Canada's waters represent a **renewable resource** that should provide food indefinitely. In this section and section 2.5 we examine Canada's fishing situation on the East and West Coasts.

The Grand Banks, located off Newfoundland, are some of the richest fishing grounds in the world. The shallow water allows abundant sunlight for plankton to grow as fish food. The meeting of the warm Gulf Stream and the cold Labrador current (see Figure 1.7.h) helps create an environment rich in nutrients. Over thirty types of fish, shellfish, and various mammals live here.

Since the 1400s or earlier, Europeans have fished these banks. The **northern cod** has been the most plentiful of these fish, as well as other "ground fish" (fish that feed near the ocean floor) such as haddock, hake, and halibut. For centuries, the traditional inshore and offshore fleets harvested a steady supply of fish. Longlines, trawlers, and lobster traps were the staple methods of the fishing fleets. However, in the last quarter of the twentieth century, overfishing has greatly reduced the fish stocks.

Like many countries, Canada has declared that it controls the ocean floor and all the ocean's resources from its coastlines to 200 nautical miles (370 km) off its shores. This 200-mile line is called the **offshore limit**. In the early 1990s, in an effort to protect the rapidly dwindling fish stocks, Canada placed a ban or **moratorium** on cod fishing within its offshore limits.

The decline of the fish stocks and the efforts by Canada's Department of Fisheries and Oceans to restore breeding stock have profoundly affected the fishing economy of the East Coast (see section 4.2), and have led to conflict with Spain (see section 5.6).

It is not yet certain whether the moratorium will have the positive effect on the cod stocks it was designed to achieve.

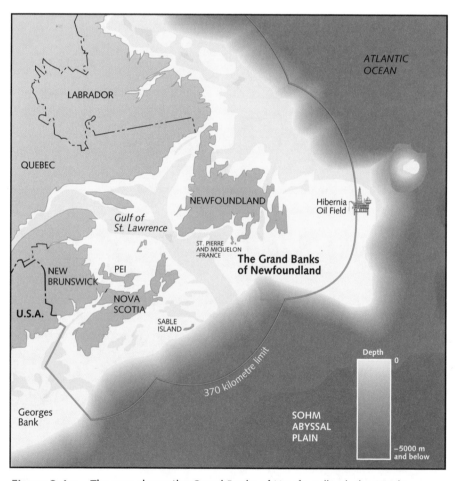

Figure 2.4.a The map shows the Grand Banks of Newfoundland, the 370 km offshore limit, and the Hibernia oil fields on the edge of the continental shelf. Note the two island territories of St. Pierre and Miquelon that belong to France.

Newfoundland Song

I'se the b'y that builds the boat,
And I'se the b'y that sails her!
I'se the b'y that catches the fish
And takes 'em home to Lizer.

Figure 2.4.b This popular folk song describes life in the villages of Newfoundland.

FACT FILE

Newfoundland outports are fishing villages that have sustained themselves on local fishing and hunting. Outport fishers used dories as their main fishing boat.

St. Pierre and Miquelon, two islands just off the coast of Newfoundland, belong to France. As such, they lay claim to their own 370 km limit in the Grand Banks (see Figure 2.4.a).

Figure 2.4.c The dory was the traditional boat of Newfoundland islanders.

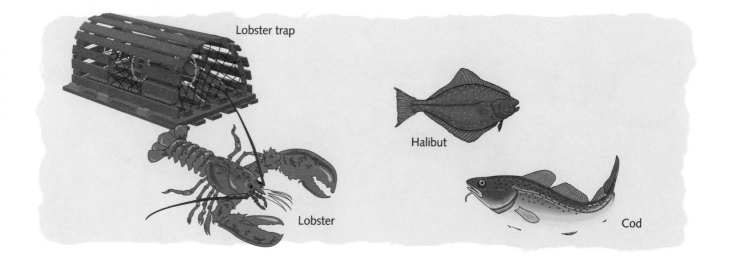

Lobster trap

Halibut

Lobster

Cod

Figure 2.4.d Cod, halibut, and lobster represent the traditional catch of the Maritimes.

Figure 2.4.e Harp seals are a well-known mammal on Canadian coastlines. There are many controversial opinions about how this wildlife resource should be used (see section 5.5)

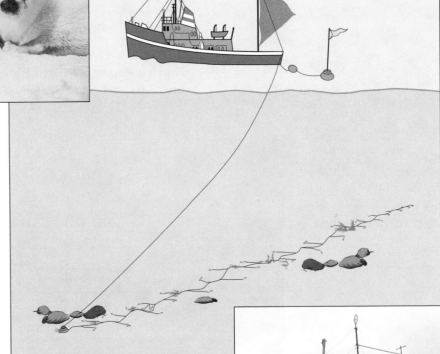

Figure 2.4.f Longline fishing was the time-tested way for the inshore fishery to catch fish. This method involves using a long line with a series of baited hooks spread along the ocean floor.

Figure 2.4.g An inshore fishing boat is in a dry dock for repairs.

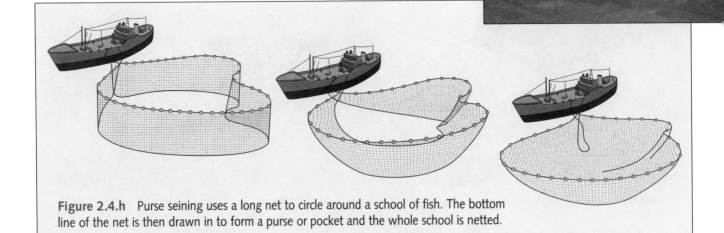

Figure 2.4.h Purse seining uses a long net to circle around a school of fish. The bottom line of the net is then drawn in to form a purse or pocket and the whole school is netted.

Figure 2.4.i Douane or French Customs identify St. Pierre and Miquelon as foreign territory within Canadian waters.

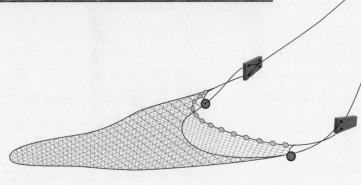

Figure 2.4.j Otter trawlers pull a huge dragline net, which scoops up everything in its path. Much of the overfishing and declining fish stock numbers is related to this method of fishing with increasingly larger nets.

Figure 2.4.k The French Customs launch monitors the harbour as two fishing trawlers deliver their catch to the processors for the markets in France.

QUESTIONS & ACTIVITIES

1. What three factors make the Grand Banks excellent for fishing?
2. a) What is the offshore limit of a nation's control over its seabed and coastal waters?
   b) What problem did Canada have inside its limits?
3. a) Why is the fishing industry important to the Maritimes?
   b) Why is it important to the world?
4. Examine Figure 2.4.a. The islands of St. Pierre and Miquelon belong to France. Draw a sketch map to suggest how Canada's claim of control over its offshore limits is complicated by France's claim of an offshore limit around the two islands.
5. a) Draw diagrams to illustrate three different methods of catching fish.
   b) Explain how each of the following works: longline, purse seine, otter trawler.
6. Hunting harp seals is a controversial issue in Atlantic Canada. Hunting baby seals for their white fur pelts draws international attention. Many scientists believe that the adult seals feed on cod fish whose stocks have been declining. Research and create a set of notes to explain the point of view of the following stakeholders in this issue:
   a) seal hunter from Newfoundland
   b) cod fishing-boat owner
   c) animal rights activist
   d) fashion designer
   e) the minister responsible for Oceans and Fisheries

FISHING ON THE WEST COAST

Major Concepts

- Types of fishing on the West Coast
- The importance of salmon to the Native cultures
- Factors and problems within the fishing industry
- Aquaculture on the West Coast

The West Coast fishing industry is different from other fisheries. It relies largely on salmon species. While other species like herring, pollock, and crab are abundant, salmon is the most valued. Demand for salmon has also spawned a large **aquaculture** industry (see Fact File). Generally, the prices for fish products from the West Coast are higher than for fish products from other parts of Canada. The demand from Japan and other Pacific Rim countries keeps the prices high for fresh fish, fish roe (eggs), and shellfish.

There are five species of salmon in the Pacific catch: chinook, cohoe, chum, pink, and sockeye.

Traditionally these species account for three-quarters of BC's annual catch. Salmon spawn in the clear, cold water of mountain streams. After their first year, the fingerlings swim to the Pacific to grow and reach maturity. Around their fourth year, **spawning runs** take the salmon from the salty oceans back upstream to the fresh water breeding sites where they were hatched. They return to the site of their birth, spawn and die.

In recent years, these fish (and the salmon industry) have become endangered. Clear-

cutting of forests has destroyed the river breeding areas by causing increased runoff and depositing of soil in the water. Dams block fish from returning to headwaters unless fish ladders are built to help them bypass the dams. Overfishing

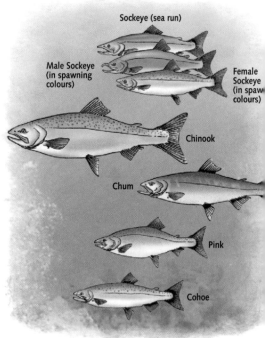

Figure 2.5.a   Five species of salmon

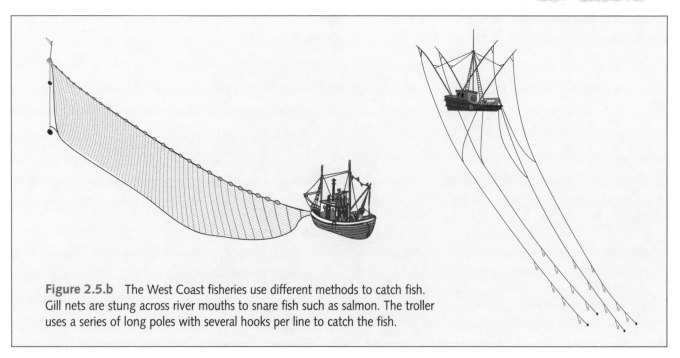

Figure 2.5.b   The West Coast fisheries use different methods to catch fish. Gill nets are stung across river mouths to snare fish such as salmon. The troller uses a series of long poles with several hooks per line to catch the fish.

Forest area	Types of trees
Boreal Forest: The major belt across Canada's North	Spruce, balsam, fir, white birch, jack pine, poplar
Pacific Coast Forest: Mild and moist belt along the BC coast	Rich in tree species including Douglas fir, cedar, hemlock, Sitka spruce
Subalpine Forest: On the eastern slopes of the Rocky Mts.	Englemann spruce, alpine fir, lodgepole pine
Montane Forest: A relatively dry region	Ponderosa and lodgepole pines, Douglas fir
Columbia Forest: A wet belt in the interior of British Columbia	Douglas fir, hemlock, cedar, larch
The Eastern Deciduous Forest: The smallest of Canada's forest regions, located in southern Ontario	Includes hardwoods such as maple, oak, black walnut, and hickory
Eastern Mixed Forest: Transitional forest between the coniferous and deciduous forest	Eastern white pine, red pine, spruce, tamarack, eastern hemlock, yellow birch, sugar and red maples, oak
Atlantic (or Acadian) Forest: In the Maritimes	Maple, balsam, red spruce, fir, yellow birch

Figure 2.6.f   Description of forest types

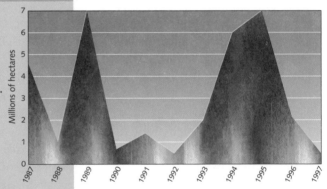

Source: Canadian Council of Forest Ministers

Figure 2.6.g   Land cover for Canada (percentage). Total area: 997.1 million hectares

evergreens because they keep their green needle foliage all year. The **deciduous** group are hardwood trees with broad-leafed vegetation. Deciduous trees normally shed their leaves in the fall.

There are over thirty species of conifers. The main ones are pine, fir, and spruce. There are over one hundred species of deciduous trees.

Some examples are maple, birch, and poplar. Figure 2.6.b shows the distribution of forest regions across Canada. Figure 2.6.f explains each type of forest cover.

FILE

FACT

Enemies of the Forest: Forest Fires and Disease

- Every year forest fires and disease destroy as many trees as loggers harvest.
- Most fires are caused by lightning or human carelessness.
- There are about 9000 forest fires every year in Canada.
- Some trees, such as the jack pine, need the intense heat of fire to open their seed cones in order to regenerate.
- Insects can damage wood, kill seeds, and destroy leaves. The spruce budworm is a major destructive force.

Figure 2.6.h   Area burned by forest fires across Canada, 1987-1997

QUESTIONS & ACTIVITIES

1. a) Describe the distribution of forests in Canada. In your answer, explain why tree types vary across the country.
   b) In what ways might tree types affect human activities?
2. a) Who owns the forested lands in Canada?
   b) How do forest companies get access to forest lands?
3. List three reasons why forests are important to the environment.
4. Examine Figure 2.6.b to see where the trees stop growing in Canada. Describe the factors that create this "tree line."
5. a) Forest fires are a serious fact of life. What are two causes?

   b) From your own knowledge, what are three dangers when forest fires occur?
   c) How are the fires controlled and/or extinguished?
   d) Why does the jack pine need fire?
6. Use your Resource Centre, the Internet, or consult a forest expert in your community to investigate these aspects of the forest environment:
   a) wildlife habitats
   b) the filtering role of forests
   c) "breathing" carbon dioxide and oxygen
   d) holding soil and preventing run-off
   e) recreational sites

THE FOREST INDUSTRY IN CANADA

Major Concepts

- Forest industries in the Canadian economy
- Products from Canadian forests

The forests of Canada provide direct work for over a quarter of a million Canadians. Nearly 1000 communities rely partially on forest-related businesses to provide work for their citizens. The businesses include logging companies, pulp and paper mills, sawmills, veneer mills, wood shingle mills, and manufacturers of wood specialty products like hockey sticks and laminates. Import and export activities, government services, and stock market traders have forest specialists. **Foresters** have careers in many aspects of the forestry business.

Another three quarters of a million jobs are indirectly related to the forests. Forests supply raw materials for a variety of products: paper, lumber, plywood, cellophane, cardboard and furniture. Energy is obtained by burning wood and sawdust. Camping, and now eco-tourism, are growing businesses using the forests of Canada.

Canada is the world's leading producer of newsprint, a low grade of paper used to bring people their daily news. Canada is a large producer of wood pulp and softwood lumber for export as well. Over 50% of Canada's wood products are exported, mainly to the United States, but also to Europe and the countries of the Pacific Rim.

Sustainable development means the uninterrupted, permanent supply of a resource (in this case, trees). Forests are renewable resources. Trees can be planted and harvested to provide continuous supplies. **Silviculture** is a branch of forestry that is devoted to growing and tending trees. Governments and forest industries spend a great deal of time and money to sustain this resource. Both use satellites that monitor the health of the forests by using infrared light reflections.

Even though they cover a large area, Canada must still protect its forests. Much of the native forest is unproductive. The slow growth in the cold regions of Canada and the small trees near the tree line

Figure 2.7.b   In this infrared satellite image of a forest, healthy green leaves are shown as reddish or magenta hues. The young trees are light toned (along the bottom of the image). As the trees grow older, the tone becomes darker. The ancient forest at the top along Queen Charlotte Strait is the darkest. Newly cut blocks are bluish to whitish. As the blocks are reforested, they begin to appear reddish. Lakes and ponds are black. The golf course is yellowish.
Landsat data copyright NOAA. Received by Canada Centre for Remote Sensing. Processed and distributed by RADARSAT International. Reproduced with permission of Space Imaging. Image courtesy P. Murtha, Department Forest Resources Management, University of British Columbia.

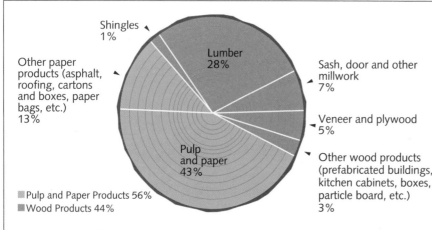

Shingles 1%

Lumber 28%

Other paper products (asphalt, roofing, cartons and boxes, paper bags, etc.) 13%

Sash, door and other millwork 7%

Veneer and plywood 5%

Pulp and paper 43%

Other wood products (prefabricated buildings, kitchen cabinets, boxes, particle board, etc.) 3%

- Pulp and Paper Products 56%
- Wood Products 44%

Figure 2.7.a   This pie graph illustrates the relative value of each of the products of the forest industry. Explain the difference between pulp and paper products and wood products.

CASE STUDY

Special Products: Hockey Stick Construction

The hockey stick is a symbol of Canada's most famous game. The stick has two main parts: the shaft and the blade. The shafts are often made of aspen wood. This light-weight wood is laminated with epoxy, fibreglass or carbon compounds to give it strength. Some all-wood shafts are made from ash or maple. The blades are made from plywood or birch and are laminated with fibreglass for strength. Some of the plywood for the blades is imported from Russia.

Sticks made only of wood are cheaper and weaker because of differing wood grains. The custom-made sticks of the professionals are made from epoxy and laminates so that each stick is made exactly the same. Canadian hockey sticks are exported all over the world.

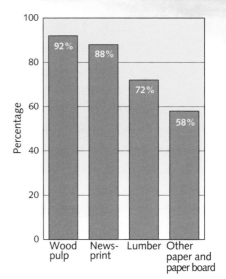

Source: Canadian Pulp and Paper Association

Figure 2.7.d Exports of Canadian forest products

(where tree growth is completely stunted by Arctic weather) are places where jobs and recreation related to forests are limited.

In section 4.3, you will examine some of the methods the forest industry has used to cut down trees and the environmental concerns these methods have caused.

Figure 2.7.c Kerry, tree planter, Princeton, BC, 1988. Forest companies employ people, often students, to replant trees. This is one way companies work to achieve sustainable forest growth. ▶

Photograph by Lorraine Gilbert.

FACT FILE

In Northern Ontario, 171 communities out of 285 rely on forest related jobs such as logging, processing timber, and pulp and paper (approximately 90 000 jobs). Forest companies must submit plans for sustainable harvest to the Minister of Natural Resources before they can cut trees down.

QUESTIONS & ACTIVITIES ?

1. List five products that forests supply.
2. Write definitions for "renewable" and "sustainable."
3. List four types of businesses that produce forest products.
4. a) Make a list of five jobs directly involved in the forest industry.
   b) Make a list of five jobs in businesses that are indirectly related to forest industries.
5. Choose one of the jobs from question 4 and investigate the qualifications needed to get this type of work.

6. Investigate how pulp is made into newsprint. Use a series of labelled diagrams on a poster board to explain the process.
7. Recycling of paper has been a success. Create a flow chart to show the path that a discarded daily newspaper in your community would take to be made into a recycled paper product.

TECHNOLOGY AND AGRIBUSINESS

Major Concepts

- Family farm to agribusiness
- Technology and farming practices
- Effects of change on the people involved in farming
- Reasons for declining number of farms

Province	Farms	Reporting Use
Newfoundland	742	112
Prince Edward Is.	2 217	451
Nova Scotia	4 453	884
New Brunswick	3 405	600
Quebec	35 991	7 941
Ontario	67 520	14 131
Manitoba	24 383	4 618
Saskatchewan	56 995	11 352
Alberta	59 007	13 491
British Columbia	21 835	5 144

Source: Statistics Canada

Figure 2.8.b Use of personal computers for farm management, 1996

Agriculture was once practised largely by farm families. Today it is dominated by **agribusiness**. Some restaurants own their own beef ranches and potato farms to make sure of a steady supply of hamburger and french fry material. A new cooperative formed by the merger of the Alberta Wheat Pool and the Manitoba Pool Elevators will serve over 70 000 grain producers and its revenues will be measured in the millions.

Early in the twentieth century most agricultural production took place on **family farms**. Each family produced a variety of crops and livestock to meet their own needs. Surplus output was sold to buy those things that the family could not produce using their own resources. In 1931, about one in three Canadians lived on family farms. By the end of the century, only two percent of the population was employed in farming.

Agriculture had changed in remarkable ways.

Some of the changes in agriculture came about because of **mechanization**—the replacement of human and animal labour with the work of machines. Mechanization was accomplished through the purchase of tractors, combines, and other farm implements, and the use of electrical motors.

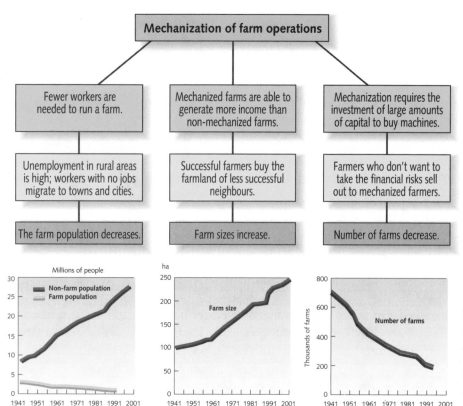

Figure 2.8.a Results of the mechanization of agriculture

Figure 2.8.c A large modern tractor prepares the fields for crops.

Livestock	Poultry	Animal Products
cattle	hens	milk or cream
pigs	chickens	eggs
sheep	turkeys	wool
horses	chicks	furs
game animals	game birds	meat
other livestock	other poultry	

Figure 2.9.d Some of the livestock, animal, and poultry products referred to in this section

products. The pattern of dairy farms in Figure 2.9.a shows their close proximity to cities.

Most poultry are raised in very controlled environments. Although there is a growing demand today, the days of the free ranging chicken have generally gone the way of the small family farm. The huge demand for chicken and turkey meat means that from egg to mature bird, the feed, water, supplements, lighting conditions, and temperatures are tightly controlled in poultry barns. These controls are designed to produce a uniformly high quality product. Getting turkeys ready to meet the high demand periods of Christmas and Thanksgiving is an example of response to consumer demand factors.

There are some very special animal farms as well. Buffalo are raised for meat and hides. Fox and mink are two other specialty livestock ranches. Caribou are being raised in captivity in the Arctic to ensure a source of meat there.

The emu is an Australian bird imported into Canada. Emu are being bred and raised as a source of low fat, high protein meat. They are also a source for skin care products that have moisturizing and possibly other healing properties.

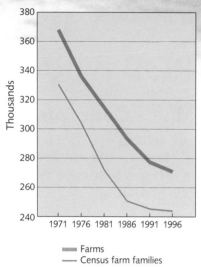

Sources: Census of Agriculture; Census of Agriculture-Population Database

Figure 2.9.e Table indicating number of farms in Canada and the continuing decline of farm families as shown by the census

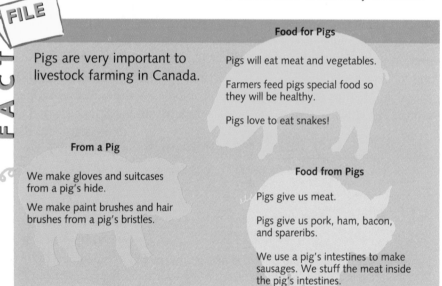

FILE

FACT

Pigs are very important to livestock farming in Canada.

From a Pig

We make gloves and suitcases from a pig's hide.

We make paint brushes and hair brushes from a pig's bristles.

Food for Pigs

Pigs will eat meat and vegetables.

Farmers feed pigs special food so they will be healthy.

Pigs love to eat snakes!

Food from Pigs

Pigs give us meat.

Pigs give us pork, ham, bacon, and spareribs.

We use a pig's intestines to make sausages. We stuff the meat inside the pig's intestines.

QUESTIONS & ACTIVITIES

1. **a)** What are three factors that influence dairy farm locations?
   b) List two reasons why dairy farms must be close to their market.
   c) What is the most important transportation factor in the dairy industry and why?
2. **a)** Why are milk quotas important to milk production in Canada?
   b) List five milk products and rank them for their perishability.
3. **a)** How many farms were there in the peak years and how many are there today?
   b) What is the number of farms that have disappeared?
4. **a)** What are large tracts of land in the western Prairie provinces devoted to?
   b) Why are the ranches there so large?
5. Make a flow chart to show how milk products get from the cow to the consumer.
6. Investigate and report on one of the specialty livestock farming operations in Canada. Make a poster board to show the operation from birth to market.

CROP FARMING IN CANADA

Major Concepts

- The patterns of crops and specialty regions
- The importance of wheat to Canada
- Changes to crops like tobacco and Canola

Compared to fifty years ago, there are fewer and much larger farms in Canada. The 280 000 farms in the 1991 census were 5% less than in the 1986 census. However, these larger farms generate more money for the owners. They are more specialized in their products, equipment, buildings, and machinery. In this section we will examine **crop farming** in Canada. Figure 2.10.a shows the types of crops and other agricultural products grown.

Crops	Other Agricultural Products
field crops	greenhouse or nursery products
tree fruits or nuts	Christmas trees
berries or grapes	mushrooms
vegetables	sod
seed	honey
	maple syrup products

Figure 2.10.a Some of the crops and products referred to in this section. Make a list of other crops and products not listed here.

Many of these products are associated with regions of Canada. Potatoes, for example, are associated with Prince Edward Island, fruit with the Niagara fruit belt and the Okanagan Valley, fodder crops with the dairy industry of Quebec, and tobacco, as a declining or "**sunset**" crop in southwestern Ontario (see Figure 2.9.a).

Wheat is the most famous and important Canadian crop. The wheat farms of the Prairies, especially Saskatchewan, are world renowned. Canada's wheat is shipped to China, Brazil, Japan, and countries in Europe and the Middle East. The natural grasslands of the Prairies have the ideal soil and climate conditions for growing wheat and other grain crops. Seeds are planted right after the last frost in May. Spring rains soak in the applications of fertilizers to bring on growth. The hot, dry summer allows the grain to ripen and by mid-August the harvest begins. The combine harvester is an example of modern, air-conditioned, specialized equipment that allows farmers to harvest crops quickly and efficiently.

The wheat is trucked to **grain elevators** where it is weighed and graded. From these unique Prairie buildings, it is loaded into boxcars to be carried by train to the ports of Vancouver, Churchill, and Thunder Bay. The grain elevators at the harbours do some drying and sorting of the grain (increasing its value) and store it until ships arrive to carry it to markets in Canada and the rest of the world. Canadians consume about one-quarter of the wheat produced in Canada.

If tobacco is a "sunset" crop because of social trends and pressures, Canola is a "**sunrise**" crop. Canada's major oil seed crop, Canola has seen spectacular growth

Figure 2.10.b Canada's top ten field crops, 1996

in planting and production in the last decade. The global demand for high-quality edible oil is expanding as health-conscious consumers seek low-fat, low-cholesterol products.

Canada has some other interesting specialty crops as well. **Market garden** areas, like the Holland

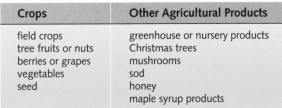

Figure 2.10.c Corn is an important fodder crop. The varieties used for feed grain differ from varieties for human consumption.

Marsh near Toronto, are found around cities to provide fresh vegetables. Ginseng and peanuts are being planted on the sandy soil once famous for tobacco in south-western Ontario. Grape vines are being planted on more and more land in the Niagara region and the Okanagan valley to supply the demand for good quality Canadian wine. Hemp is also becoming a valuable crop with many uses.

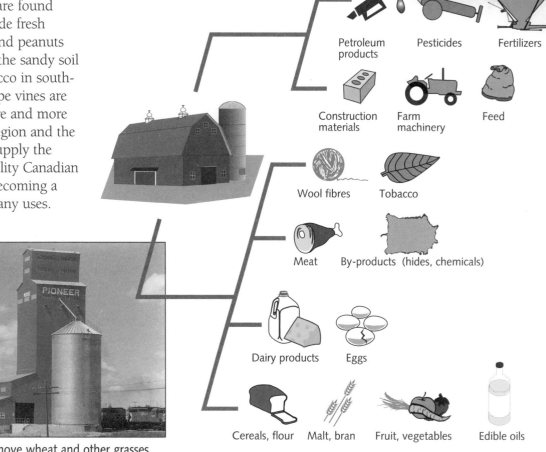

Petroleum products Pesticides Fertilizers

Construction materials Farm machinery Feed

Wool fibres Tobacco

Meat By-products (hides, chemicals)

Dairy products Eggs

Cereals, flour Malt, bran Fruit, vegetables Edible oils

Figure 2.10.d Trains move wheat and other grasses from storage elevators to markets. Most trains deliver to port cities such as Churchill, Manitoba, Thunder Bay, Ontario, and Vancouver, BC.

Figure 2.10.e Products used in farming and products coming from farm operations

QUESTIONS & ACTIVITIES

1. List four ways large farms are more profitable than small farms.
2. List three regional specialty crops.
3. **a)** Discuss how social trends have made tobacco a "sunset" industry.
   b) Discuss how trends have made Canola a "sunrise" industry.
4. **a)** Explain why the Prairies are an excellent region for growing wheat.
   b) Make a flow chart that traces the journey of wheat from the seeding of wheat to its arrival at grain elevators ready for export.
5. Look at a map of Canada in the Appendices and decide what port would be the most likely point of shipment for the following countries: China, Brazil, Japan, Europe, Iran, and Indonesia. Draw a line on a blank world outline map to show the best route to each of the listed wheat-importing nations. Compare your map to an atlas map to check your predictions.
6. Think about what types of farms are in your region. Make a list of the products grown around your community.
7. Use the *Canada Year Book* to track the land devoted to tobacco and to Canola from 1951 to 1996. Construct a series of pie graphs to illustrate the changes in crop land where these two crops have been planted.
8. Use the information in Figure 2.10.e to make a chart. List the products a farm needs in one column. In the second column, show the products coming from the farm. Write point-form notes about each of the items in your chart to explain their significance.

2.11

CONVENTIONAL ENERGY IN CANADA

Major Concepts

- Conventional forms of energy
- Sources of power to generate electricity
- Correlating the demand for energy with pollution

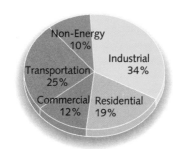

Figure 2.11.b The percentage of energy demand from various sectors. Which sector demands the most energy?

In Canada, the conventional, or usual, sources of energy are flowing water, fossil fuels such as coal, natural gas, and oil, and uranium. These fuels support the large consumption of energy by Canadians, who have one of the highest consumption rates in the world. Canada has three main reasons for this demand: vast distances, a cold northern latitude location, and the high standard of living of its citizens.

Although Canada has plentiful sources of energy, each source creates problems (see also sections 2.12, 4.6, 4.7, 8.2, and 8.3).

Electrical energy is a major form of power. Electricity is generated by flowing water, by burning fossil fuels like coal, oil, or natural gas, and through nuclear reactors using uranium. Many waterways, such as the St. Lawrence River, Niagara Falls, and the Columbia River, have already been harnessed with power

dams to generate electricity. Projects, such as Hydro-Québec's James Bay mega-project, can provide a lot of energy. However, such projects create concerns about environmental destruction, loss of habitat for animals, and the civil

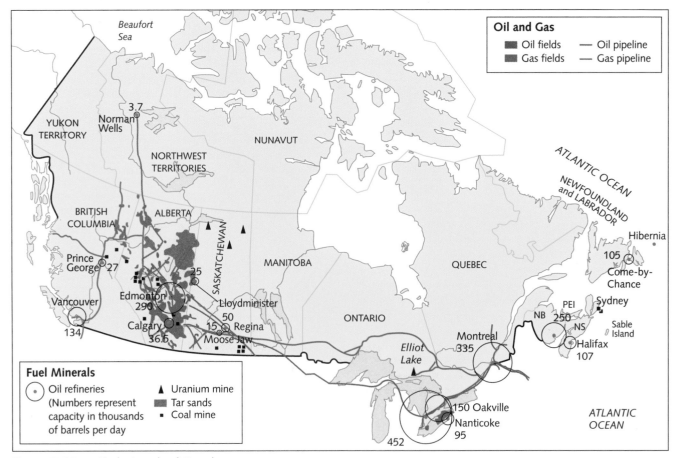

Figure 2.11.a Fuel minerals of Canada

rights of people who are displaced by the project (see section 4.7).

Canada has a huge supply of uranium, the power source for nuclear energy. Ontario has built several nuclear generating plants throughout the province. However, nuclear waste products are very dangerous radioactive materials. Their handling, storage, and disposal in safe sites are serious environmental concerns.

Coal is mined in British Columbia, Alberta, Saskatchewan, New Brunswick, and Nova Scotia (Cape Breton). Coal has been a source of energy with many uses. In the past, homes, schools, and other large buildings were heated with coal. Generating plants burned coal for electricity, and iron and steel plants used coal for fuel in smelting steel.

However, coal as a power source in Canada creates some problems. Air quality, especially sulphur emissions from burning coal, are a major concern. Coal mines are very deep and difficult to maintain. Strip mining coal can create scars on the land. Nevertheless, coal is still an important product and a leading Canadian export.

Natural gas is a common fuel in home heating today. Alberta and British Columbia provide much of Canada's present supply. Natural

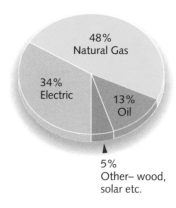

48%
Natural Gas

34%
Electric

13%
Oil

5%
Other– wood, solar etc.

Figure 2.11.d How we heat our homes. Into which sector does your residence fit?

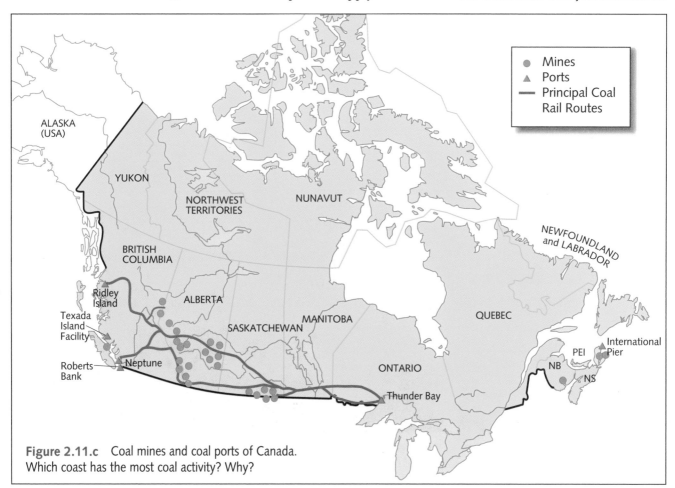

Figure 2.11.c Coal mines and coal ports of Canada. Which coast has the most coal activity? Why?

gas must be moved by pipeline. Canada has a large network of pipelines to distribute the natural gas to markets. New sources in the Beaufort Sea, the MacKenzie Delta, and Hibernia on the Grand Banks are being developed. The Maritimes are exploring the possibility of burning Sable Island natural gas to replace the expensive, sulphur-laden coal from Cape Breton.

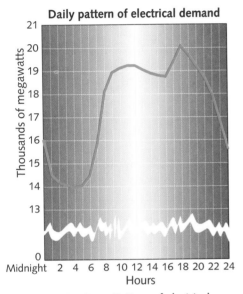

Daily pattern of electrical demand

y-axis: Thousands of megawatts
x-axis: Hours (Midnight 2 4 6 8 10 12 14 16 18 20 22 24)

Figure 2.11.e Pattern of electrical demand during a typical winter day in Ontario. "Peak" hours are when demand is highest. Power companies must have power ready for those times of day. When is the peak demand?

Figure 2.11.g The Adam Beck generating plant, Niagara Falls, Ontario. The Niagara escarpment allows water diverted from the Niagara River and Falls to drop through turbines and generate electrical power.

Crude oil supplies a huge range of energy products from gasoline to aviation fuel. The number of cars and trucks in Canada creates an enormous demand for this fuel. Crude oil is refined into a variety of products. Some are used for energy, some for lubrication, and some go into the giant **petrochemical indus-try.** Exhaust gas from burning petroleum products contributes to air pollution and has been identified as a possible contributor to **global warming.**

Consumption of energy varies by seasons. The winter season requires a steady supply of heating fuels. Summer is also a high energy use

Figure 2.11.f Niagara Falls, Ontario. The scenic falls are the result of water dropping over the Niagara escarpment.

Figure 2.11.h The Pickering nuclear plant. Nuclear power is a source of energy in parts of Canada. The safe handling of radioactive materials is a constant concern for the industry.

Natural gas windfall stirs controversy in New Brunswick

FREDERICTON (CP) — The natural-gas windfall in the Maritimes is stirring controversy over just who will benefit from the new source of energy.

A draft government report on gas distribution in New Brunswick, leaked to the news media this week, has suggested that big industrial users like the powerful Irving companies be given direct access to Sable Island natural gas straight off the pipeline.

That has alarmed and dismayed people who believe the fairest approach would be to allow for a single, integrated distributor to build a system in the province that would reach the most homes, businesses and industries possible.

The integrated approach is being promoted by one of the leading consortiums bidding for distribution rights, Gas New Brunswick, which is made up of Ontario-based Consumers Gas Energy Inc. and a team of New Brunswick investors including Harrison McCain of McCain Foods Ltd.

"There's still a lot of objectives that the government has to meet and they haven't found the answers for how that's going to happen," said Bud Bird, spokesman for Gas New Brunswick.

"I believe the innovative capabilities of an experienced distributor such as Consumers Gas Energy probably has a better chance than anybody to help the province realize the full benefits of natural gas." Oct. 30, 1998

Figure 2.11.j The St. Lawrence Seaway Power Dam. The St. Lawrence River was harnessed in the 1950s to provide electrical power and ship canals from the Atlantic to the Great Lakes.

Figure 2.11.i The article describes a controversy as power companies switch fuel sources.

season due to the demand for air-conditioning in homes and offices. When demand is high it is referred to as peak demand. **Peak demand** happens daily and seasonally. Power must be available or reduced power supplies can cause brown-outs, which can damage electrical appliances.

Figure 2.11.k Mica Dam and Generating Station, part of the Columbia River Dams system. The Columbia project uses the flow of water from mountains to generate power. Canada and the United States had to cooperate on this hydro project because the Columbia flows in both countries.

QUESTIONS & ACTIVITIES

1. What are three conventional sources of energy?
2. What are three ways to produce electricity?
3. What are two problems with conventional petroleum fuel products?
4. Use flow charts to describe how each of the three energy sources referred to in the text generate electric power.
5. Design a survey for your class. Ask everyone to find out how their homes are heated. Total all the sources.
   a) Draw a pie graph to show the percentage of each type of heat source.
   b) Write a sentence to summarize the heat sources from your class survey.
   c) Compare your class results with the results of the Canadian survey conducted by Hydro-Québec (Figure 2.11.d). Write your comparison in your notes.
6. Locate the St. Lawrence Seaway, Niagara Falls, and the Columbia River on a map. Discuss how the US border is a factor in the production of power at all three sites.

ALTERNATE FORMS OF ENERGY

Major Concepts

- Alternate sources of fuel
- Environmental concerns related to energy sources
- Evaluating alternate supplies of energy in Canada

There is growing concern around the world about the long-term effects of burning fossil fuels. Air pollution, smog and possible global warming are the main concerns. Extracting and using fossil fuels results in sulphur and exhaust emissions that seriously pollute the atmosphere. Moreover, fossil fuels are

Figure 2.12.a
Part of a windmill electricity generating farm

non-renewable. Once they have been extracted and consumed, they are gone. The long life of radioactive waste and the high cost of safely handling nuclear fuels create problems. Hydroelectric energy mega-projects can destroy huge tracts of land.

All of these problems demand alternate ways of providing fuels and energy. New sources of energy should also provide for conservation methods and more efficient ways of producing and distributing energy. At the moment, alternate sources are often expensive. As they

become more common and more accepted, costs should decline.

Figure 2.12.b shows the patterns of solar energy and wind energy in Canada. **Solar energy** means capturing the rays of the sun and turning the heat into useful forms of energy. More Canadians are using solar heat to warm their swimming pools. Some houses, like The ARK project in PEI (Figure 2.12.e), use solar energy as a heat source for the whole building.

Wind will also generate electrical energy. Calgary, Alberta, and the Gaspé region of Quebec are two areas where windmill farms are set up to convert constant winds into electrical current that feeds into their provincial power grids.

Wood has been a traditional source of heat in Canada keeping people warm for many centuries. Wood stoves and furnaces are still used. Some wood industries, to be more efficient, burn wood waste products like sawdust and wood chips for heat and energy.

Methane is a gas that may provide fuel in the future. Both human waste and animal manure give off this gas. Some sewage treatment plants use this waste gas to heat their plants. In

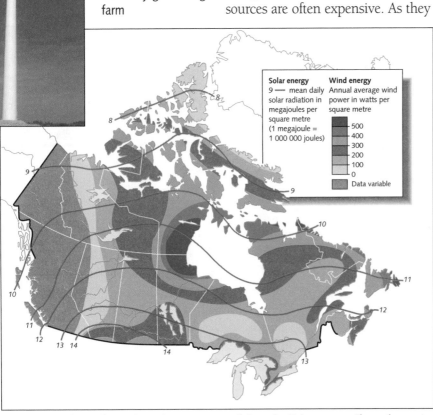

Solar energy
9 — mean daily solar radiation in megajoules per square metre
(1 megajoule = 1 000 000 joules)

Wind energy
Annual average wind power in watts per square metre

- 500
- 400
- 300
- 200
- 100
- 0
- Data variable

Figure 2.12.b Solar and wind energy map of Canada. Solar energy (from the sun) and wind are two key forms of alternate energy.

> To replace the energy from a nuclear generating plant in Ontario, you would need an area bigger than PEI covered with windmills. The sound from those propellers would drive you crazy!

Nuclear engineer,
Canadian General Electric

STUDY Natural-gas powered vehicles

Conventional resources can have alternate uses to help the environment. Natural gas can be a fuel for vehicles. In Kitchener, Ontario, air quality and fuel costs were two big concerns for City Council. As a result of their actions, public vehicles (over 50 public works vehicles and 23 public transit buses) have been converted to natural gas power to save money on conventional fuel (gasoline and diesel fuel) and to reduce exhaust emission into the air. Any buses purchased in the future will be powered by natural gas.

Figure 2.12.c Natural-gas powered bus, Kitchener, Ontario

Photograph by Ovi Colavincenzo

Figure 2.12.d The tidal power plant at Annapolis Royal, Nova Scotia. The Bay of Fundy has the highest tides in the world. This site harnesses energy from the regular rise and fall of the tidal waters.

future, animal manure may be gathered on a larger scale to produce methane gas for fuel.

Garbage is also a potential source of energy. Scientists are developing energy cells that convert waste to power. Incinerating garbage can provide energy. However, maintaining air quality is a limiting factor.

It is important to realize that these sources of energy, which are all renewable, can help maintain a clean environment in one way and contribute to environmental problems in another.

Figure 2.12.e The ARK is an experimental house at Spry Point in PEI. Many alternate forms of energy such as solar collectors, building site orientation (windows face south), windmills, and battery storage are built into the house.

QUESTIONS & ACTIVITIES

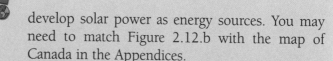

1. Name five sources of alternate energy.
2. Write a definition and give two examples for the following terms:
   a) renewable energy sources
   b) non-renewable energy sources
3. a) How do alternate forms of energy help the environment?
   b) How could these forms become environmental problems as well?
4. Study Figure 2.12.b. Select three cities that could develop wind power and three cities that could develop solar power as energy sources. You may need to match Figure 2.12.b with the map of Canada in the Appendices.
5. Explain why solar power is a poor alternative for people living north of sixty degrees latitude. (You may want to refer back to section 1.7.)
6. Use your Resource Centre and the Internet to research an alternate source of fuel for automobiles, e.g., hydrogen fuel-cell, solar- or battery-powered cars. Write a "consumers report" on the chosen fuel.

MINING IN THE CANADIAN SHIELD

Major Concepts
- The size and location of the Canadian Shield
- Mining in the Canadian Shield
- Minerals and their location
- Open-pit and shaft mining

Canada produces over 50 different kinds of minerals, rocks, and fuels from over five hundred mines, pits, and quarries. It produces more nickel and zinc than any other country. In 1997, 368 000 people were directly employed in the mining industry.

The Canadian Shield is Canada's largest geologic region (Figure 2.13.a). It circles around Hudson Bay, and its 4.6 million square kilometres occupy almost half of the total area of Canada (9.97 million square kilometres). The Shield, formed at the birth of the planet,

has some of the oldest rock formations on Earth. This enormous area of low rocky hills, forests, and tundra contains some of the richest mineral resources on the planet.

The Shield is a very stable area of massive rocks. Almost no earthquakes occur here. Any volcanic activity happened billions of years ago. Large deposits of metallic minerals occurred when the original **igneous rock** intruded into the surrounding materials. Minerals like gold, diamonds, silver, lead, iron, nickel, copper, and many others were formed.

Many minerals are found in ore bodies. **Minerals** are naturally formed, inorganic crystalline solids that have one or more chemical elements and have definite physical properties. Single element minerals are gold, silver, or copper. Others, such as gypsum, are made up of several elements. However, minerals all have a crystalline structure.

Canada also has natural mineral resources that are not true minerals. Liquid mercury, water, petroleum, and coal are valuable materials that are not true minerals. Petroleum and coal have an organic origin.

Minerals are usually found by prospectors with a background in geology and geophysics who explore with Geiger counters, Global Positioning Systems (GPS), rock hammers, and maps. They find signs of **ore deposits** and stake claims to the mineral rights of the land.

Sudbury is Canada's major mining centre. It began accidentally during railway construction in the 1880s when a huge nickel and copper belt was discovered. The region still produces more nickel than any

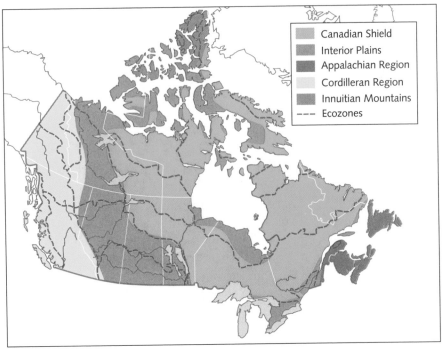

Figure 2.13.a Geologic regions of Canada. Mining products, methods, and activities are related to geologic regions and the minerals contained in the rocks.

Legend:
- Canadian Shield
- Interior Plains
- Appalachian Region
- Cordilleran Region
- Innuitian Mountains
- - - - Ecozones

FILE

FACT

Ore
Ore is a mixture of valuable and worthless minerals from which at least one of the minerals can be extracted at a profit. If a type of mineral has proven reserves and a market demand, a mining company will build the mine to develop it.

EXPLORATION

Area Selection

7 Years +

PRELIMINARY	ADVANCED	DEPOSIT EVALUATION
• air geophysics • chemical surveys • prospecting geology	• land purchase • ground geophysics, geological, and geochemical studies • environmental studies • preliminary closure plan • drilling • roads	• bulk sampling • mineral inventory • ore estimate • underground exploration • mine and plant design • feasibility studies

DEVELOPMENT | PRODUCTION | CLOSURE

1–3 Years	**Up to 75 Years**	**Post-Closure**
• infrastructure • mine development • plant construction • install environmental protection equipment • design closure plan	• hire production employees • begin extraction, milling, smelting, refining • expand mine • tailings disposal and treatment • monitor environmental impacts • market promotion and sales • invest in new production and environmental protection technologies • internal exploration and delineation	• site rehabilitation • closure monitoring

Figure 2.14.b Each stage of the mining process is described in this chart.

Figure 2.14.c Geologist at work

The Interior Plains and Lowlands are huge areas of **sedimentary rocks**. These layers of rocks were deposited in shallow seas that once covered these parts of Canada. These warm shallow seas were filled with animals and plants. As the animals and plants died, their bodies were buried in sediment and they turned into fossil fuels. These remains form the deposits of the oil and natural gas industries of Alberta, Saskatchewan, and the territories in the North as well as the Tar Sands in the Athabaska region.

Oil drilling rigs are moved onto sites where geologists hope to strike oil or gas. Heavy-duty drills can reach three kilometres deep. Gas and oil pipelines move the raw material to refineries. Then the pipelines, ships, trains, and trucks move the refined products to consumers.

Most deposits in Canada have been developed in fairly accessible parts of the country. Frontier exploration takes geologists to more difficult places. The Arctic Lowlands present huge challenges with the climate and potential environmental problems. Large resources are still to be developed in the Beaufort Sea.

The Hibernia oil fields are located on the Grand Banks off Newfoundland. Floating oil rigs must be permanently stationed in the ocean to drill for the deposits under the Atlantic floor. Moving workers and supplies across the water to the site, avoiding icebergs and protecting the environment from oil spills are major challenges to this industry which could bring wealth to Newfoundland and the other Atlantic provinces.

Figure 2.14.d Production of leading materials

Province or Territory	Metals ($'000)	Industrial Minerals ($'000)	Fuels ($'000)	Total Province or Territory ($'000)	Percent of Total
Newfoundland	902 957	31 138	0	934 095	1.90
Prince Edward Island	0	3 395	0	3 395	0.01
Nova Scotia	0	205 899	391 573	597 472	1.22
New Brunswick	589 917	310 531	24 310	924 758	1.88
Quebec	2 183 670	1 136 326	0	3 319 996	6.75
Ontario	4 140 785	1 420 722	82 105	5 643 612	11.48
Manitoba	843 816	68 583	111 511	1 023 909	2.08
Saskatchewan	642 771	1 141 958	3 430 739	5 215 467	10.61
Alberta	348	486 442	25 552 617	26 039 407	52.96
British Columbia	1 526 486	462 893	2 258 839	4 248 218	8.64
Yukon Territory	400 328	3 760	18 981	423 069	0.86
Northwest Territories	521 496	20 489	256 419	798 403	1.62
Canada	11 752 573	5 292 136	32 127 094	49 171 802	100.00

Sources: Natural Resources Canada; Statistics Canada
Note: Numbers may not add to totals due to rounding.

Figure 2.14.e   Mining production by province, 1996

▲
Figure 2.14.f   Hibernia offshore oil rig

◀**Figure 2.14.g**   Here iron ore from Wabush Mines in Labrador is being loaded on a 200T Cat truck.

QUESTIONS & ACTIVITIES ?

1. Give an example of:
   a) a single mineral element
   b) a compound mineral element
   c) a non-mineral resource.
2. a) Copy Figure 2.14.b in your notebook.
   b) Work with a partner to find out what each item in the chart means and write a point-form note beside it. Take notes when the class gives their ideas and a summary is made by your teacher.
3. a) Make a list of three minerals (choose them from Figure 2.14.a), the metal contained in them, and the uses of the metal.
   b) Pick a metal object in your classroom. Try to figure out what metal it is made from and try to determine its origin in Canada.
4. Work in a team of four people to investigate the areas of mineral exploration in Canada. Choose one from: natural gas in the Beaufort Sea, oil from the Athabaska Tar Sands, oil from Hibernia, nickel from Voisey's Bay, or natural gas from Sable Island.

   Make a report for the site to include: how the resource will be developed and refined, how it will get to market, environmental and wildlife concerns and the impact on Native peoples and other local residents.

WATER AS A RESOURCE

Major Concepts
- Water is a resource
- Canada's supply of fresh water
- Demands for water resources

Water is a combination of hydrogen and oxygen. It comes in liquid, solid and gaseous states. Water covers 75% of the Earth, and Canada has almost 10% of that water. This makes us a resource-rich nation in water.

Water moves continually through the environment in the **water cycle**. The weather systems of Canada distribute the water in a variety of patterns. Because of Canada's northern latitude, less than 50% of the water evaporates. Much of it is held in the form of ice. Water is abundant on the West Coast where mountains cause **relief rainfall**.

To irrigate crops Alberta uses over half of the water consumed in Canada; but it has only 3% of the water supply. Ontario and Quebec have abundant amounts, but quality of water can be a factor because of pollution.

Water is gathered into a system of natural **drainage basins**. From these basins a network of rivers returns the water to the sea. Canada has drainage systems that flow to three oceans: the Pacific, the Arctic, and the Atlantic. Canada's longest river system is the Mackenzie River, while the St. Lawrence has the largest discharge.

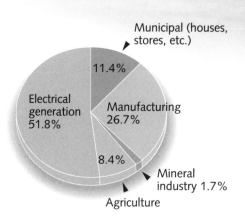

Figure 2.15.b Canada's water use. What sector consumes the largest amount?

Canada has a series of lakes at the edge of the Canadian Shield. When the glaciers moved off the hard granite of the Shield onto softer sedimentary rock, they gouged out lake basins. Great Bear Lake, Great Slave Lake, Lake Winnipeg, and the Great Lakes were formed this way. The Shield itself is covered with thousands of smaller lakes.

Water has been a transportation resource since earliest times. From Native peoples and fur traders in the past, to pleasure yachts, and grain ships today, boats use the waterways of Canada. The St. Lawrence drains the Great Lakes, the largest collection of fresh-water lakes in the world. Lake Superior at the head of the lakes is the largest fresh-water lake in the world. Waterfalls have been a source of energy and tourism. Niagara Falls provides power to Ontario and draws thousands of tourists to view its scenic beauty. Della Falls in BC, with a drop of 440 m, is the highest falls in Canada, while Niagara drops about 50 m.

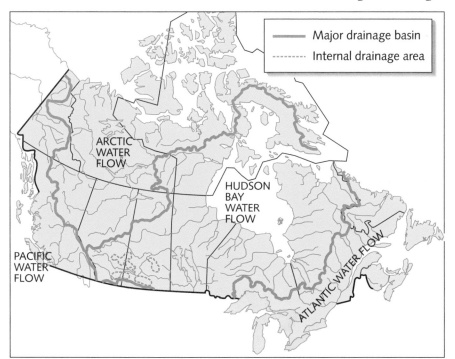

Figure 2.15.a The drainage basins of Canada. Refer to section 1.12 to review the major concepts that are used in this section.

Water is essential to the support and enjoyment of life. Although Canada is rich in this resource, we take it for granted. Canada has one of the highest consumption rates per person of water in the world. Care and conservation must be used to preserve this renewable resource.

Conflicts often arise over how to use this treasure. The Fraser River in BC would make an excellent hydro source, but that would cause problems for the salmon swimming upstream to spawn. The Great Lakes provide huge supplies of freshwater, but have been heavily polluted by shoreline cities. Today, many cities are restoring their waterfronts to their natural conditions. Commercial fishing fleets are at odds with recreational use over the types and conditions of fishing in the lakes. Both groups are important to the economy of the lakes.

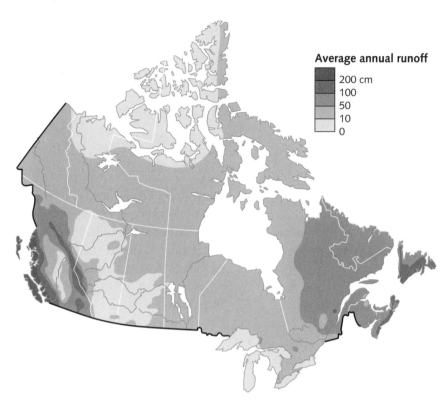

Average annual runoff

	200 cm
	100
	50
	10
	0

Figure 2.15.c Average annual runoff in Canada. The runoff from snow and rainfall are primary sources of water. Some parts of Canada have a surplus and some have shortages. Identify your local region on the map and describe the runoff conditions there.

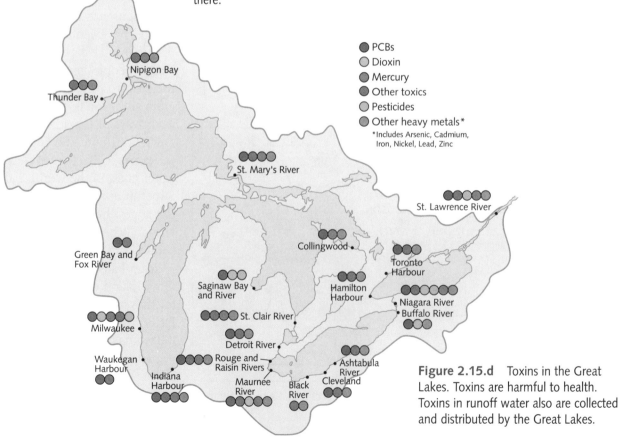

- PCBs
- Dioxin
- Mercury
- Other toxics
- Pesticides
- Other heavy metals*

*Includes Arsenic, Cadmium, Iron, Nickel, Lead, Zinc

Nipigon Bay
Thunder Bay
St. Mary's River
St. Lawrence River
Collingwood
Green Bay and Fox River
Toronto Harbour
Saginaw Bay and River
Hamilton Harbour
Niagara River
Buffalo River
Milwaukee
St. Clair River
Detroit River
Waukegan Harbour
Rouge and Raisin Rivers
Ashtabula River
Cleveland
Indiana Harbour
Maumee River
Black River

Figure 2.15.d Toxins in the Great Lakes. Toxins are harmful to health. Toxins in runoff water also are collected and distributed by the Great Lakes.

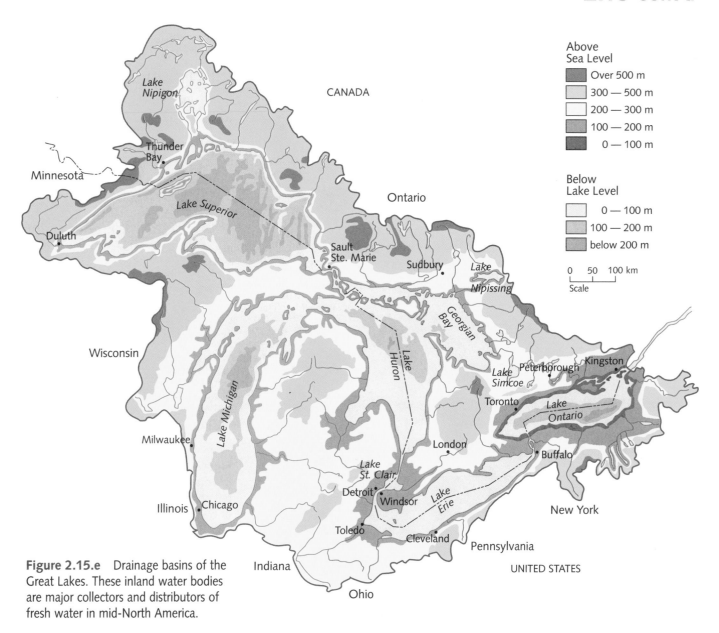

Figure 2.15.e Drainage basins of the Great Lakes. These inland water bodies are major collectors and distributors of fresh water in mid-North America.

Figure 2.15.f Some of the best recreational sailing grounds in the world are on the Great Lakes.

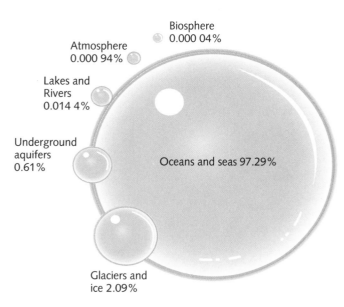

Figure 2.15.g World distribution of water. Fresh water sources become very valuable and significant when you study the percentages on this diagram.

Water export blasted

U.S. commission opposes Ontario firm's plan

BY JASON HOPPS
REUTERS NEWS AGENCY

The director of the U.S. Great Lakes Commision says his environmental watchdog group has joined the fight against an Ontario company that wants a permit to export Lake Superior water to Asia.

"If you start a trickle, it could soon turn into a fatal problem," said Michael Donahue, director of the Michigan-based Great Lakes Commission.

"Since the 1970s, Canada and the United States have spent $11 billion (U.S.) cleaning up the Great Lakes. We didn't clean the water so a private interest can scoop it up and sell it, " he said.

A company called Nova Group, based in Sault Ste. Marie, is fighting the Ontario government's repeal of a water-export license it had granted the company in March. The permit was revoked in May after a flood of protest from Canadian and U.S. environmental groups.

The Nova Group, whose plan is to ship millions of litres of Lake Superior water to irrigate Asian crops, will try to win back the permit at a Dec. 7 hearing in Sault Ste. Marie.

"The water is a shared bi-national resource and the Great Lakes states were not consulted before the permit was issued," he said.

The Ontario government and eight U.S. states signed the Great Lakes Charter in 1985, a non-binding agreement on water use and management. Donahue said Ontario violated the spirit of that agreement when it originally granted the Nova Group a permit to export water.

Oct. 28, 1998

Figure 2.15.i Water is a resource and it is often in short supply. This story reflects a growing concern about the sale of Great Lakes' fresh water.

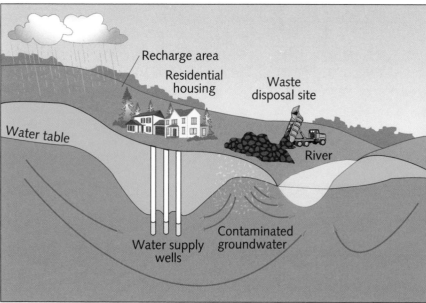

Figure 2.15.h Groundwater contamination cycle

Figure 2.15.j River rafting is a popular way to enjoy flowing river waters.

	Elevation	Length	Breadth	Maximum depth	Total area	Area on Canadian side of boundary
	m	km	km	m	km²	km²
Superior	184	563	257	405	82 100	28 700
Michigan	176	494	190	281	57 800	—
Huron	177	332	295	229	59 600	36 000
Erie	174	388	92	64	25 700	12 800
Ontario	75	311	85	244	18 960	10 000

Source: Natural Resources Canada, Canada Centre for Remote Sensing, GeoAccess.
Note: Lake St. Clair is omitted.

Figure 2.15.k   Comparative table of the Great Lakes. Which lake is not part of Canada?

QUESTIONS & ACTIVITIES

1. a) What percentage of the Earth's water does Canada have?

b) Why does so little water evaporate in Canada?

c) What percentage is held as ice?

d) What percentage of the world's water is held in the oceans and seas?

2. What are four uses Canadians make of their water resources?

3. What are the three oceans that create Canada's coastline?

4. In previous Geography classes, you made diagrams to illustrate the water cycle.

a) Draw a copy of the water or hydrologic cycle in your notes.

b) Copy Figure 2.15.h into your notebook.

c) Relate how the water flow in Figure 2.15.h fits into the water cycle and how it causes problems for ground water use.

5. a) What are four causes of water pollution?

b) Describe how they have affected various lakes and rivers across Canada.

6. Describe how the demand for hydroelectric power can cause conflict with people's demands for recreational water use.

7. Explain why commercial fisheries are often in conflict with recreational fishing.

8. Read the newspaper article in Figure 2.15.i.

a) What is involved in this issue?

b) Who is interested in selling the water and for what purpose?

c) Who opposes this development and why?

d) The federal government recently passed a law banning water exports. Do you agree with this law?

e) Set up a debate and choose one side of the proposition:

"Be it resolved that it should be illegal to sell water from the Great Lakes."

9. The Great Lakes are a great resource for Canada and the US. Organize into groups of five people, with each person responsible for a Great Lake. (Omit Lake St.Clair). Each person is responsible for:

a) making a scale map of the lake (all five students should use the same scale).

b) describing the general location, borderline location, and identifying the main cities on their lake.

c) describing the main economic activities around their lake, and describing any environmental areas of concern and what is being done about them.

d) put the maps together to form a composite map of the Great Lakes and mount them in a display.

e) put labels on the main points of interest for all the lakes.

CHANGING PERSPECTIVES

When people want to protect or evaluate something, they find it helpful to develop a checklist of criteria to make sure everything they want to study is included. Preserving and protecting Canada's wilderness and good farmland areas are two important goals for the future. Select either wilderness or farmlands and make a list of 8 to 10 criteria that would be important factors to check in order to maintain these areas. Analyze these factors and explain how they would help you to form a plan to keep the land in its current condition. Can you also predict where opposition to keeping the land in its present condition may come from?

Perspectives on Research: Questions

Well-thought-out questions are important in good research. You can improve how you read a question and answer a question, or write a question.

Reading questions: On a test, some questions need only a one-word answer, while others may require an essay. Learn to read carefully to determine the type of answer required. Practise re-reading questions.

Writing questions: Determine whether you want to ask a question solely to collect facts, or whether you want to gather statements, opinions, arguments, or conclusions. You should also consider what answer you expect to get from your question. An interesting experiment is to write a few test survey questions and record the answers you think you will get. Then try the questions out with a few of your classmates or teachers. Compare your actual results with your predicted results and analyze the reasons for any differences.

For more about designing questionnaires and surveys, see "Perspectives on Research: Questionnaires and Surveys" on page 194.

UNIT 3 PATTERNS IN RESOURCE USE

Our activities in extracting and processing natural resources produce geographic patterns. These patterns shape the human systems that give Canada and Canadians distinctive characteristics.

SETTLEMENT PATTERNS

Major Concepts

- Factors affecting settlement patterns
- Seigneurial long lots
- Townships, counties, and the grid square system

In Canada, culture as well as geography influenced **settlement patterns**. In Quebec, the **seigneurial system** of early French settlement created a pattern of long, narrow lots extending back from the main rivers such as the St. Lawrence. Farms had this special shape because before the 1730s rivers were the only means of transportation and all lots had to have some waterfront property. As well, the farm houses could be close to one another for protection. The seigneurs owned the long lots and rented lots to people who were willing to clear the land and farm it. The land on each farm ranged from the fertile soil deposits at the river's edge to the forests on the rocky Canadian Shield. To this day, dairy farming along the fertile shores and maple syrup woodlots provide important farm products in Quebec.

Surveyors in Ontario working for the English monarchy took a different approach to dividing the land. They wanted to impose a certain

FACT FILE

Geography and Patterns of Settlement

As the transcontinental railway was being built, settlers were encouraged to move west and settle along the railway.

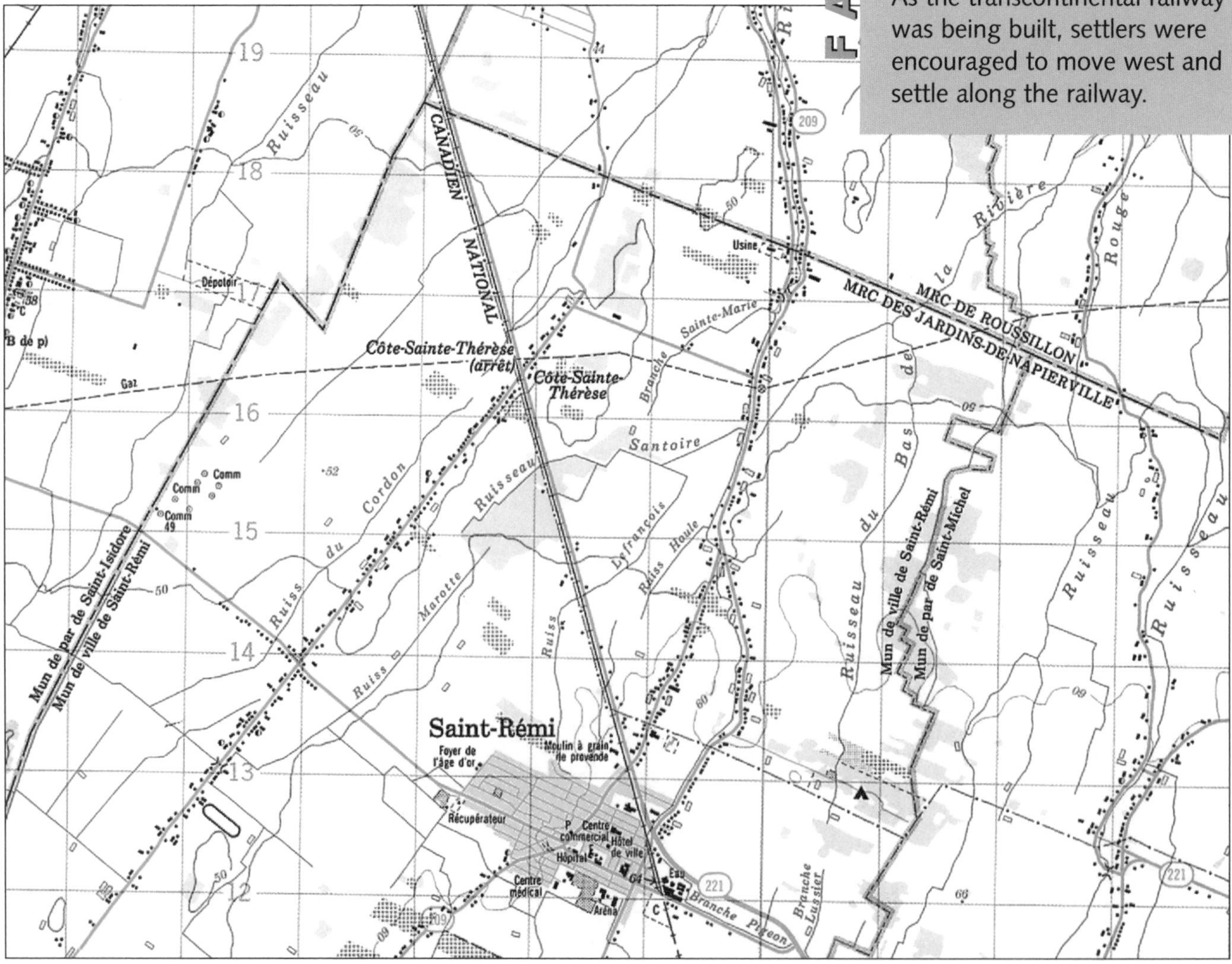

Figure 3.1.a Topographic map of St. Rémi, Quebec (31 H/F). Scale 1:50 000

Figure 3.1.b This air photo of long lots in St. Rémi, Quebec, shows some of the area shown in Figure 3.1.a.

order on the landscape and used a geometric square as their measure, forming grids over the land. Counties and townships were laid out with concession roads and township lines running north-south and east-west no matter what the landscape was like. Ontario farms, most owned by the people who farmed them, were laid out along these grids, which were often plotted in 100-acre (40 ha) units. Many Canadian cities also have a core **grid pattern** of streets that follow the main compass points of North, South, East, and West.

The settlement of the Prairies was controlled by a grid pattern as well. A huge grid was placed over on the relatively flat Prairies. Townships were created that were six miles by six miles (9.6 km x 9.6 km) square. Each block in the grid contained 36 sections of a square mile (2.6 km^2) each (Figure 3.1.g). One of these parcels was set aside for schools, and some for churches.

Most were given to new farmers in quarter sections of 160 acres (64.75 ha). Ploughing, planting, and harvesting these quarter sections was the beginning pattern of settlement in this region of Canada.

Population patterns in other parts of Canada are noticeable by their connection to resources. The sea and its bounty of food led to settlements along coastlines. Mining sites, logging sites, hydroelectric sites, passes through mountains, and crossing points along rivers are all factors that influenced the settlement patterns of Canada.

Figure 3.1.c Most seigneuries had a church and sometimes a mill for grinding grain into flour. The seigneur who owned the land lived in a manor house. Most settlers built their houses at the river's edge where they could move by canoe to neighbours, the seigneur's manor, or the nearest town.

Scale 1:50 000 Échelle

Metres 1000   0   1000   2000   3000   4000 Mètres

Figure 3.1.d Topographic map of Stoney Creek (30 M/4). Scale 1:50 000

Figure 3.1.e Part of the area in Stoney Creek, Ontario, from an 1875 map showing the Ontario **grid square farm pattern**

One dot represents 200 people

Figure 3.2.c Population distribution, **1871**.

of living is very high and universal medicare programs generally ensure a healthy population across the nation. As a result, infant mortality is very low in Canada and most Canadians can expect to live into their late seventies and early eighties. The difference between the birth rate and the death rate (see Fact File in section 3.3) helps determine how fast a population will grow in the future. Population is also determined by the **net immigration rate** (number of **immigrants**, people coming into the country, compared to the number of **emigrants**, people leaving the country).

One dot represents 200 people

Greater than
2 000 000 people

1 000 000 – 2 000 000
500 000 – 999 999
100 000 – 499 999

Figure 3.2.d Population distribution, showing major cities (**Census Metropolitan Areas**—CMAs), 1996

Figure 3.2.e Canadian population and population growth, 1991-1996

Area Name	Population		Population Change	
	Census 1996	Census 1991	Number 1991–1996	Percent 1991–1996
Canada	28 846 761	27 296 859	1 549 902	5.68
Newfoundland	551 792	568 474	–16 682	–2.93
Prince Eward Island	134 557	129 765	4 792	3.69
Nova Scotia	909 282	899 942	9 340	1.04
New Brunswick	738 133	723 900	14 233	1.97
Quebec	7 138 795	6 895 963	242 832	3.52
Ontario	10 753 573	10 084 885	668 688	6.63
Manitoba	1 113 898	1 091 942	21 956	2.01
Saskatchewan	990 237	988 928	1 309	0.13
Alberta	2 696 826	2 545 553	151 273	5.94
British Columbia	3 724 500	3 282 061	442 439	13.48
Yukon Territory	30 766	27 797	2 969	10.68
Northwest Territories	64 402	57 649	6 753	11.71

Source: Statistics Canada

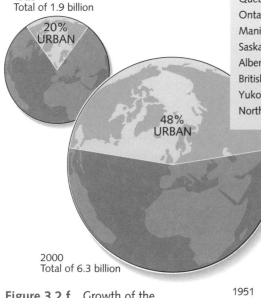

1925
Total of 1.9 billion

20% URBAN

48% URBAN

2000
Total of 6.3 billion

Figure 3.2.f Growth of the world's population

Figure 3.2.g Canada's urban population. At the end of the twentieth century, more than three-quarters of Canada's population lived in urban areas.

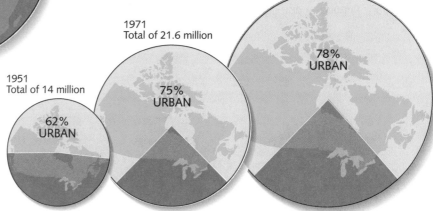

2000
Total of 31 million

1971
Total of 21.6 million

1951
Total of 14 million

62% URBAN

75% URBAN

78% URBAN

QUESTIONS & ACTIVITIES ❓

1. **a)** Why is the night light land area view in Figure 3.2.a effective?

   b) How could you actually see this type of pattern?

2. **a)** List three reasons for Canada's population pattern.

   b) Examine Figures 3.2.c and 3.2.d. List two differences and two similarities evident on the maps.

3. Make a chart to explain the population pattern in these regions of Canada:

   a) interior BC;

   b) Prince Edward Island;

   c) north shore of Lake Ontario;

   d) Montreal to Quebec City.

   Use these headings: Part of Canada, Description of Pattern, Reasons for Pattern.

4. **a)** Write definitions for the terms "urban" and "rural."

   b) What percentage of Canada is urban? What percentage is rural?

   c) What percentage of the world is urban? What percentage is rural?

   d) Make a prediction about urban and rural percentages for the next century. Will they change? Why or why not?

5. The world's population has grown rapidly. How do you think the standard of living in a country affects the population growth?

POPULATION PATTERNS AND DENSITY

Major Concepts

- Population density
- Population pyramids
- Birth rate and death rate

How many people live in Canada compared to the rest of the world?

How many males and females are there in Canada and how do those figures compare to world statistics?

How many young people, middle-aged, or old people are there?

How many people will live in Canada in the future?

The answers to some of these questions are found by using two population study tools called population density and population pyramids.

Population density is a calculation that gives the average number of people per square kilometre. If you take the total population of a country and divide it by the country's area, your result is the number of people per square kilometre, or the **density**. For Canada the density is approximately 31 000 000 ÷ 9 970 000 km² = 3.1 people per square kilometre. In comparison, Hong Kong has a density of 500 people per square kilometre, the highest population density in the world.

Population densities allow people to make some interesting comparisons. For example, we can get an idea of the population patterns within Canada by comparing the population densities of the provinces and territories. Density measurements also allow us to compare the population of Canada to populations in other parts of the world. They can also be used on a local level to compare the density of population in urban areas to those in rural areas. Figure 3.3.a shows how population density differs in different parts of Canada. When you look at these densities remember that the number 3.1 people per square kilometre is the average population density for *all* of Canada.

Population pyramids are special graphs to show the make-up of a population by age and by gender. The population is divided by five-year intervals (usually) from birth to 100 years. The number of males is plotted on one side and the number of females is plotted on the other. The pattern created gives some vital clues to the nature of a population (see Figure 3.3.b). The population pyramid for Canada is shown in Figure 3.3.c.

City and town planners use density statistics and population pyramids when planning what

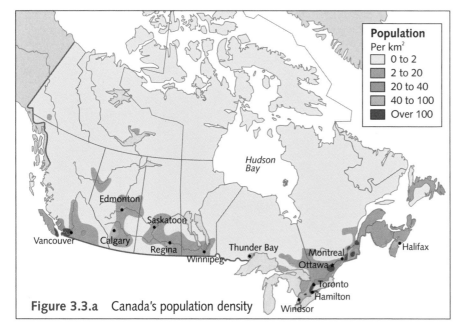

Figure 3.3.a Canada's population density

Population Per km²
- 0 to 2
- 2 to 20
- 20 to 40
- 40 to 100
- Over 100

services—for example, kinds of health services, schools, and roads—will be needed by the people living in their communities. People planning where to build new shopping malls or deciding whether to move a business to a town or city also find these population study tools useful.

Changing Population, Changing Needs

Overall, Canada has a high standard of living for all of its people. Yet the growth rate of the population is one of the lowest in the world. Canada has what is called a **stable population base**. With an aging population and better health care, Canada's population could actually fall as fewer babies are born. As the make-up of the population changes the kinds of services needed may change. The number of females in the child-bearing age range can affect the birth rate. The number of elderly can determine the death rate. Each grouping needs special types of services. An elderly population may need more health care. A baby boom may require more child care and more schools.

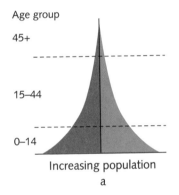

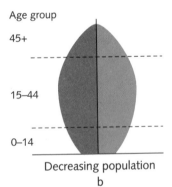

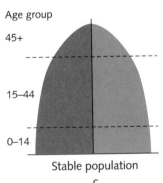

Figure 3.3.b Typical shapes of population pyramids

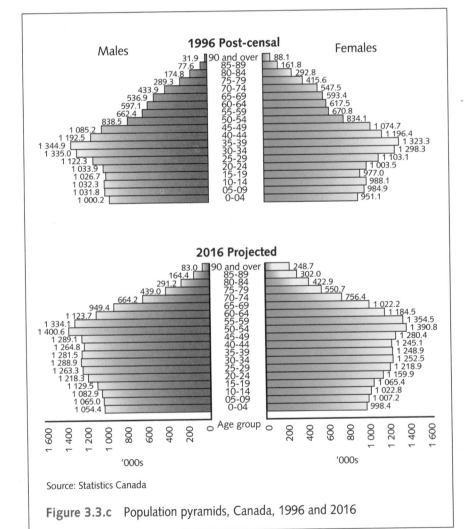

Figure 3.3.c Population pyramids, Canada, 1996 and 2016

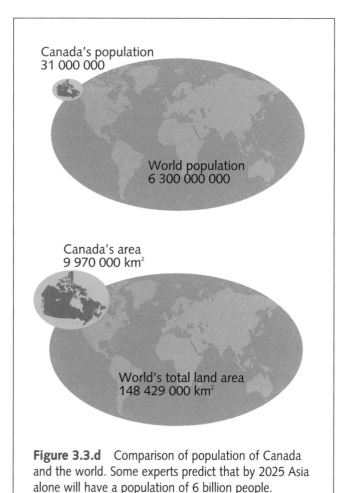

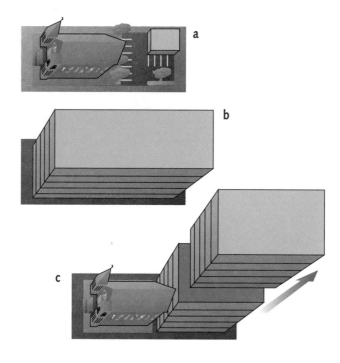

Figure 3.3.d Comparison of population of Canada and the world. Some experts predict that by 2025 Asia alone will have a population of 6 billion people.

Figure 3.3.e City density diagram. The heart of a city is constantly changing: growing, deteriorating, redeveloping. In **a**, a church occupies half a lot in an area zoned for a floor/area ratio of five. That is, the amount of floor space in a building or buildings built on that lot may not be more than five times the lot's area. The church may be torn down and a five-storey building may be constructed on the entire lot **b**. But to encourage preservation of the church, the city may ignore the church's floor space, and allow a ten-storey building to be put up on half the lot **c**.

QUESTIONS & ACTIVITIES ?

1. Make a pair of block diagrams in your notebook to show the relative size of:
   a) Canada's population compared to the world population;
   b) Canada's area compared to that of the world.
2. Study Figure 3.3.b.
   a) Describe why graph **a** shows an increasing population.
   b) Why does graph **b** mean a decreasing population?
   c) Why does graph **c** show a stable population?
3. a) Draw Canada's population pyramid in your notebook.
   b) Explain why Canada has a stable population.
   c) What factors may cause Canada's population to decrease?

4. Why does the population represented by each type of pyramid in Figure 3.3.b demand special services? List three examples of special services needed for each type.
5. a) What parts of Canada have higher population densities?
   b) List five reasons why people might prefer to live in these locations.
6. Research a list of 10 ways urban areas cope with demands created by a large population. Then, work with one or two partners to brainstorm as many additional ideas as possible. Now, condense your group's list to the 10 most important and briefly explain in writing why each is important.

LOCATION OF CITIES

Major Concepts

- Physical features create the site
- Economic relationships create the situation
- Cities provide levels of functions and services

Figure 3.4.a shows the location of Canadian cities with a population of over 50 000 people. Geographers try to explain why people choose to live together in clusters, and why some of these sites grow larger than others. A physical feature, such as rich fertile land for crops or a strategic river crossing, is often an important reason for choosing a city site. **Site** refers to the unique physical characteristics of a place.

Linked to site is what geographers refer to as the situation of a city. **Situation** refers to the location of a city within a nation or continent and its relationship to other places. The relationship is an economic one related to trade, markets, and transportation patterns. The original location of a city is usually determined by its physical site while its situation determines its rate of growth.

Quebec City is one of the oldest cities in Canada. It is located where the Gulf of St. Lawrence narrows to the channel of the St. Lawrence River. The original site of Quebec offered a port for ships, a bluff for a fort to control the shipping lanes and protect the citizens, and a fresh water river (the St. Charles) for water

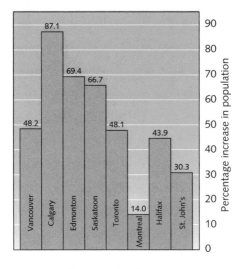

Figure 3.4.b   Growth of cities, 1971-1991

supply. Today, Quebec is a port, the provincial capital, and the heart and soul of French culture in Canada.

St. John's, Newfoundland, is another of Canada's oldest cities. It has a natural protected harbour and is Canada's link to the North Atlantic trade routes and fishing industry. Vancouver, on the opposite coast, has a site on the Fraser River delta, which provides a fertile farm area, and the Burrard Inlet, which provides sheltered port facilities. The Fraser River valley allows access to the mountain passes in the Western Cordillera.

Some of the site selections of Canada's cities are based on a single industry. Thompson, Manitoba, is a mining city. Sudbury is a mining city that has added other services such as offices of Revenue Canada.

Each community offers a range of services. Villages have **low-order services** such as variety stores, general stores, and gasoline stations. Towns add **middle-order services** such as general hospitals, community colleges, regional museums, libraries, and art galleries.

Figure 3.4.a   Canadian cities with more than 50 000 people

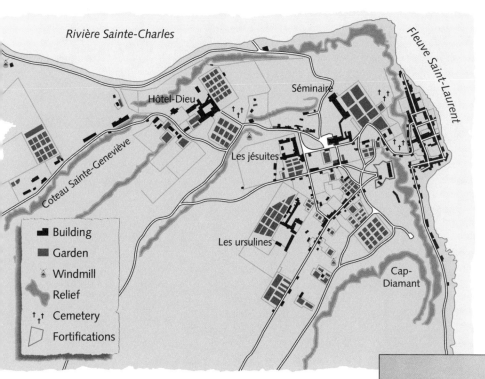

Figure 3.4.c Site map of Old Quebec, 1685, after Robert de Villeneuve

High-order services require a large population to pay for them. The Hospital for Sick Children in Toronto, Canada's largest city, serves all of Toronto and Ontario as well as cases from across Canada and from other nations. The head offices of banks and companies, the stock market, and high fashion stores are other examples of high-order services found in the largest urban centres. The higher the order of services and the more specialized these services are, the larger the population must be to support them.

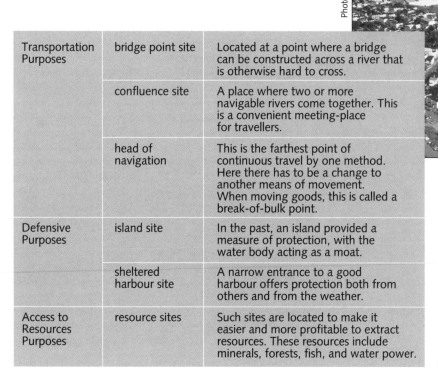

Figure 3.4.e Low-level air photo of St. John's harbour, Newfoundland.

Transportation Purposes	bridge point site	Located at a point where a bridge can be constructed across a river that is otherwise hard to cross.
	confluence site	A place where two or more navigable rivers come together. This is a convenient meeting-place for travellers.
	head of navigation	This is the farthest point of continuous travel by one method. Here there has to be a change to another means of movement. When moving goods, this is called a break-of-bulk point.
Defensive Purposes	island site	In the past, an island provided a measure of protection, with the water body acting as a moat.
	sheltered harbour site	A narrow entrance to a good harbour offers protection both from others and from the weather.
Access to Resources Purposes	resource sites	Such sites are located to make it easier and more profitable to extract resources. These resources include minerals, forests, fish, and water power.

Figure 3.4.d Reasons for the location of towns and cities

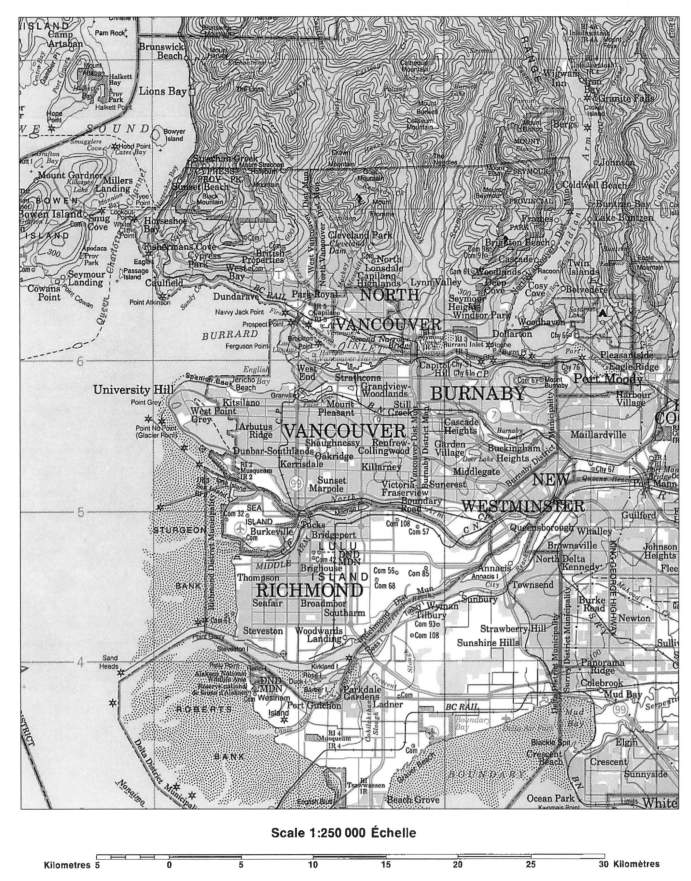

Scale 1:250 000 Échelle

Kilometres 5 0 5 10 15 20 25 30 Kilometres

Figure 3.4.f Topographic map of Vancouver and the Fraser delta (92 G). Scale 1:250 000. See also image of Vancouver and the Fraser delta in Figure 1.5.b.

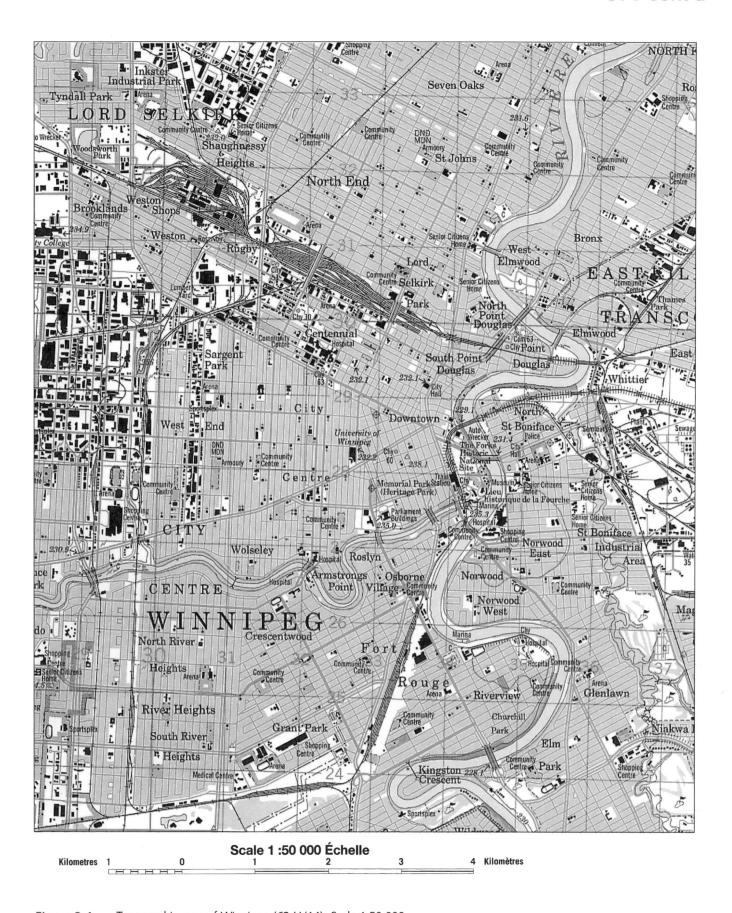

Scale 1 :50 000 Échelle

Kilometres 1   0   1   2   3   4   Kilomètres

Figure 3.4.g   Topographic map of Winnipeg (62 H/14). Scale 1:50 000

Figure 3.4.h Site and situation of Toronto's metropolitan area, 1931–1991. Populations increased between 1951 and 1971 as suburbs grew near large cities. Between 1971 and 1991, however, the highest rates of growth occurred outside metropolitan cores as people moved farther from city centres. Outlying towns and rural land were transformed by new residential and business development.

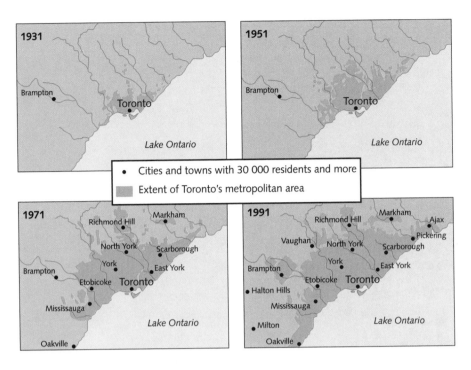

QUESTIONS & ACTIVITIES ?

1. Write a definition for site and situation. Describe the site and situation of the community where you live.

2. Figure 3.4.d lists a variety of conditions that may lead to the establishment of a community, such as the location of a bridge at a crossing point.

   a) In your notebook, match the location conditions in Column A to the cities in Column B. Use your atlas to identify the site and situation for each place and write them in your notebook.

Column A	Column B
bridge point site	Fort McMurray, Alberta
confluence site	Montreal, Quebec
head of navigation site	Sault Ste. Marie, Ontario
island site	Quebec City, Quebec
sheltered harbour site	St. John's, Newfoundland
high bluff site	Thunder Bay, Ontario
resource site.	Winnipeg, Manitoba

   b) Using an atlas, identify a least one other community in Canada that may have started from each condition in Column A. Record your answer in chart form.

3. In the past, towns and cities were often located where there was deep water or high land. Give two examples of Canadian cities that started on sites like these.

4. Describe the site and situation of Quebec City (see Figure 3.4.c).

5. Examine the sites of the following cities and describe the physical features that influenced their location:

   a) Figure 3.4.e—St. John's
   b) Figure 3.4.f —Vancouver
   c) Figure 3.4.g—Winnipeg
   d) Figure 3.4.h—Toronto

6. a) Describe the three levels of service found in urban places.

   b) Why do you think higher-order services require more population?

   c) Assign a level of service to each of the items below. Explain your choices.
   SkyDome, grocery store, movie complex, five-star restaurant, diner, fire hall, fire fighter training school.

7. What locational advantages does your community have? Research this topic and write a one-page report to describe the origin of your community and the important events and circumstances that have shaped its development.

TRANSPORTATION: MOVING PRODUCTS

Major Concepts

- Moving things requires a transportation network
- Landforms affect the network system
- Products are solid, liquid, gas, or digital

Canada's vast size, climate, and terrain present challenges to all forms of transportation. In Canada, the main forms of product transportation are water, rail, road, pipeline, telecommunication lines, and air. **Transportation systems** have adapted and changed over our history, but they are designed to get resources to manufacturers and finished products to consumers. The nature of our transportation system both ties the country together and affects the economy.

Water transportation has been important in Canada since the first Aboriginal peoples used the waterways to fish, trade, and travel. Water transportation was equally important to the first European explorers and fur traders who travelled inland in large canoes, carrying trade goods inland and returning with furs to ship across the ocean to Europe.

Today water commerce is centred around ports on the Atlantic and Pacific coasts, and on the Great Lakes-St. Lawrence Seaway system.

Halifax and St. John's are important ports on the East Coast. Vancouver is the major western port. Despite being almost mid-continent, Thunder Bay is a big port where wheat, barley, canola, other grains, and other products start their journey through the Great Lakes and St. Lawrence River. Canals and locks are vital pieces of this route as obstacles like Niagara Falls must be bypassed by artificial channels such as the Welland Canal. Ice is a critical factor as winter arrives. Saint John, New Brunswick, and the other ocean ports mentioned are ice-free and keep Canada's trade moving all year.

Since the 1870s after Confedera-

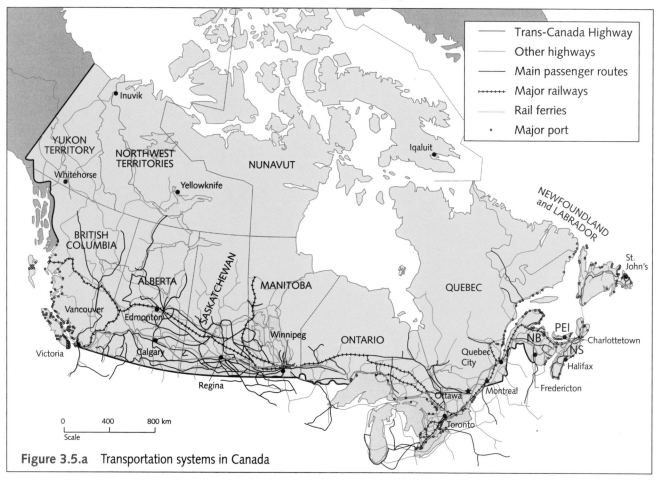

Figure 3.5.a Transportation systems in Canada

Legend:
- Trans-Canada Highway
- Other highways
- Main passenger routes
- Major railways
- Rail ferries
- Major port

Transport Mode	Climate Variables
Air	• Ceiling and visibility • Wind speed and direction • Storm occurrence • Permafrost, ice and snow cover (runways) • Open-water season (floatplanes)
Marine	• Sea-ice concentration, floe size, age, ridging • Iceberg occurrence, movement • Wave height and period • Wind speed and direction • Air temperature • Sea-level height • Storm frequency, severity
Freshwater	• River and lake ice: freeze-up and break-up dates, length of season, thickness • Precipitation
Land	• Air temperature • Precipitation • Visibility • Ice on rivers and lakes • Snow cover thickness, length of season • Permafrost characteristics

Figure 3.5.b Climate variables affecting Arctic transportation

tion was established, rails have linked Canada from coast to coast. Railways are still one of the best ways to move large, bulky freight items like grain, coal, potash, iron ore, chemicals or new vehicles. Some specialized trains are called **unit trains**. They can be over a kilometre long and carry one product, such as coal or iron ore. **Containers** are another method of moving product. Specialized cranes allow efficient moving of these "boxcar"-like containers from train to ship to truck.

Transport trucks and trailers haul materials all over the country. Fast and flexible, trucks can move containers, fresh produce, refrigerated goods, even houses. The trucking industry is vital to Canada's economy.

Pipelines are important to the gas and oil industry. Crude oil and natural gas can be distributed from their well site locations to refineries and markets very efficiently. Pipelines are expensive to build because of Canada's geography. Mountains, rivers, permafrost, and granite rock all mean high construction costs. No leaks are permissible because of the potential damage to the environment and loss of valuable product. Once pipelines are in

Figure 3.5.c Container port. Note the specialized cranes used to lift the containers onto ships.

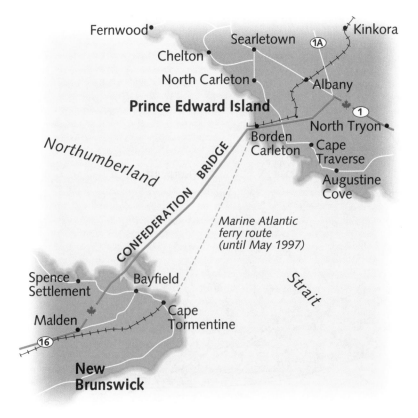

Figure 3.5.d Drawing of the site of Confederation Bridge connecting New Brunswick to PEI. The 12.9 km-long bridge is the longest bridge in the world spanning ice-water. It takes ten minutes to cross by car. Maritimers are adjusting to the alterations the bridge is bringing to their landscape and to how they move products.

Moving things		Moving people	
Road	44%	Road	84%
Rail	41%	Air	12%
Water	13%	Urban transit	2%
Air	2%	Rail	1%
		Other	1%

Figure 3.5.e Modes of transportation

place, however, materials move economically. Even coal, made into a liquid slurry, can be forced through a pipeline.

Digital information is information broken down into language code that can easily be sent through various media and that is understood by all computers. Moving digital information throughout Canada and the world has taken on added importance. New fibre-optic cables are rapidly being installed to handle the dramatic increase in volume and speed of traffic. Relay towers and satellites move information at high speed through the air. The **information highway** is becoming one of Canada's busiest transportation routes.

Air transport of goods is expensive. Yet the remote parts of Canada depend on planes for supplies. One of the largest transport businesses is courier service. The need to move parcels and packages quickly has created a demand for businesses with a fleet of trucks to collect and deliver these items. These businesses also often have their own planes to move the packages to other cities in order to meet overnight-delivery promises.

Figure 3.5.f Workers prepare to install fibre-optic cable.

QUESTIONS & ACTIVITIES

1. **a)** How has a good transportation system helped to tie Canada together? Give three examples.
   b) What challenges does Canada face in developing and maintaining a good transportation system?
2. **a)** On a map of Canada locate and label the location of Canada's main ports. Why are the Great Lakes and Arctic ports more restricted than the East and West Coast ports? Locate and label the Great Lakes and St. Lawrence Seaway system on your map.
   b) Find and draw a cross-section of the St. Lawrence Seaway to show how the lock system helps ships up and down through the waterway, and around obstacles like Niagara Falls.
3. **a)** What is a unit train?
   b) What kinds of products are carried on them?
   c) Why are they efficient ways of moving cargo?
4. **a)** What are some obstacles to building pipelines?
   b) Why are they efficient in the long term?
   c) What products are moved by pipeline?

5. **a)** How is digital information moved in Canada?
   b) Why do you think transportation technology is a growing field?
6. Write a paragraph to explain why airplanes are of limited use in moving products. Compare them to trains and trucks. What products are aircraft especially good at moving and why? Make reference to the need for air shipments to remote Arctic communities.
7. **a)** Construct two circle graphs to show the statistics in Figure 3.5.e. Plot the percentages as a pie graph. You might try using a spreadsheet program on a computer.
   b) Which transportation system is most used to move many products? Which system is second?
   c) What is the most important system for moving people, and by what percentage?

TRANSPORTATION: MOVING PEOPLE

Major Concepts

- Mobile Canadians
- The favoured automobile
- Technology and transportation
- Changes in passenger transportation
- Privacy and new transportation technology

Transportation systems help us move to and from home, work, or on vacation. There are many ways for people to move, but the automobile is the overwhelming favourite for most Canadians. They love to drive them and building them is important to our economy.

In Canada today, there are 445 cars for every 1000 people. This is three times the 1955 figure of 145 cars per 1000 people. More cars mean more traffic, and more traffic means more problems in moving people smoothly and safely. In Toronto, for example, the 401 Highway has been described as the world's longest parking lot during rush hours. In

British Columbia, pollution builds as cars and other vehicles idle for long periods of time on the bridges leading to downtown Vancouver.

Traffic planners and controllers,

police, governments, and automobile manufacturers are working to solve the problems caused by the rapidly growing traffic. Fibre-optic cable is buried under roads like the 401 to count cars, and measure the speed and the distance between vehicles. TV cameras monitor highways every kilometre. These measures help police to pinpoint problems so that they can take action before they become too serious.

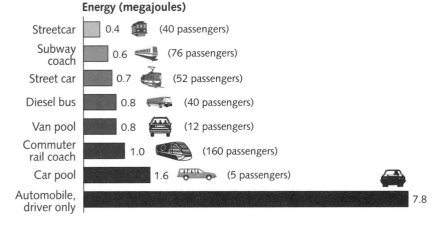

Figure 3.6.b Average energy used moving people per person per kilometre

Figure 3.6.a Ninety years ago, Ford of Canada produced an automobile every 14 hours. When mass production techniques were applied in 1913, production time was cut to just 93 minutes per vehicle. Today, Ford's Oakville Assembly can turn out new Windstars at a rate of 75 per hour or one every 48 seconds!

- Mini-van and sport utility vehicle sales have soared from 9000 in 1982 to 190 000 in 1994.
- Canadians spend an average of 90 minutes per day commuting to work. Workers in Toronto and Vancouver may spend 120 minutes commuting per day.
- Since 1988, public transit ridership has declined about 2% per year.
- Car Co-ops: Cars are owned by a group of up to 20 people and usage is scheduled and paid by time and distance.
- Transponders with GPS (Global Positioning Systems, see Figure 3.9.d) are now a reality. Many people are becoming increasingly concerned by what they see as a growing invasion of their privacy as the number of systems that monitor traffic flow by identifying particular vehicles continue to grow.

Carrier	Average capacity (persons)	Energy input in litres per vehicle per km	Energy input in litres to carry 100 persons 100 km
high-speed train	470	2.00	200
car	4	0.17	420
bus	53	0.45	90
aircraft	100	9.20	920

Figure 3.6.c Comparing efficiency of methods of moving people

Other technologies are also being used to help maintain the flow of traffic. Computers make calculations and flash notices on signs along highways to alert motorists to problems ahead. Computers also control traffic lights at busy intersections. Digital imagery cameras capture vehicle licence plates, and cars with **transponders** communicate with receivers along toll roads. Canada's first private **toll highway**, highway 407 across the top of Toronto, automatically bills vehicles using this technology. However, some people strongly oppose the use of the digital imagery cameras in this way. They argue that their privacy is being invaded.

Governments are passing increasingly tough anti-pollution laws designed to lessen pollution caused by vehicles. In April 1999, the Ontario government introduced the Ontario Drive Clean program. Under this program, when drivers in the Greater Toronto Area and the Hamilton-Wentworth Region renew their licence plates and car registration, they may have to have their vehicles checked to make sure they meet government anti-pollution standards. The program applies particularly to older vehicles.

In cities, single drivers are being encouraged to get out of their cars or take passengers. Some cities have assigned one lane of traffic exclusively to vehicles that have more than two people in them. Already expensive parking spaces in city centres are being reduced. In many cities, more people are riding bicycles to get to work. The automobile industry too is working to develop prototypes of cars and trucks that emit less pollution. These are just

some of the measures being tried to keep people and their vehicles moving safely and without too much harm to the environment.

Cars, of course, are not the only means of moving people. **Commuter trains** bring people into cities. Then rail lines underground, on ground, and even elevated, as well as subways and monorails, move passengers throughout the city. Streetcars use tracks on the street. Buses offer more flexibility, and taxi buses are being tested as an even more convenient way of picking people up and delivering them to their doorstep.

Although trains continue to be a significant way of moving people,

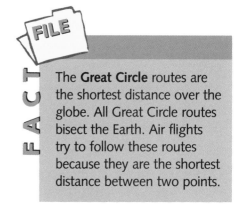

FILE

FACT

The **Great Circle** routes are the shortest distance over the globe. All Great Circle routes bisect the Earth. Air flights try to follow these routes because they are the shortest distance between two points.

10 Busiest Passenger Airports

Toronto
Vancouver
Calgary
Montreal (Dorval)
Edmonton (International)
Winnipeg
Ottawa (Macdonald-Cartier)
Halifax
Montreal (Mirabel)
Victoria

Figure 3.6.d This Arctic projection map between Canada and Russia shows possible Great Circle links between the two countries.

Figure 3.6.e Canada's busiest passenger airports, 1997

Figure 3.6.f Electronic signs inform drivers about traffic flow.

Frequency	Reasons	Usual method of transportation
Daily	• school • friends • •	
Weekly/monthly	• sports • church • entertainment • shopping • •	
Annually	• medical appointment • vacation • •	

Figure 3.6.g My Transportation Needs

planes have displaced many long-distance rail passenger routes. Today most people think of travelling across Canada by rail only as a recreational activity.

Airports in Canada are busy with business and vacation travellers in increasing numbers. The global village means business people move nationally and internationally to increase the operations of their companies.

Many of Canada's 2400 ports are designed to move people across waterways. Recreational boating is popular. Ocean travel has become more recreational since air travel is a faster form for people in a hurry.

QUESTIONS & ACTIVITIES

1. Study Figures 3.6.b and 3.6.c.
   a) What is the most efficient way to move people?
   b) If a train uses more energy per kilometre than a car, why is it more efficient to move 1000 people by train than by their individual cars?
   c) Why are subways found mostly in city cores?
2. What are the advantages and disadvantages of using commuter rail trains?
3. a) Why were trains important for moving people in the early part of this century?
   b) What forms of transportation have replaced passenger rail service? Why?
   c) What is the main attraction of trains for travellers today?
4. a) Why is flying a preferred type of travel for so many Canadians?
   b) Why are Great Circle routes used?
   c) Why does air travel to Russia and eastern European countries seem like a good option for Canadian air routes?
5. a) How is technology being used to improve the flow of traffic?
   b) From your own knowledge and from the text, how are cars being improved to reduce their impact and the problems they create?
   c) Research the use of transponders and other new transportation technologies. Do you think these technologies invade your privacy and your right to drive in private? Write an essay expressing your opinion.
6. a) Copy the headings in Figure 3.6.g into your notebook.
   b) Work with a partner to fill in your chart. Cover as many of the occasions you travel as possible.
   c) Predict how you will meet your travel needs: i) next year; ii) in 5 years; iii) in 10 years.

COMMUNICATIONS AND THE ROLE OF GOVERNMENT

Major Concepts

- Communication overcomes distance
- Governments control media patterns
- The CBC reflects Canadian culture
- The effects of Canada's relatively small market

The distance from Cape Spear in Newfoundland, Canada's most eastern point, to the Alaska border is 5500 km and covers six time zones. Today, we can communicate across that distance almost as easily as if the distance didn't exist. In fact, we can communicate globally just as quickly. We can do so because Canada has one of the best **communication systems** in the world.

The federal government's main regulatory agency is the **Canadian Radio-television and Telecommunications Commission (CRTC)**. The CRTC controls transmission on the AM, FM, and short-wave radio band widths. It also has the power to regulate antenna, satellite, and cable television.

In music videos, movies, and print services, the government is expected to balance the need for community standards with an individual's right to freedom of choice. The CRTC performs the role of enforcing community standards for what we receive on our home equipment. This role is a big task because in large urban centres there are numerous radio channel frequencies. Cablevision has the ability to add up to 500 specialty channels. The Internet and satellites that circle the globe beaming down radio and television transmissions from all parts of the world are making the role of government a complex task.

The CRTC also ensures that radio and TV reflect Canada's diversity and language rights by controlling English- and French-language channels and by making sure minorities have access to broadcast signals. The number of cultural channels is growing rapidly, including a First Nations channel launched in 1998.

The Canadian Broadcasting Corporation is the government-owned company that provides a broadcast venue for Canadian culture. CBC radio stations are on AM and FM bands as well as short wave. CBC radio and television are available to all parts of Canada with national and regional programming.

Some provinces have their own television stations. TV Ontario is a public (government-supported) broadcast station in Ontario that produces and transmits a large assortment of educational and other programming.

Figure 3.7.a Logo for Canada's national broadcast system

Canada has also developed laws to protect and encourage the growth of Canadian magazines that reflect Canadian culture and points of view. One problem area at the end of the 1990s was **split-run magazines**. These were usually popular American magazines that produce a special edition for Canada. Some

CBC radioONE		CBC radio Two	
Toronto 99.1 FM	Vancouver 690 AM	Toronto 94.1 FM	Moncton 95.5 FM
Windsor 1550 AM	Victoria 90.5 FM	Windsor 89.9 FM	Fredericton 101.5 FM
Ottawa 91.5 FM	Prince George 91.5 FM	Ottawa 103.3 FM	Vancouver 105.7 FM
Thunder Bay 88.3 FM	Kelowna 88.9 FM	London 100.5 FM	Prince George 90.3 FM
Sudbury 99.9 FM	Prince Rupert 860 AM	Thunder Bay 101.7 FM	Victoria 92.1 FM
London 93.5 FM	Regina 540 AM	Peterborough 103.9 FM	Smithers 88.1 FM
Kingston 107.5 FM	La Ronge 105.9 FM	Kingston 92.9 FM	Regina 96.9 FM
Calgary 1010 AM	La Ronge 105.9 FM	Calgary 102.1 FM	Saskatoon 105.5 FM
Edmonton 740 AM	Winnipeg 990 AM	Edmonton 90.9 FM	Winnipeg 98.3 FM
Banff 860 AM	Brandon 97.9 FM	Lethbridge 91.7 FM	Brandon 92.7 FM
Lethbridge 100.1 FM	Thompson 100.0 FM	Halifax 102.7 FM	St. John's 106.9 FM
Halifax 90.5 FM	St. John's 640 AM	Sydney 105.1 FM	Charlottetown 104.7 FM
Sydney 1140 AM	Corner Brook 990 AM	Cape Breton 105.1 FM	Montreal 93.5 FM
Fredericton 970 AM	Montreal 88.5 FM	Saint John 101.5 FM	Yellowknife 95.3 FM
Saint John 91.3 FM	Quebec City 104.7 FM		
Moncton 1070 AM	Yellowknife 1340 AM		
Charlottetown 96.1 FM	Whitehorse 570 AM		

Figure 3.7.b Location and frequencies of CBC Radio One and CBC Radio Two

American magazines added a small amount of Canadian editorial content to magazines largely already paid for by US advertisers and then charged inexpensive rates to Canadian advertisers. The government wanted to protect exclusively Canadian magazines that are trying to survive in the small population market of Canada alone. The Canadian government saw the matter as one of protecting Canadian culture. The US saw the matter as one of international trade.

E-zines are a new form of communication. These electronic publications are on the World Wide Web. At this time, governmental control is almost non-existent. These electronic magazines can originate from anywhere and can contain whatever content the publishers wish to include.

Figure 3.7.c These scenes from Canada Post's *Scenic Highways* series reflect the influence that Canada's geography has on how Canadians see themselves and their country. Stamps reproduced courtesy of Canada Post Corporation

FILE

FACT

Canada's postal service is an important agency of communication. Over 5000 post offices handle billions of pieces of mail annually. Like other countries, Canada has been divided geographically into postal code zones to improve postal service. Automated machines read mail for area codes and help sort the destinations.

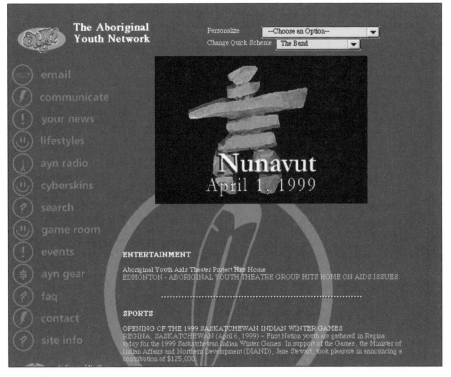

Figure 3.7.d Sample of an E-zine page on the World Wide Web

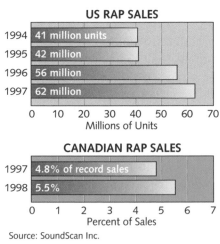

US RAP SALES

1994	41 million units
1995	42 million
1996	56 million
1997	62 million

0 10 20 30 40 50 60 70
Millions of Units

CANADIAN RAP SALES

1997	4.8% of record sales
1998	5.5%

0 1 2 3 4 5 6 7
Percent of Sales

Source: SoundScan Inc.

Figure 3.7.e Rap sales in Canada and the United States

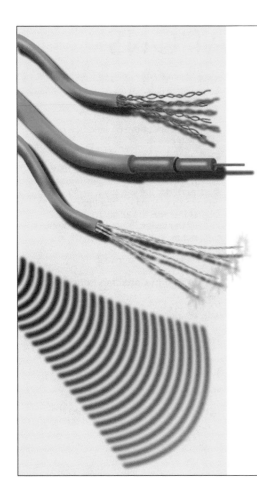

Figure 3.7.f The carrying capacity, or **bandwidth**, of different communications systems varies greatly. Telephone lines in most homes are twisted copper wires with a narrow bandwidth (top). Cable TV uses **coaxial cable**, a tube of conductors that can carry a hundred times the load of a copper phone line. Long-distance phone calls pulse along **fibre-optic cables** (see also Figure 3.5.f) capable of carrying tens of thousands of times that of copper. **Satellite signals** (bottom) carry more than coaxial cable but less than fibre optics.

FILE

FACT

The US government now provides a weather forecast for space. It will predict violent solar storms that may bombard Earth with supercharged atomic particles. These storms can disable satellites and result in fuzzy TV reception. They can disrupt cellular phones or disabled navigational devices (see the case study in Unit 3.8.).

QUESTIONS & ACTIVITIES

1. a) On a blank map of Canada and using the information in Figure 3.7.b, plot the CBC radio stations. Use a different colour for Radio 1 and Radio 2.
   b) Label Cape Spear, Point Pelee, the Yukon border, and Alert to mark the extreme points of Canada.
2. a) What is the full name of the CRTC?
   b) What are four functions it performs?
   c) Examine the sale of Rap music in Figure 3.7.e. How might this increase in sales create problems for CRTC and community standards?
3. a) What is a split-run magazine?
   b) Research and give three examples of Canadian national magazines.
   c) Research and give three examples of split-run magazines from the US.
   d) Explain why population is a factor in magazine

sales between Canada and the US.
4. a) What is an E-zine?
   b) How do you get a copy?
   c) Why does the growth of E-zines present problems for Canada's CRTC?
5. a) Explain how postal codes assist mail distribution.
   b) How does having postal codes lead to more use of technology in delivering mail?
6. If there is no air in space, why do people need space weather reports?.
7. a) Calculate how many hours of television you watch per week. Compare your time with other members of the class.
   b) Predict some programming that will fill the possible 500 channels in the future. Compare your choices with those of your classmates.

MASS MARKET COMMUNICATIONS

Major Concepts

- Satellites are vital and vulnerable
- Mass media as indirect communication
- The variety of mass market communication

Canada was the third nation to have a satellite in space and the first to use satellites for communication within its own territories. The current **Anik** series (Figure 3.8.a) of satellites, which took their name from the Inuktitut word for "brother," last about seven years before running out of fuel or becoming obsolete. Satellites relay television, daily newspapers, and telecommunication signals. They allow Global Positioning Systems (GPS) to work (see Figures 3.9.b, 3.9.c, and 3.9.d). The earth is constantly photographed from space and the photographs returned to earth via satellites, giving us an enormous variety of images. These images help us to create up-to-date and specialized maps, track ice conditions and land-use changes, and give global peacekeepers and military personnel information that helps them carry out their operations safely and effectively.

Information that is made available to many people is a form of **indirect communication** called mass communication or **mass media**. Television is the best known form of mass communication. In 1998, over 97% of homes in Canada had a television set. Signals are received through antennae, satellite signals to dishes, cablevision or its subsidiary, pay television. The number of cable channels is exploding with the 60 to 70 channels of today soon to become 500.

While radio is still very popular, it is currently a declining mass medium in terms of numbers of listeners and advertising revenue.

Commuters in cars listen for news and traffic reports. Some listeners select from a variety of stations that play music geared to select markets. Others tune in daily to their favourite talk show.

Magazines and newspapers deliver mass market information. Canada has a few national magazines and

Techno Facts:
Some facts about the proliferation of video screens:

Techno-terms:
Screenagers: the generation who have grown up in a multiscreen environment.
Data persona: the identity a person takes on in the anonymity of the Internet.
Digital literacy: the ability to use and understand technology such as computers, cell phones, automatic bank machines and the Internet.
VDT: video display terminal.

Percentage of Canadian households:
with computers:
In 1996: **31.6**   (1997): **36.0**
with Internet access
In 1996: **7.4**   (1997): **13.0**
with cell phones
In 1996: **14.1**   (1997): **18.6**

Source: The Canadian Press, January 1999

Figure 3.8.b   Some facts about modern technology

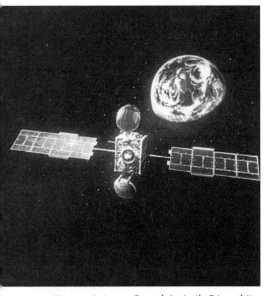

Figure 3.8.a   Canada's *Anik-E* in orbit around the Earth. TELESAT Canada

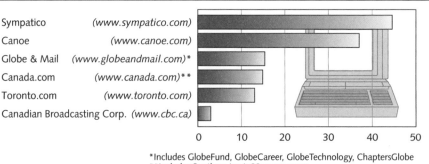

		0	10	20	30	40	50
Sympatico	(www.sympatico.com)						
Canoe	(www.canoe.com)						
Globe & Mail	(www.globeandmail.com)*						
Canada.com	(www.canada.com)**						
Toronto.com	(www.toronto.com)						
Canadian Broadcasting Corp.	(www.cbc.ca)						

*Includes GlobeFund, GlobeCareer, GlobeTechnology, ChaptersGlobe
**Includes Southam Inc.'s 33 newspapers

Figure 3.8.c   News on-line: Canada's most popular Web sites for news and information based on page views per month. With its news and information pages, the Internet has become a major means of mass communication.

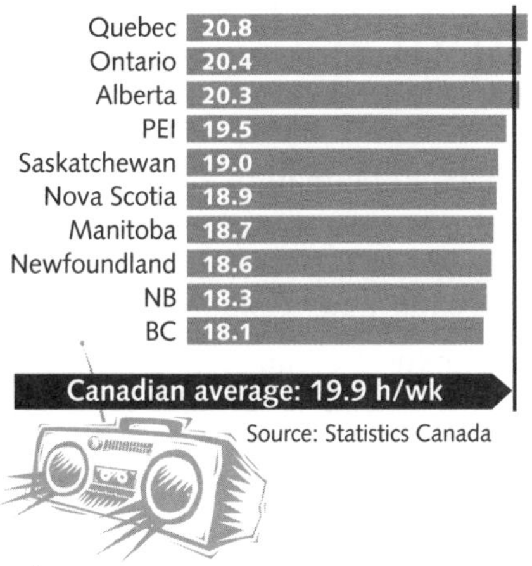

Quebec	20.8
Ontario	20.4
Alberta	20.3
PEI	19.5
Saskatchewan	19.0
Nova Scotia	18.9
Manitoba	18.7
Newfoundland	18.6
NB	18.3
BC	18.1

Canadian average: 19.9 h/wk

Source: Statistics Canada

Figure 3.8.d Average hours per week that Canadians listen to the radio. Time spent listening to the radio in 1997 fell for the fourth consecutive year to 19.9 hours a week from 20.2 in 1996.

CASE STUDY The Leonids

The largest recurring meteor shower in space is called the **Leonids**. Every 33 years in mid-November, the orbit of the Earth intersects with this cloud of meteor particles. On November 17, 1998, scientists from around the world flocked to the remote Gobi Desert for the best viewing site on the planet for witnessing the Leonids crossing. The shower of rock, sand, and ice particles in the meteor shower sandblasts the upper atmosphere of earth causing a spectacular display of meteorites or shooting stars. The problem that has developed since the last visit of Leonids in 1965/66 is the large number of satellites now in orbit around the Earth. A direct hit by one of the particles could knock a satellite out of commission. Its television, telephone and data transmission could be permanently damaged. In 1998 some satellites were turned so that they presented their smallest surface to the on-coming storm.

two national newspapers competing to cover the news. Provincially, many daily newspapers bring reports of the world to citizens. A major role of national magazines and newspapers is to maintain a Canadian presence and national identity across the country. Smaller magazines and newspapers concentrate on special interest groups, particular industries and institutions, or local news and conditions.

Today, the **Internet**, with its e-zines, news, information, shopping, and banking abilities, is a rapidly growing form of mass communication.

Television, the Internet and other electronic avenues are redirecting how we work, play, and reach out to one another.

QUESTIONS & ACTIVITIES

1. a) How many countries had satellites in orbit before Canada?
   b) What is the present satellite series called? What does its name mean?
   c) How long do these satellites last in space? Why?
2. List five things that rely on satellite transmission of data.
3. a) What is indirect communication?
   b) Examine Figure 3.8.d. Although 98% of Canadians have a radio, the number of listeners is declining. Why do you think this is so?
   c) List your favourite radio station(s) and calculate how much you listen per day and per week. Compare your answers with those of your classmates. Make a graph or chart of the whole class's responses.
4. a) Examine Figure 3.8.c. What are the three most popular news pages?
   b) Why do you think people view the Web pages for news?
   c) Rank the following for speedy reporting of news: radio, television, daily newspaper, news magazines, Internet news. Give reasons for each ranking.
   d) How do news magazines (weekly or monthly) make up for the slower delivery of news?
   e) What are some problems involved with early or fast reporting of breaking news stories?
   f) How do smaller magazines and community newspapers compete for readers?
5. a) What is the Leonids?
   b) How often does this event occur?
   c) What major changes have occurred since its 1965/66 meeting with Earth?
   d) How can particles affect satellites and transmission signals?

PERSONAL AND BUSINESS COMMUNICATIONS

Major Concepts

- Global personal and business communications
- Fax, e-mail, e-commerce, and the Internet
- Person-to-person as direct communication

Faxes and **e-mail** or electronic messages are alternatives to postal or courier services. A wide variety of organizations and businesses are developing e-commerce or e-business to provide goods and services on a global basis.

With the launch of sixty-six new low-orbit satellites in late 1998, the range of personal and business communications became truly global. The neighbourhood for phone calls now includes every corner of the earth. When a conversation occurs between two people and messages are relayed immediately, the process is called **direct communication**. The Internet provides an extension of this person-to-person communication by allowing many people to communicate directly with many others.

Canadians are used to having excellent communications. The telephone is the most widely used system. From home you can pick up the phone and by dialing eleven digits or so, you can reach almost anywhere in the world. With the satellite system, you can have that phone in your pocket and reach anywhere.

The use of **GIS** (Geographical Information Systems) mapping has allowed the 911 service of rescue and aid to be implemented. All houses are numbered and electronically mapped for emergency vehicles to respond to calls for help. The **GPS** (Global Positioning Systems, Figures 3.9.b, 3.9.c, and 3.9.d) allows boaters, hikers, or trekkers to identify their position on earth within 100 m. A cell phone can relay the information to outside agencies.

The Internet is a major tool in personal communication. As more households get personal computers, many quickly add Internet access. These services can come over phone cable, television cable, fibre-net optics, or satellite digital transmissions. Once a person is logged onto the service, the Internet world awaits. However, hazards exist in many forms. The Internet is somewhat like the Wild West of the past. There are few regulations and controls on the information that is posted on the Internet. It is difficult to check the accuracy of material, misinformation is common, hate messages are hard to screen out, and advertisers compete for attention.

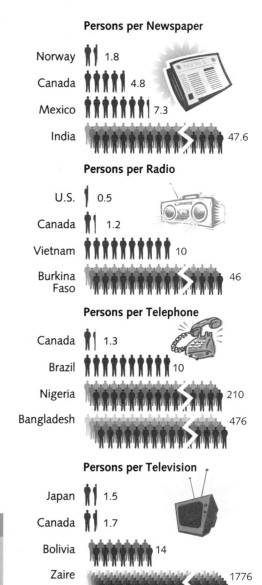

Persons per Newspaper

Norway	1.8
Canada	4.8
Mexico	7.3
India	47.6

Persons per Radio

U.S.	0.5
Canada	1.2
Vietnam	10
Burkina Faso	46

Persons per Telephone

Canada	1.3
Brazil	10
Nigeria	210
Bangladesh	476

Persons per Television

Japan	1.5
Canada	1.7
Bolivia	14
Zaire	1776

Figure 3.9.a How people use different personal communication devices

Figure 3.9.b This geologist examines the dome above a Global Positioning device in the Long Valley Caldera in Northridge, California. The device helps scientists measure how much the ground moves along earthquake faults.

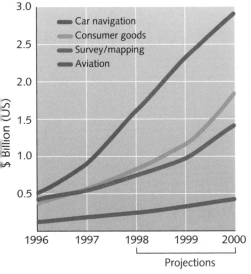

Source: US Commerce Department

Figure 3.9.c Although the Global Positioning System was developed by the United States government, new GPS products and services are being driven by personal and business demand.

The Global Positioning System (GPS) uses a principle of geometry and trigonometry called triangulation. A matrix of orbiting satellites transmit radio waves to the ground, allowing GPS receivers to calculate their exact location on Earth.

GPS

Constellation of more than 20 orbiting satellites provides around-the-clock real-time navigation data, including extremely accurate three-dimensional location information. There should be at least four satellites visible to a receiver at any one time, anywhere on earth.

GPS Receivers

Can be as small as a mobile phone providing accurate information to travellers without being affected by weather conditions—ideal for climbers.

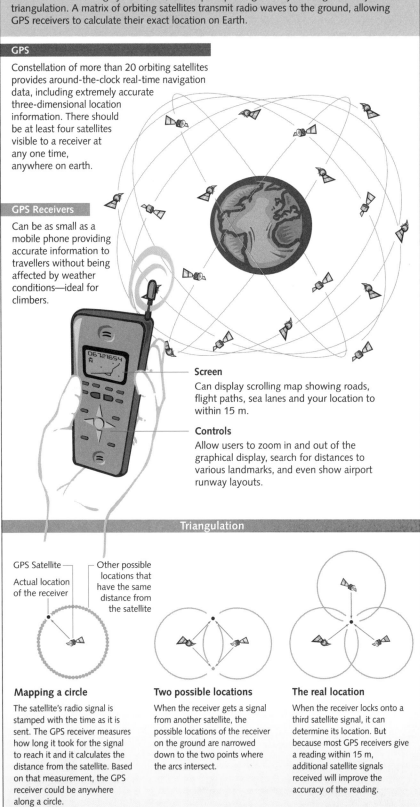

Screen
Can display scrolling map showing roads, flight paths, sea lanes and your location to within 15 m.

Controls
Allow users to zoom in and out of the graphical display, search for distances to various landmarks, and even show airport runway layouts.

Triangulation

GPS Satellite — Other possible locations that have the same distance from the satellite

Actual location of the receiver

Mapping a circle
The satellite's radio signal is stamped with the time as it is sent. The GPS receiver measures how long it took for the signal to reach it and it calculates the distance from the satellite. Based on that measurement, the GPS receiver could be anywhere along a circle.

Two possible locations
When the receiver gets a signal from another satellite, the possible locations of the receiver on the ground are narrowed down to the two points where the arcs intersect.

The real location
When the receiver locks onto a third satellite signal, it can determine its location. But because most GPS receivers give a reading within 15 m, additional satellite signals received will improve the accuracy of the reading.

Source: Magellan Systems, Reuters, *New York Times*

Figure 3.9.d How Global Positioning works

Banners Static or animated poster-style advertisements

Buttons Thumbnail graphic hotlink to advertiser site

Interjacent Animated "commercial break" between display of third-party web pages

Sponsored Sponsor seeking to associate brand values with third-party web site

Source: OXIRM

Figure 3.9.e Emerging types of on-line advertising

FACT FILE

Canadians are moving towards a cashless society. Automated tellers and banking machines are found in banks, corner stores, shopping malls, and grocery stores. Banking cards and charge cards allow us to make purchases and pay directly from our accounts or to run a line of credit. Smart cards can be activated with a cash purchase and used to buy a wide variety of products and services.

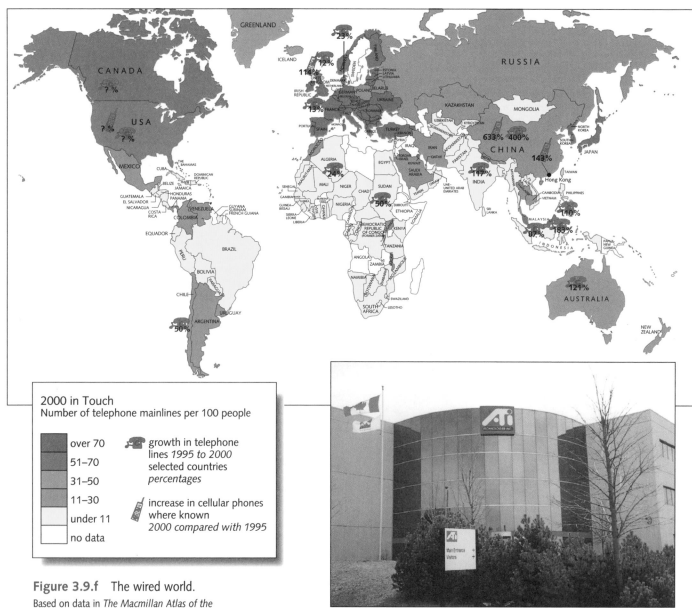

2000 in Touch
Number of telephone mainlines per 100 people

over 70	growth in telephone lines *1995 to 2000* selected countries *percentages*
51–70	
31–50	
11–30	increase in cellular phones where known *2000 compared with 1995*
under 11	
no data	

Figure 3.9.f The wired world.
Based on data in *The Macmillan Atlas of the Future*, edited by Ian Pearson

Figure 3.9.g A.T.I. is an example of a Canadian hi-tech company.

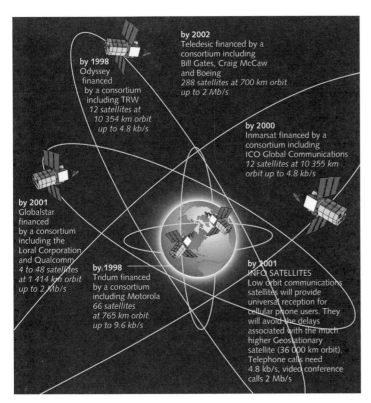

Figure 3.9.h By 2001, low-orbit communications satellites will provide universal reception for cellular phone users.

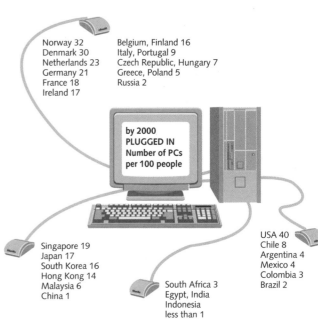

Figure 3.9.i Projection of the number of PC computers plugged into the Internet per 100 people in 2000.

QUESTIONS & ACTIVITIES

1. a) What is direct communication? How is it different from indirect communication?

b) How is direct communication becoming easier on a global basis?

2. a) What is GIS?

b) How has GIS mapping helped provide 911 service?

c) What is GPS?

d) Study Figure 3.9.d and make your own simplified labelled diagram to explain how GPS works.

e) How might GIS combined with GPS help reduce car theft?

3. a) What is e-mail?

b) What is e-commerce or e-business?

c) Name four ways advertisers use the Web (see Figure 3.9.e).

4. Examine the pictographs in Figure 3.9.a. Write a paragraph summary of Canada in relation to other parts of the world shown on all the pictographs.

Make sure you write at least one sentence about each graph.

5. a) Explain how Canadians are moving to a cashless society. List four examples.

b) Do a voluntary survey of your classmates to find out:

i) who has credit cards

ii) who has personal banking cards

iii) who has phone cards

iv) who has pay cheques electronically deposited

v) who has other types of cards

Graph your results. Discuss the implications of these patterns.

6. Write a report to analyze how people advertise on the Web.

a) How can the Internet affect your research plans for an essay.?

b) How can you evaluate information you find on the Internet for accuracy, truth, and freedom from bias?

RECREATIONAL ACTIVITY IN CANADA

Major Concepts

- Recreation and leisure activities in Canada
- Leisure and work time
- The Shaw and Stratford festivals

In a country where landscape painting has made the Group of Seven artists world famous, it is not surprising that geography has an effect on our **recreational activities**. According to Statistics Canada, we are a nation full of energy. Almost one in two Canadians plays hockey, skis, or swims. Our natural environment provides many of our recreational sites and opportunities (See Figure 2.15.j).

Sports naturally appeal to most young people and 75% of people aged 15 to 18 are involved in some organized sport. This figure compares to 50% of the people aged 25 to 34, and 25% of the people over 55.

The preferred activities of people from ages 11 to 14 are baseball, hockey, swimming, and basketball. However, they also bowl, cross-country ski, curl, golf, and play tennis—all sports that people engage in later in life. Skate-boarding, roller-blading, snow-boarding, and biking are increasingly popular with young people.

Our enjoyment of recreational time is influenced by many factors.

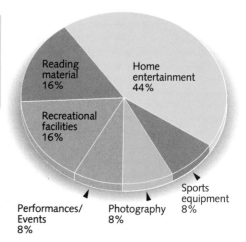

Figure 3.10.b How Canadians spend on fun

According to the 1996 Census one important factor affecting our recreation is the fact that since the 1991 Census Canadians have lost almost one hour per day of leisure time. However, the same survey indicates what we are spending on recreation. Canadians are spending 33% more on recreational gear such as golf clubs or camping equipment. We are also spending on recreational services such as movies, live concerts, and other local events. We are working more to pay for our recreational activities.

Watching cable television, spending time on the Internet, and renting videos and video games are other favourite pastimes of Canadians. Newspapers, magazines, and paperback books are preferred reading materials. Listening to the radio is declining in popularity, but not listening to recorded music.

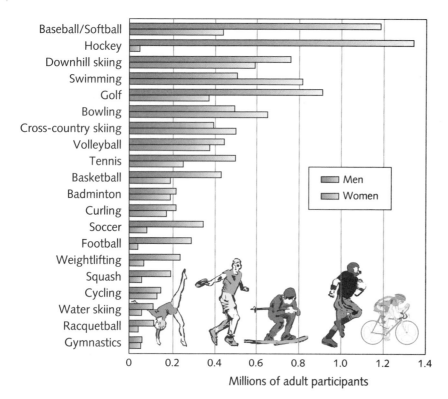

Figure 3.10.a Sports Canadians most enjoy

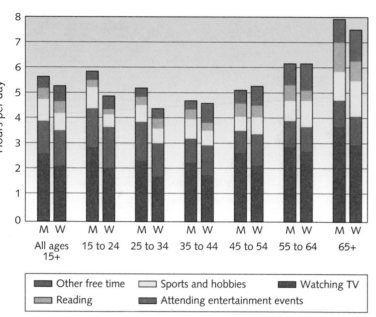

Figure 3.10.c   What Canadians do for fun

Legend:
- Other free time
- Sports and hobbies
- Watching TV
- Reading
- Attending entertainment events

X-axis labels: M W (All ages 15+), M W (15 to 24), M W (25 to 34), M W (35 to 44), M W (45 to 54), M W (55 to 64), M W (65+)

Y-axis: Hours per day (0 to 8)

FILE

FACT

Leisure activities Canadians enjoyed, 1991-1996:
- 81% listened to recorded music
- 80% read a magazine
- 71% watched a video
- 51% used a heritage site
- 49% went to a show
- 31% attended a professional sporting event

Canadians are travelling to see live theatre and concerts in ever-increasing numbers.

In the 1990s, the Stratford and Shaw festivals had record-breaking attendance. Stratford is a small town in southern Ontario with the largest classical theatre company in North America and an audience and cast who come from all over the world. The festival has grown from a Shakespearean theatre in 1953 to its present world-famous mix of classical and modern plays.

The Shaw Festival is based in Niagara-on-the-Lake in southwestern Ontario. It is the only theatre in the world largely devoted to the Irish playwright George Bernard Shaw. Like the Stratford Festival, Shaw has expanded to include works by other playwrights as well as Shaw. Over three-quarters of a million people are entertained at the Stratford and Shaw Festivals annually. Many are students who arrive on the familiar yellow school buses from across Ontario.

QUESTIONS & ACTIVITIES

1. What activities involve almost half of all Canadians?
2. What are the preferred sports of young people in Canada?
3. a) List five ways natural environments provide recreational sites.
   b) List five recreational sites that were constructed for entertainment.
4. Use the data in the Fact File to construct a bar graph illustrating the activities Canadians are involved in.
5. Construct a leisure time pie graph for your life at this time.
   a) Make a list of your activities for the day, e.g., school, sleep, eat, sports.
   b) Estimate how many hours a day you spend on each activity.
   c) Calculate the percentage of each based on the 24-h day.
   d) Plot the percentages on a pie graph. You may want to use a spreadsheet program on a computer.
6. Explain why Canadians are working more (one hour less of leisure time per day on average) to spend more on recreational activities (see Figure 3.10.c).
7. Describe a visit you have had to the Shaw or the Stratford festivals or describe a live production you have seen (band, concert, play, or sporting event). Write your description in an expository paragraph.

PARKS IN CANADA

Major Concepts

- National parks
- Provincial parks
- Municipal parks
- Preserving Canada's natural and cultural sites

Since 1990 Canada's federal, provincial, and recreational agencies responsible for the environment have been committed to completing Canada's network of protected land areas. This large network also includes protection of marine ecosystems.

In 1930 the federal government passed the **National Parks Act** to set aside areas for "the benefit,

education, and enjoyment of the Canadian people." In that year the Rocky Mountain Parks Reserve, formed in 1887 by the federal government, was renamed Banff National Park. Since then, park land has been continually set aside for the enjoyment of Canadians and to protect the environment. Eight percent of Canada is designated as park land. Wood Buffalo

Park in Alberta and the Northwest Territories is very large covering an area of 44 800 km^2, while the park at the St. Lawrence Islands near Kingston, Ontario, is only 6.9 km^2. Some sites, such as the beaches at Rustico in PEI, are easily reached by automobile. Others, like Auyuittuq on Baffin Island, are remote and difficult to reach.

Provincial parks follow the same philosophy as the national parks. Algonquin Park in northern Ontario was the first provincial park created in Canada in 1893. It was named in honour of the Algonquin people. Shortly after,

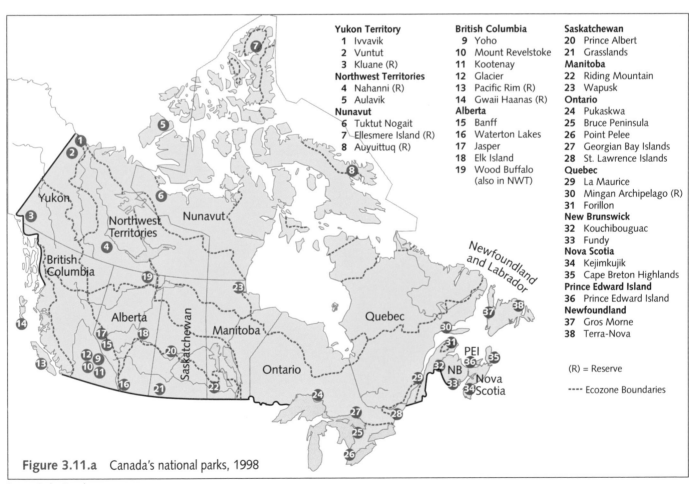

Yukon Territory
1 Ivvavik
2 Vuntut
3 Kluane (R)
Northwest Territories
4 Nahanni (R)
5 Aulavik
Nunavut
6 Tuktut Nogait
7 Ellesmere Island (R)
8 Auyuittuq (R)

British Columbia
9 Yoho
10 Mount Revelstoke
11 Kootenay
12 Glacier
13 Pacific Rim (R)
14 Gwaii Haanas (R)
Alberta
15 Banff
16 Waterton Lakes
17 Jasper
18 Elk Island
19 Wood Buffalo (also in NWT)

Saskatchewan
20 Prince Albert
21 Grasslands
Manitoba
22 Riding Mountain
23 Wapusk
Ontario
24 Pukaskwa
25 Bruce Peninsula
26 Point Pelee
27 Georgian Bay Islands
28 St. Lawrence Islands
Quebec
29 La Maurice
30 Mingan Archipelago (R)
31 Forillon
New Brunswick
32 Kouchibouguac
33 Fundy
Nova Scotia
34 Kejimkujik
35 Cape Breton Highlands
Prince Edward Island
36 Prince Edward Island
Newfoundland
37 Gros Morne
38 Terra-Nova

(R) = Reserve

---- Ecozone Boundaries

Figure 3.11.a Canada's national parks, 1998

Source: Parks Canada

Canada has a great national heritage system. This system is designed to preserve places that have historic or scenic value. The Trent-Severn Canal system in Ontario is one example. A second example is Bellevue House in Kingston, Ontario, the home of Canada's first Prime Minister.

Figure 3.11.b Banff, Alberta. Photograph by Douglas Leighton

Quebec set aside the large Laurentides park system to protect its wilderness sites.

National and provincial parks conserve wilderness lands, like the Laurentides, preserve recreational sites such as Sand Banks Provincial Park in Ontario, or, as in the case of the Pelee Island National Park (Ontario) flyways, and protect animals and their habitat.

Parks in urban areas are operated by municipal parks departments. These islands of greenery are meant to provide healthy retreats for city dwellers in the midst of the hectic pace of work and traffic. Many of these parks are designed by landscape architects and designers. Municipal parks may protect river valleys or shorelines, have fountains or statues, flower gardens or bandstands. It is becoming more common to see gardens and greenery on the rooftops of city buildings or under canopies of glass or skylights in malls, shopping centres, and condominiums.

Conservation Authorities have been developed along river drainage basins as well. The Otonabee Region Conservation area in Ontario, for example, protects the natural conditions of the Otonabee River for the benefit of the citizens living within the river's watershed.

Province/Territory	Parks		Wildlife management areas		Wilderness areas	
	Number	Area (km²)	Number	Area (km²)	Number	Area (km²)
British Columbia	387	52 506	10	247	1	1 315
Alberta	193	1 417	8	680	8	5 607
Saskatchewan	227	11 560	1 662	15 372	—	—
Manitoba	60	14 318	72	31 833	1	4 065
Ontario	261	63 619	45	9 240	37	618
Quebec	16	4 194	16	67 000	—	—
New Brunswick	48	235	19	3 219	—	—
Nova Scotia	117	111	26	1 417	—	—
Prince Edward Island	42	35	8	33	—	—
Newfoundland/Labrador	75	246	1	618	2	3 965
Yukon	1	114	2	5 918	—	—
Northwest Territories	44	130	3	26 464	—	—
Total	**1 471**	**148 485**	**1 872**	**162 041**	**49**	**15 570**

Source: *The State of Canada's Environment*

Figure 3.11.c Provincial and territorial parks, wildlife management areas, and wilderness areas, 1991

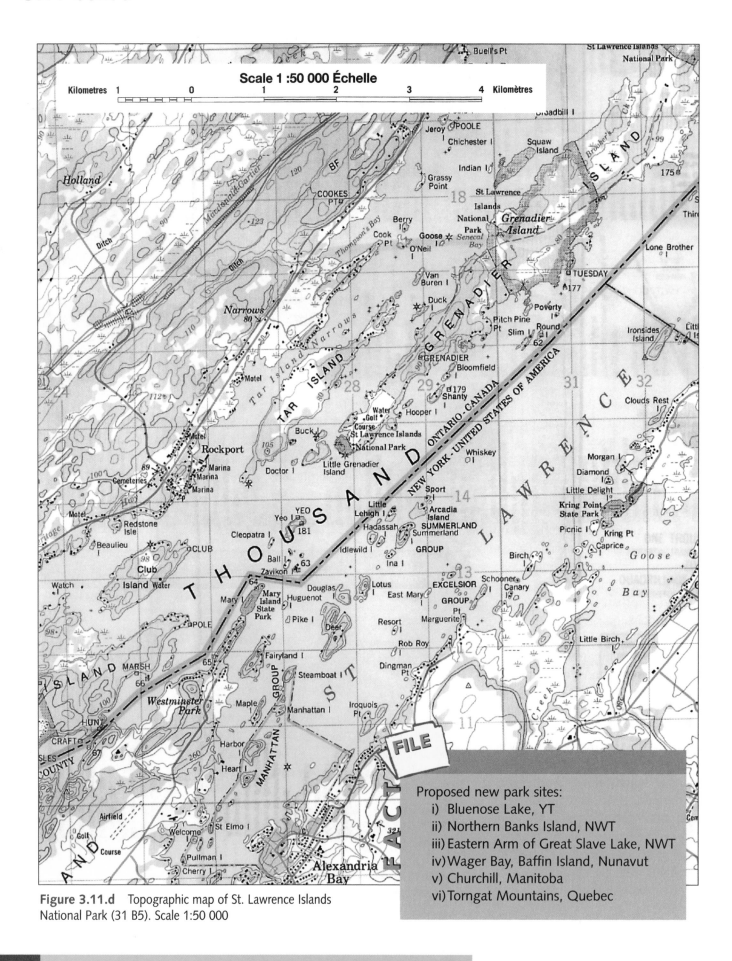

Figure 3.11.d Topographic map of St. Lawrence Islands National Park (31 B5). Scale 1:50 000

Proposed new park sites:
  i) Bluenose Lake, YT
  ii) Northern Banks Island, NWT
  iii) Eastern Arm of Great Slave Lake, NWT
  iv) Wager Bay, Baffin Island, Nunavut
  v) Churchill, Manitoba
  vi) Torngat Mountains, Quebec

Algonquin Park

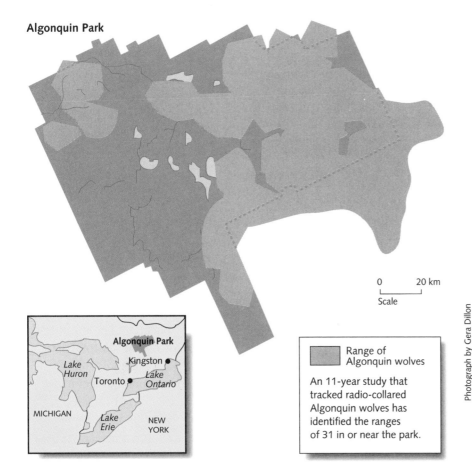

0   20 km
Scale

Range of
Algonquin wolves

An 11-year study that
tracked radio-collared
Algonquin wolves has
identified the ranges
of 31 in or near the park.

Figure 3.11.e   Sketch map of Algonquin Park, showing range of wolves about
the park

Photograph by Gera Dillon

Figure 3.11.f   Cloud Gardens is an
indoor city park in Toronto's financial
district. The park is built on the roof of a
parking garage and has a three-storey
waterfall and a conservatory.

QUESTIONS & ACTIVITIES

1. Copy Figure 3.11.a onto a blank map for your note-book. Find the proposed park areas and add them to your map with a special symbol.
2. a) What was the first national park in Canada?
   b) What are the purposes for having national park land?
3. a) What are three reasons for provincial parks?
   b) Name two parks and the reasons they were created.
   c) Construct a bar graph to show the number and size of provincial parks by province and territory (use 2 bars and 2 scales, one on each side of the graph).
4. Examine Figure 3.11.e.
   a) What part of the park do the wolves inhabit?
   b) What do you think happens at the park boundaries?
   c) How might this situation present problems:
      i) for the wolf

   ii) for people living just outside the park
   iii) for people trying to protect the wolf
5. a) Why are city parks important?
   b) How are cities finding ways to create green spaces?
6. What is the purpose of Conservation Authorities?
7. Examine Figure 3.11.b and Figure 3.11.d. Write down the features that make these two sites popular national parks.
8. Suppose a large company wanted to buy 200 ha of land near a national park to build a factory. The factory would create work for many people. It would add a large volume of truck traffic and would require large outdoor storage tanks. Describe a process or hearing that would allow all sides to have a say and enable a consensus or agreement to be reached that would reflect community wishes.

WILDERNESS IN CANADA

Major Concepts

- Wilderness areas in Canada
- Human and animal need for wilderness
- Endangered species, threatened species, at-risk species
- Heritage river systems

"We did not think of the great open plains, the beautiful rolling hills and winding streams as wild. Only to the white man was nature a wilderness."
- *Luther Standing Bear, Oglala Chief*

"The closest way to the universe is through a forest wilderness."
- *John Muir, North American naturalist*

Wilderness is, according to the *Oxford Dictionary*, "an uncultivated and uninhabited tract of land." Humans have not taken possession of the land. Visiting some of the wilderness areas of Canada can be challenging. In fact, wilderness survival is a course in some school curricula, for business executives, for soldiers whose military operations may take them to remote and difficult areas, and for everyone who is serious about exploring the outdoors.

Today, the term wilderness is often used to refer to tundra, remote forests, alpine mountain regions, and deserts. Wildernesses are natural regions where plants and animals have natural habitats and a chance to survive the pressures of the growing human population. Wilderness areas can range from small ecological sites such as wetlands or historic sites, to large national parks or animal refuges. Few people visit wilderness areas, yet they are places where people can go to escape the pressures of

daily life and to test themselves against the elements of nature.

Canada is a vast, northern and remote country with large open and wild spaces. Most of the population of Canada lives within six hundred kilometres of the US border. Yet Canada has its share of extinct and endangered species (Figure 3.12.f). The Great Auk is gone, the beaver was almost wiped out by the fur trade, and the Sand Cranes were down to twenty-three known birds.

In 1990, the federal government established the **Green Plan** to set aside twelve percent of Canada's land as space free of human influence. The legislation was designed to protect endangered, vulnerable, or threatened species and to restore their habitats. The Bay of Fundy Shore Land Reserve is a famous example of a waterfowl habitat that shelters over two million birds along an annual migration flyway. Canada's protected areas have grown to 800 000 km^2, or 8% of the total area of Canada's 217 land ecoregions. One hundred and sixty ecoregions contain at least one protected area. Five new wetlands have been added in the maritime ecoregions,

Pure Water and Clean Air

Conservation and Preservation

Scientific Value

Scenic and Aesthetic Value

Historic Value

Educational Value

Recreation

Economic and Commercial Value

Figure 3.12.a The wilderness is important to humans as well as to wildlife.

Figure 3.12.b Every year thousands of tourists go on whale watching expeditions.

Regions	Number	% of total number in Canada
Pacific/Mountain	9	9.4
Arctic	8	8.3
Boreal	10	10.4
Prairie	9	9.4
Great Lakes/ St. Lawrence	46	47.9
Atlantic Maritime	16	16.7
Marine Coastal	11	11.5
Total Number in Canada	**96**[a]	

[a] The sum of the number of species, subspecies, and populations in each region exceeds the total number in Canada because some species are found in more than one region.

Source: *The State of Canada's Environment*

Figure 3.12.c Endangered species by region

Figure 3.12.d These are logos of two of the most widely recognized conservation agencies.

reflecting the need to protect a variety of land and water sites.

Modern technology is having an impact on how humans enjoy the wilderness. Hikers go into these areas equipped with cell phones that allow contact with the outside world. Global Positioning Systems (see Figure 3.9.d) are now the size of remote controls for televisions. They tell people who journey into wilderness areas their exact latitude and longitude. For less adventurous Canadians, **virtual wilderness** is here, allowing people, from the comfort and safety of their homes, to experience the excitement and challenges of more remote parts of the world through computer simulation.

Environmental conservation and stewardship programs have been extended outside the boundaries of parks, reserves, and protected sites. The Niagara Escarpment hiking trail is an example of many land parcels being protected through

legal agreements with private citizens rather than through government acquisitions. Ducks Unlimited is a private organization dedicated to buying, developing, and protecting wetlands for migrating waterfowl.

FILE

FACT

The **Canadian Heritage River Systems** is a plan to protect and preserve some of the significant river systems in Canada. By preserving their natural state, a nation's ecosystems can be maintained.

Shirley Sloat, Images of New Brunswick

Figure 3.12.e Some of the millions of birds that shelter at the Bay of Fundy Shore Land Reserve.

Extinct[1]	Mammals	Birds	Fish and marine mammals	Reptiles and amphibians	Plants
Extinct[1]	Caribou, Woodland (Queen Charlotte Islands population) Mink, Sea	Auk, Great Duck, Labrador Pigeon, Passenger	Cisco, Deepwater Cisco, Longjaw Dace, Banff Longnose Walleye, Blue		
Extirpated[2]	Bear, Grizzly (Prairie population) Ferret, Black-footed Fox, Swift	Prairie–Chicken, Greater	Chub, Gravel Paddlefish Walrus, Atlantic (Northwest Atlantic population) Whale, Gray (Atlantic population)	Lizard, Pygmy Short-horned	Blue-eyed Mary Trefoil, Illinois Tick
Endangered[3]	Caribou, Peary (Banks Island and High Arctic populations) Cougar (Eastern population) Marmot, Vancouver Island Wolverine (Eastern population)	Bobwhite, Northern Crane, Whooping Curlew, Eskimo Duck, Harlequin (Eastern population) Falcon, *Anatum* Peregrine Flycatcher, Acadian Owl, Burrowing Owl, Spotted Plover, Mountain Plover, Piping Rail, King Shrike, Loggerhead (Eastern population) Sparrow, Henslow's Thrasher, Sage Warbler, Kirtland's	Otter, Sea Sucker, Salish Whale, Beluga (St. Lawrence River, Ungava Bay and Southeast Baffin Island – Cumberland Sound populations) Trout, Aurora Whale, Bowhead (Eastern and Western Arctic populations) Whale, Right Whitefish, Acadian	Frog, Blanchard's Cricket Snake, Blue Racer Snake, Lake Erie Water Turtle, Leatherback	Agalinis, Gattinger's Agalinis, Skinner's Cactus, Eastern Prickly Pear Clover, Slender Bush Coreopsis, Pink Fern, Southern Maidenhair Gentain, White Prairie Lady's-slipper, Small White Lousewort, Furbish's Milkwort, Pink Mint, Hoary Mountain Mountain Avens, Eastern Mouse-ear-cress, Slender Orchid, Western Prairie White Fringed Plantain, Heart-leaved Pogonia, Large Whorled Pogonia, Small Whorled Poppy, Wood Quiltwort, Engelman's Sundew, Thread-leaved Tree, Cucumber Water-pennywort Wintergreen, Spotted
Threatened[4]	Bison, Wood Caribou, Peary (Low Arctic population) Caribou, Woodland (Gaspé population) Marten (Newfoundland population) Shrew, Pacific Water	Chat, Yellow-breasted (B.C. population) Murrelet, Marbled Shrike, Loggerhead (Prairie population) Sparrow, Baird's Tern, Roseate Warbler, Hooded Woodpecker, White-headed	Beluga (Eastern Hudson Bay population) Cisco, Blackfin Cisco, Shortjaw Cisco, Shortnose Darter, Channel Darter, Eastern Sand Madtom, Margined Porpoise, Harbour (Northwest Atlantic population) Redhorse, Black Redhorse, Copper Sculpin, Great Lakes Deepwater Sculpin, Shorthead Smelt, Lake Utopia Dwarf Stickleback, Benthic Texada Stickleback, Enos Lake Stickleback, Limnetic Texada Whale, Humpback (North Pacific population) Whitefish, Lake Simcoe	Rattlesnake, Eastern Massasauga Turtle, Blanding's (Nova Scotia population) Turtle, Spiny Softshell Snake, Black Rat	Ash, Blue Aster, Anticosti Aster, White Wood Bluehearts Chestnut, American Colicroot Deerberry Fern, Mosquito Flag, Western Blue Gentain, Plymouth Ginseng, American Golden Crest Golden Seal Greenbrier, Carolinean Jacob's Ladder, van Brunt's Lipocarpha, Small-flowered Mulberry, Red Paintbrush, Golden Pepperbush, Sweet Pegonia, Nodding Prairie–Clover, Hairy Redroot Spiderwort, Western Thistle, Pitcher's Thrift, Athabasca Coffee-tree, Kentucky Coffee Twayblade, Purple Verbena, Sand Violet, Bird's-foot Violet, Yellow Montane Water-willow, American Willow, Tyrrell's Woodsia, Blunt-lobed
Vulnerable[5]	Mole, Eastern Vole, Woodland		Cod, Atlantic Lamprey, Lake Madtom, Northern	Frog, Northern Leopard (Prairie population) Salamander, coeur d'alène Salamander, Mountain Dusky Skink, Five–lined Toad, Great Basin Spadefoot	Buffalograss Fern, Coastal Wood Fern Helleborine, Giant

Figure 3.12.f The five classifications of extinct and **at-risk species**. In the mid-1990s there were 256 species of mammals, birds, reptiles and amphibians, fish and plants listed in these five categories.

1 Any species that no longer exists
2 Any species no longer existing in the wild in Canada but occuring elsewhere
3 Any species facing imminent extirpation or extinction
4 Any species likely to become endangered if limiting factors are not reversed
5 Any species at risk because of its declining numbers

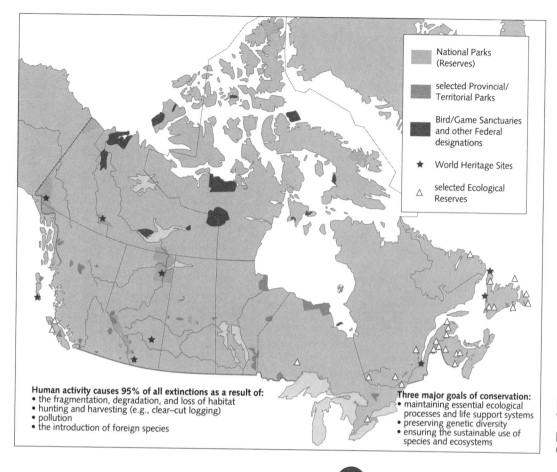

Human activity causes 95% of all extinctions as a result of:
• the fragmentation, degradation, and loss of habitat
• hunting and harvesting (e.g., clear–cut logging)
• pollution
• the introduction of foreign species

Three major goals of conservation:
• maintaining essential ecological processes and life support systems
• preserving genetic diversity
• ensuring the sustainable use of species and ecosystems

Figure 3.12.g
Wilderness and **protected lands** in Canada.

Map legend:
- National Parks (Reserves)
- selected Provincial/Territorial Parks
- Bird/Game Sanctuaries and other Federal designations
- ★ World Heritage Sites
- △ selected Ecological Reserves

QUESTIONS & ACTIVITIES

1. a) In your own words, write a definition for the term wilderness. Then compare your definition with two or three different dictionary entries.

b) Elaborate on your definition to explain what wilderness means to you.

c) What did wilderness mean to Chief Luther Standing Bear?

2. a) Describe Canada's Green Plan.

b) If Canada is so large and has so many uninhabited areas, why is a Green Plan necessary?

3. a) How has technology changed the way people deal with wilderness?

b) How does "virtual" wilderness work?

c) How would it help protect the real environment?

4. a) Copy Figure 3.12.a in your notebook.

b) Work with a partner to find an example of each item in the chart.

c) Each item represents something of value to society. With your partner, state a value of having each item included in wilderness sites.

d) Have the class present all their values for each item. Make a summary in your notes.

5. Read John Muir's quote and write a sentence or two to explain the meaning.

6. Investigate the status and situation of whales in Canada. From the Internet or other research resources develop an inquiry essay to explain your position on the status of whales. Consider and include the position of conservationists, eco-tourists, and Aboriginal peoples.

7. Examine the logos in Figure 3.12.d. These logos represent two famous wildlife protection agencies.

a) What does WWF stand for? Research both organizations and prepare a brief point-form report explaining their roles in conservation Canada's natural habitat.

b) Create a design that would symbolize your views on wildlife protection. Check the Internet or wildlife magazines for logos from other agencies.

NATURAL HAZARDS IN CANADA

Major Concepts

- Nature has powerful forces
- Resources and living spaces may conflict with natural forces
- Natural hazards have causes and patterns
- Canada's global position affects natural hazards

As Canadians seek to develop their resources, they push into all corners of the country. As a result we come directly into contact with forces of nature that are sometimes amazing, sometimes overwhelming, and sometimes fatal.

This section examines some of the **natural hazards** Canadians face. Some events happen annually, while some are so rare we think they cannot happen to us. Canada has many agencies involved in studying locations of hazards, predicting their course and outcome, preparing and warning citizens, and rescuing survivors.

Because of Canada's large size and northern latitude, weather-related hazards are a major concern. Our winters are severe and can be deadly. Cold winter winds produce wind-chill factors that can freeze exposed human flesh in seconds. Icebergs break off glaciers and float into shipping channels, causing hazards to passing ships. These are only a few of the natural hazards we face annually.

ROCK AND SNOW SLIDES

Gravity doesn't seem like a natural hazard until slides occur. Rock, mud, and snow will all slip on steep slopes and fall to the valleys below. On April 29, 1903, 90 million tonnes of limestone started Canada's largest rock slide disaster. It descended from the south peak of Turtle mountain on the coal-mining town of Frank in Alberta, killing 70 people.

Avalanches are common in the Western Cordillera. Huge canopies are built across highways and train tracks in high-risk places such as the Rogers Pass where avalanche paths are predictable. Artillery range guns are used to trigger small slides before large ones can build up. Skiers risk injury and death when skiing in remote sites.

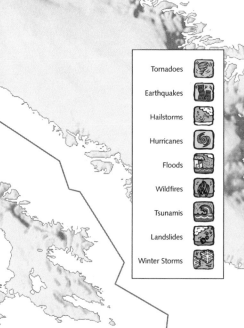

Legend:
- Tornadoes
- Earthquakes
- Hailstorms
- Hurricanes
- Floods
- Wildfires
- Tsunamis
- Landslides
- Winter Storms

CURRENTS, ICEBERGS, AND FOG

Currents are rivers of motion within the world's oceans. They often bring different temperature conditions into a region. As a cold current pattern changes every few years off the coast of Chile and Peru, it affects weather conditions in North America. The weather for the year 1997 was affected by the return of El Niño, a famous warm current that appears periodiocally here from the Pacific.

The Labrador current is a cold water current flowing south from the Canadian Arctic. It brings large chunks of glacial ice or icebergs into the southern shipping lanes. The famous passenger ship *Titanic* suffered the ultimate fate after colliding with an iceberg. The Hibernia oil rigs tethered off Newfoundland must be alert for icebergs.

When the cold Labrador current meets the warm Gulf Stream, fog is caused. The thick, moisture-laden air reduces visibility to a few metres and causes all kinds of problems.

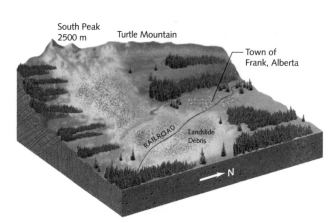

Figure 3.13.b   Diagram of the Frank landslide

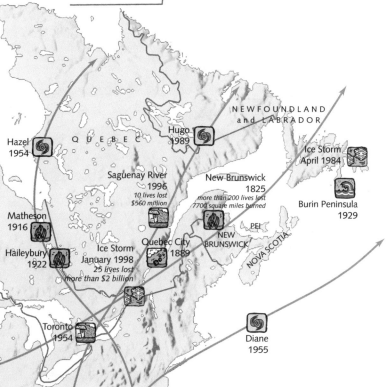

Figure 3.13.a   Natural hazards in Canada

PREDICTION MODELS AND WARNINGS

Natural hazards are dangerous to people. Warning systems alert people to the danger of natural events. Telecommunications form part of the warning system. Satellites photograph our country and these images give clues to potential problems. Emergency Preparedness Canada, part of the Department of National Defence, is a federal agency that prepares citizens for disasters and provides aid and relief. Radio and television broadcast warnings. Marine radio alerts watercraft. Agencies like the Red Cross and St. John's Ambulance help with relief aid and emergency situation training.

A

Strike-slip faults form when slabs of rock slide horizontally past each other.

B

Normal faults occur when rock formations pull apart suddenly.

C

Thrust faults result when chunks of rock press together, forcing one side over the other.

D

Blind thrusts usually raise folded hills without breaking the surface.

Figure 3.13.c Types of faults

DROUGHTS

The opposite of too much water is too little. This is when **drought** occurs. The Prairies in particular are often hit by prolonged dry conditions. Dying crops, dropping water tables, and raging fires are some of the events that result from drought. Competition for the use of water supplies above and below the ground increases the risk of drought. While it is not usually considered in this category, we should all be aware that Arctic Canada is a desert due to the small amount of moisture available annually.

HURRICANES

Figure 3.13.d shows that hurricanes are not a severe threat to Canada. These fierce storms form over warm oceans and need warm water to feed their energy. The Maritimes will often get the tail end of storms as the storms move up the Atlantic coast. In 1954, central Canada was struck by the rare inland movement of Hurricane Hazel. Hurricanes occur in the late summer and fall season.

EARTHQUAKES AND TSUNAMIS

Canada's West Coast is part of the Ring of Fire (see Figure 1.4.c), an unstable edge of the Pacific continental plates that create volcanic and earthquake activity. Earthquakes happen where the earth's tectonic plates collide or grind past one another. When these plates move along a crack or **fault line**, **shock waves** or **earth tremors** are produced. Sometimes the movement leaves a gaping line in the ground. Often it is the vibrations from the waves that cause buildings to sway and crumble, bridges to collapse, and land to cave in. Canada's West Coast is the most vulnerable and unstable area in Canada. The Canadian Shield is least likely to have an earthquake. However, shock waves travel further through this rigid rock. Waves are called **seismic waves** and are recorded by seismographs. They are measured by the Richter scale.

If an earthquake occurs in an ocean, the shock waves set up a wave motion in the water. A tsunami is a **tidal wave**, a massive wave that blasts ashore. Often it comes unexpectedly causing enormous damage to coastal locations.

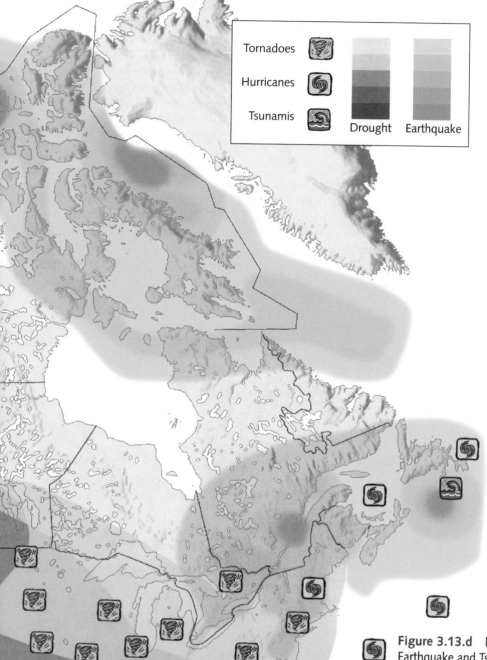

WILDFIRES

Lightning bolts can set the boreal forest aflame in seconds (see section 2.6). Fires can also be started by careless campers or people clearing fields or yards. A spark in dry grass can spread through prairie grass or arctic tundra as quickly as through a forest. Wind fans the flames and drives the fire. If towns or houses are in the way, this hazard becomes serious for the inhabitants. Fires destroy over 700 million dollars worth of lumber a year in Canada. Fighting fires costs millions more.

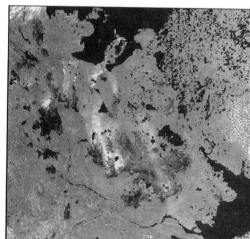

Figure 3.13.e Satellite image of a tundra fire in the central Northwest Territories, 1995. The dark purple areas are the burned areas (here estimated at 1.3 million ha). Unburned vegetation is in green, orange, and red tones. The smooth, black areas are lakes and rivers.

Figure 3.13.d Drought, Tornado, Hurricane, Earthquake and Tsunami areas in Canada

TORNADOES

Tornadoes are sometimes called **twisters** and many movies have been made about them. Tornadoes are created when two extreme air masses meet. When the warm, humid air from the Gulf of Mexico meets the cool, dry air of central Canada, cyclonic storms spin into being. These storms contain fierce winds surrounding a small vortex of upwardly moving air. The intense low pressure created causes things as heavy as cars, small buildings, and roofs to fly into the air. Canada reports over 100 tornado storms per year. While most tornadoes occur in the Prairies and the St. Lawrence valley area, they can occur anywhere. They form quickly, move fast, and touch down like a wrecking-ball. Most are over in 15 s to 30 s, but the devastation they leave is enormous. The peak season is June and July. However, they can happen anytime conditions are right. A tornado over water pulls large amounts of water into the air and is known as a **water spout**.

Causes of Floods

1. melting snow
2. rain and convection or cyclonic storms
3. ice jams/power dams/ obstructions
4. coastal storms
5. changes to drainage patterns, e.g., clear-cutting forests or pavement in cities
6. tsunamis/high tides/ storm surges

FLOODS

Every river or lake has the potential to cause a **flood**. When water rises to unexpectedly high levels and spills over the normal bank or high water mark, flooding occurs. In Canada floods can occur when snow and ice melt too quickly or when severe storms drop large amounts of precipitation in a short time.

Manitoba and its capital, Winnipeg, suffered severe flooding in the spring of 1997. The Red River flows from south to north through Manitoba. If the southern tributaries thaw before the northern part has melted, or if there are ice jams, the water from the southern part of the river is blocked from getting through and flooding occurs. During the winter months of 1996–1997 blizzards

dropped a record snowfall along the river. The snow quickly melted in the south and flooded as ice dammed the northern mouth of the valley. Two thousand square kilometres in the Red River valley were flooded. Only the land behind the Brunkild Dike and the eight permanently ring-diked towns were spared.

In the Saguenay River area in Quebec in July 1996, flooding occurred very quickly and differently. A **cyclonic storm**, which is similar to a tornado but less severe, had been raging for 28 straight hours. As it remained stalled over the region, the water mounted up behind the Lac Ha!Ha! Reservoir. The eastern dike gave out and thirty million cubic metres of water flooded through the Saguenay region.

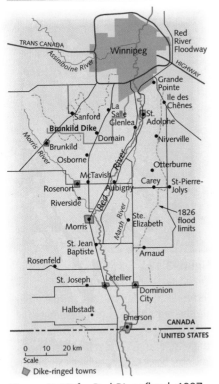

Figure 3.13.f Red River flood, 1997

Figure 3.13.h ▶ Cyclonic depression that stalled over the Saguenay-Lac Saint-Jean region

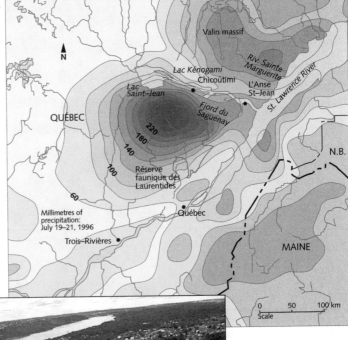

Figure 3.13.g The ring-diked town of Morris in the heart of the Red River flood. Note the river's usual meandering tree-lined course.

Figure 3.13.i The flooding Rivière Chicoutimi washes over the streets of the Saguenay town of Chicoutimi, July 21, 1996.

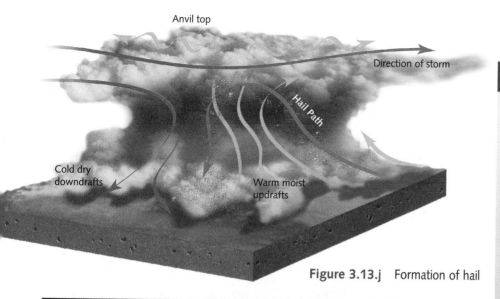

Anvil top

Direction of storm

Hail Path

Cold dry downdrafts

Warm moist updrafts

Figure 3.13.j Formation of hail

WINTER STORMS

Our northern latitude ensures several months of cold and sometimes stormy weather. Snow can be a serious problem and snow removal is a top priority in order to allow for the movement of people and goods. Being stranded in a snowstorm is a big concern.

Freezing rain can be a bigger problem than snow. Driving and walking are treacherous when the temperature sits at the freezing mark and the rain freezes on sidewalks, roads, cars, and property. A huge ice storm in Quebec and Ontario in January 1998 caused severe damage as trees snapped, roofs caved in, and hydro towers toppled. Four million people were left in frozen darkness for hours, days, and some for weeks.

HAILSTORMS

Thunderstorms and lightning are common in Canada. When conditions are right, they produce hail. The right conditions are **convectional storms**. Strong updrafts carry water into the higher sub-zero layers of the clouds. There, ice pellets begin to form. With the correct combination of updrafts and repeated freezing, these hailstones can grow to the size of golfballs. When they reach a critical mass, they blast down to the earth. They are rarely lethal to people, but they cause millions of dollars damage to crops and property.

CANADA

UNITED STATES

Jan. 5, 1998
7:00 a.m.

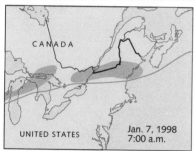

CANADA

UNITED STATES

Jan. 7, 1998
7:00 a.m.

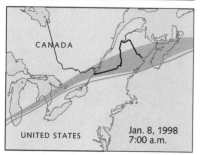

CANADA

UNITED STATES

Jan. 8, 1998
7:00 a.m.

Figure 3.13.k Progress of the 1998 ice storm in Ontario and Quebec

QUESTIONS & ACTIVITIES

1. **a)** What are the largest number of natural hazards related to in Canada?
   b) List five weather-related hazards.
2. Read the quote by William Dumont. Explain why "subject to change without notice" is a good description of natural hazard happenings.
3. Explain why Canada has a large number of tornadoes, but very few hurricanes.
4. Make a labelled diagram to show how raindrops develop into hailstones.
5. **a)** What are six causes of flooding?
   b) Explain the difference between the flood that occurred in Winnipeg and the one that occurred in the Saguenay region.
6. The Arctic is a desert. Examine Figure 3.13.e. Explain three ways fire is a huge danger in the Arctic.
7. **a)** Make a map of the ice storm of January 4-10, 1998.
   b) List five ways the ice caused immediate problems.
   c) How did the ice cause problems after the storm had passed?
8. **a)** What are three natural hazards caused by ocean currents?
   b) What are two hazards caused by gravity?
9. **a)** Why is it important to be able to anticipate natural hazards?
   b) How can people be warned?
10. Investigate how satellites are helpful in predicting natural disasters and warning people. Prepare a series of maps or diagrams and captions to illustrate your findings.

CHANGING PERSPECTIVES

Transpo 2000 is an exposition to allow the exchange of ideas for improving transportation within and between cities in Canada over the next 25 years. Your group is a team of experts on one form of transportation, for example, passenger cars, courier trucks, helicopters, subways, rail-passenger trains, rail-unit trains. Your team must submit a report on the state of your chosen form of transportation today, and identify problems, technological advances, and predicted improvement for the 25-year plan. Each group member should try to become a specialist on identified subtopics for your chosen form of transportation, such as fuel consumption, roads and regulations, or competing forms of transportation. Your final report should include displays, graphics, maps, diagrams, and text (paper, display board, or hypermedia).

Perspectives on Research: Taking Notes

Here are a few reading and note-making skills to practise:
- read quickly and concentrate
- pick out key words
- write notes in point form
- select key phrases
- master key words (have a dictionary within reach)
- use short forms and symbols

To skim read text or an article, pay attention to the first and last sentences in a paragraph; they will give you the main idea.

UNIT 4 CONFLICTS IN USING NATURAL RESOURCES

In a country as large and diverse as Canada, there are many views about how resources should be used and protected. This unit explores some of these resource issues and the roles governments play in managing our environment.

4.1

ABORIGINAL LAND CLAIMS

Major Concepts

- Origin of Aboriginal land claims
- Specific and comprehensive claims
- Claim settlement conditions

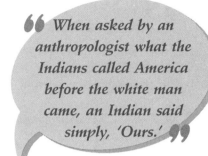

In the 1980s, Aboriginal land claims led to conflicts between Aboriginal Canadians and non-Aboriginal Canadians over the ownership and use of a variety of Canada's natural resources. The roots of Aboriginal **land claims** and the resulting conflicts are found in Canada's past. In the early years after the arrival of the first Europeans, Aboriginal peoples and fur traders lived in a kind of partnership. However, as more and more settlers arrived, this pattern changed. In 1867, the new Canadian government assumed control over health care, education, the administration of all **reserves**, and the negotiation of treaties with Aboriginal groups. Between 1871 and 1923, eleven distinct treaties were negotiated with

the Indians. These treaties encompassed a geographic area of virutally all of northern Ontario, Manitoba, Saskatchewan, Alberta, and parts of British Columbia, the Northwest Territories, and the Yukon. These were known as the numbered treaties.

When they signed treaties, Aboriginal peoples gave up much of their land in return for land set aside for their use (reserves), the right to hunt and fish, and annual payments from the federal government. However, many reserves were extremely small, of poor quality, and isolated. In the 1970s and 1980s Aboriginal peoples began to call for redress of wrongs they felt had been done to them. In the 1980s and 1990s two types of

Aboriginal land claims were brought to the courts—specific and comprehensive. **Specific land claims** refer to the restoration of lands and rights in cases where Aboriginal groups believe that the meaning and intent of their original treaty are not being met, or that parts of the Indian Act are not being carried out fairly. When the elders signed treaties, their intent was to share the lands of Canada with the Europeans. They had not intended to give up their systems of government, their laws, their language, their culture, or their traditional way of life. Over the years, the terms of many of their treaties were broken by Canadians.

Comprehensive land claims are based on aboriginal rights. No treaties were signed governing northern Quebec, the Atlantic Provinces, the Yukon, part of the Northwest Territories, and most of British Columbia. Aboriginal groups bringing comprehensive land claims argue that lands not signed away in treaties still belong to the Aboriginal peoples. In 1997 the Supreme Court of Canada affirmed aboriginal rights in relation to land Aboriginal peoples had

Treaties

- Pre-Confederation
- Post-Confederation
- Exempted from treaties (Royal Proclamation 1763)

1921

1899

1906

1875

1975 James Bay agreement

1876

1905

1877

1871

1874

1871

1873

1850

1763

1850 1923

Figure 4.1.a Treaties signed with Aboriginal peoples, pre-Confederation to 1975

occupied long before Europeans arrived and that had not been given up through formal treaties. These claims involve land title or ownership, the right to hunt, fish, or trap, royalties for mineral exploration, and other benefits.

Settling Aboriginal land claims is not easy. Land claim boundaries are often difficult to plot and are subject to disagreement. Some lands covered by broken or forgotten treaties have been farmed, developed by mining and forest industries, or used for recreation by non-Aboriginal Canadians for several generations. In other cases, people have built homes or have established whole communities on land now claimed by Aboriginal peoples. The present occupants hold legal title to these lands.

FACT

Land Claims, Traditional Values, and Conflicts Over Resource Use

- In the 1970s the Cree of northern Quebec rallied support from the international environmental community as they fought to prevent Québec-Hydro from damming rivers on their lands for electrical power.
- A crisis in Oka and Kahnawaké near Montreal in 1990 involved an armed struggle between Aboriginal peoples who were trying to protect a traditional Aboriginal burial ground and developers who planned to expand a golf course onto that land.
- In British Columbia, conflicts erupted between commercial loggers and Aboriginal salmon fishers.
- Innu fishers restarting a traditional whale hunt were challenged by environmentalists opposed to any hunting of whales.
- Mineral deposits in Labrador led to conflict between the developers who wanted to mine those minerals and the Inuit on whose traditional hunting grounds those mines would be built.
- In Georgian Bay in Ontario, non-Aboriginal fishers opposed Aboriginal fishers who claimed the right by tradition to fish in waters that were designated as non-commercial fishing areas and to sell those fish.

Figure 4.1.b Comprehensive land claims in the North, 1999. Besides the new territory of Nunavut, three land claims have been settled in the Northwest Territories. The land claim settlements involved cash, direct ownership of land, some mineral rights, wildlife management, fishing and hunting rights, and elements of self-government. In Nunavut, the Inuit were given wide powers of self-government (see section 8.1). Seven out of fourteen self-government agreements have been signed in the Yukon.

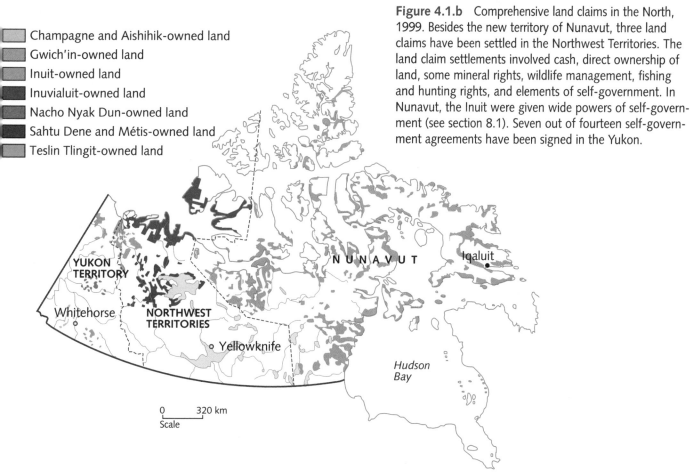

☐ Champagne and Aishihik-owned land
☐ Gwich'in-owned land
☐ Inuit-owned land
■ Inuvialuit-owned land
☐ Nacho Nyak Dun-owned land
■ Sahtu Dene and Métis-owned land
☐ Teslin Tlingit-owned land

FILE

FACT

Nisga'a Treaty

In 1998, after thirty years of negotiation, the Nisga'a signed a treaty with the British Columbia and federal governments. The treaty gave the 5000 Nisga'a people a $190 million payment, absolute ownership of 1992 km² of land, including all surface and subsurface resources, as well as fishing and hunting rights over a wider area. As well, the Nisga'a were given wide powers of self-government in matters of culture, language, and family life. In return, the Nisga'a dropped claims to a much larger territory and to their tax-exempt status. Challenges have been made to this modern treaty by people who argue that the changes are too great and that the terms override the Constitution of Canada.

Figure 4.1.c Nisga'a Tribal Council President, Joseph Gosnell Sr., hands Minister of Indian Affairs and Northern Development, Jane Stewart, the Nisga'a Treaty for her to sign.

QUESTIONS & ACTIVITIES ❓

1. What did Aboriginal leaders believe when they signed treaties with the Canadian government?
2. a) What are specific land claims?
   b) What are comprehensive land claims?
3. Describe three land claims settlements made in Canada.
4. Using the information from Figures 4.1.a and 4.1.b create a pie graph showing how much of Canada has legally been defined as Aboriginal lands.
5. Copy Figure 4.1.a on a blank map of Canada. Research what treaties have been made with Aboriginal peoples since 1975 and add them to your map. Don't forget to add the treaty areas from Figure 4.1.b.

6. Over the next few days, try to find current articles in the newspaper related to Aboriginal land claims. You might also try searching the key words "land claims" on the Internet. Prepare a brief report of your findings.
7. Are there land claims under consideration where you live? If so:
   a) Draw a map of your area and indicate on the map to what areas the claims refer.
   b) In chart form, list the arguments in favour of the claim(s) and any arguments against or difficulties caused by the claims.
8. Research the Royal Proclamation of 1763. Explain why treaties were excluded from the area covered by this treaty.

ENVIRONMENTAL IMPACTS: DECLINING FISH STOCKS

Major Concepts

- Fish stocks are declining worldwide
- Protecting fish stocks may lead to economic hardship
- Trawler size and technology are factors in the decline of fish numbers
- The changing economics of fishing lead to conflict over resource use

Figure 4.2.b This fallen church in a remote outpost fishing village in Newfoundland symbolizes a way of life that has been changed forever by the declining cod stocks.

The oceans once seemed to have an endless supply of fish. Now supplies of fish worldwide are declining. Cod fishing off the East Coast of Canada illustrates some of the problems created by declining fish stocks. The cod harvest fell from 435 000 t in 1989 to 50 000 t in 1996. These figures reflect both the decline in cod stocks themselves and the effects of the **moratorium**, or ban, on cod fishing that the Canadian government imposed within its 200-mile [370 km] offshore limits and the **quotas** imposed on fishing fleets. You saw in section 2.4 that most of the Grand Banks, the East Coast's most plentiful supply of fish, falls within these limits. It is hoped that the moratorium and fishing quotas will allow the cod, especially the northern cod, to regenerate its numbers to **sustainable** levels. However, the price being paid socially and economically by the East Coast has been enormous. The fishing industry provided much of the traditional occupations and business base of Atlantic Canada. Nearly 1000 communities in Atlantic Canada were largely or entirely dependent on the fisheries. Fish-processing plants have been closed and fishing quota licences have been drastically reduced, leaving many people unemployed. For some Atlantic Canadians, a whole way of life is disappearing.

Like the Atlantic cod stocks, the Pacific salmon are under siege worldwide. Because some nationalities prefer the saltier, oilier taste of salmon caught at sea, more and more fishing boats are now catching salmon mid-ocean as well as along the coasts.

Two reasons for declining fish stocks are changes in the number of vessels fishing for seafood and new developments in fishing technology. Today, more than a million vessels fish the world's waters—twice the number of ships fishing in 1970. Modern technology makes locating fish easier.

The number of Canadian fishing vessels operating in the Grand Banks has declined as a result of the Canadian government's moratorium and fishing quotas. The number of ships from Newfoundland, for example, fell from over 15 000 in 1986 to under 12 000 in 1996. However, problems continue with enforcing the moratorium on ships from other nations. It can be difficult to identify to what country a ship belongs. A ship can be owned in Iceland, registered in Cyprus, crewed by Faroe Islanders and fishing in Canadian waters. The only

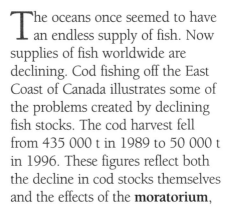

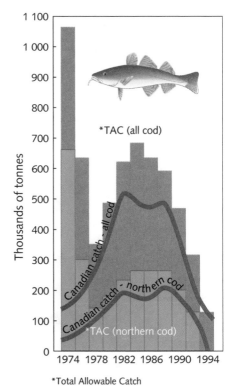

*TAC (all cod)

Thousands of tonnes

Canadian catch - all cod

Canadian catch - northern cod

*TAC (northern cod)

1974 1978 1982 1986 1990 1994

*Total Allowable Catch

Figure 4.2.a Declining cod stocks, 1974-1994

way to monitor the size of catch is for a government representative to be on board.

Also, **floating factory ships** can catch and process their own fish at sea, as well as serve as a **mother ship** and fish processor to a fleet of trawlers. The ability to process and package fish at sea has revolutionized the industry.

The changing worldwide demand for fish also helps explain the decline in fish stocks. Once fish were called the "protein of the poor." **Fish meal** was a dried powder that poorer people added to their meals to supplement their diets with protein. Today, more people eat fish than ever before, and they are willing to pay such high prices for fish that the poor often can no longer afford this dietary staple.

The profits that fishers can make have also led to overfishing and to conflicts among people who want to protect the fish stocks for today and the future and fishers who can make excellent money filling the worldwide demand for the fish.

FACT FILE

Demand and Profits
- On the Pacific, a salmon boat can earn $380 000 in a few weeks.
- A premium tuna in the Tokyo fish market will sell for $9000 to $18 000 or nearly $300/kg.
- Fish eggs, like caviar from sturgeon, have been a delicacy for centuries and command prices of hundreds of dollars per gram.
- Sushi, or raw fish, is a gourmet delight in specialty restaurants.
- Shellfish, lobster, crab, shrimp, and seaweed are all harvested as marketable items.

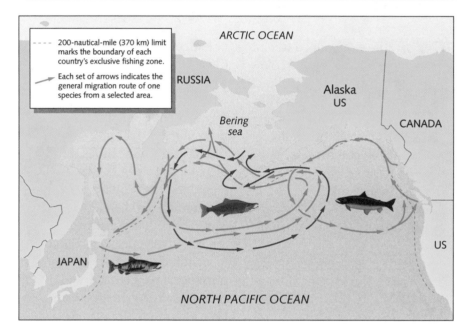

Figure 4.2.c This map of the North Pacific Ocean shows the general migration route of salmon to their rich feeding grounds in mid-ocean. Restrictions and quotas are now imposed at sea as well as along coastlines to protect the salmon stocks.

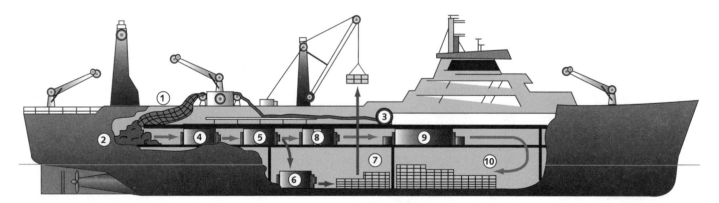

Figure 4.2.d Simplified cross-section of a factory ship. Once the fish are brought aboard (1) the catch is spilled into a fish bin (2) while the net is spooled onto a reel (3). The fish are weighed (4) and then gutted and cleaned (5). Offal is processed into fish meal (6) and stored (7). Fish fillets are washed, bleached, and treated with additives (8) before being quick-frozen (9). They are then boxed and stored in the refrigerator hold (10). They arrive at home port already packaged for market.

FACT FILE

Technology and Fishing Today

- A ship's sonar finds schools of fish. Computers linked to bow sonar set the course and speed to follow the school. The wide-mouthed nets herd the school into the netting. The largest net is over 100 m wide and could fit over the top of any high-rise office tower in Canada. The catch is winched aboard and delivered to the mother ship or a processing plant.
- Some seafood companies use helicopters to scope out the location of large schools of fish.
- Modern trawlers can catch 90 t of fish in one set of the net. This catch would fill twelve 747 jets!

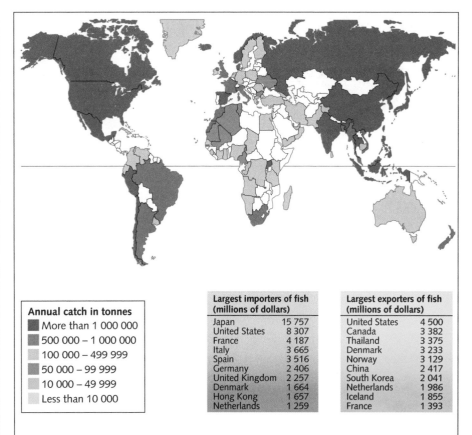

Annual catch in tonnes

- More than 1 000 000
- 500 000 – 1 000 000
- 100 000 – 499 999
- 50 000 – 99 999
- 10 000 – 49 999
- Less than 10 000

Largest importers of fish (millions of dollars)	
Japan	15 757
United States	8 307
France	4 187
Italy	3 665
Spain	3 516
Germany	2 406
United Kingdom	2 257
Denmark	1 664
Hong Kong	1 657
Netherlands	1 259

Largest exporters of fish (millions of dollars)	
United States	4 500
Canada	3 382
Thailand	3 375
Denmark	3 233
Norway	3 129
China	2 417
South Korea	2 041
Netherlands	1 986
Iceland	1 855
France	1 393

Figure 4.2.e World fishing. Largest importers and exporters of fish and the annual fishing catch

QUESTIONS & ACTIVITIES

1. a) Draw a copy of Figure 4.2.a in your notebook.
   b) Research the cod catch in Canada from 1995 to the present. Add to your copy of Figure 4.2.a the bars to show the change in catch since 1994.
   c) Explain these changes.
   d) Prepare a set of recommendations for the future sustainability of the East Coast fisheries.
2. a) Define "factory ship" and "stern trawler."
   b) Explain why the factory ship is called the "mother" ship to a fleet of stern trawlers.
   c) Why are factory ships difficult to monitor for fishing quotas?
   d) Why would being able to process and package fish at sea revolutionize the industry?
3. a) Develop a flow chart to suggest three factors that might cause problems for migratory salmon when they return to spawn.

   b) How have changing dietary choices affected the salmon stocks in mid-ocean?
4. Give three examples of fish-pricing that make fishing a profitable business for some.
5. Examine Figure 4.2.e. Why do you think that the United States, France, and the Netherlands are among both the largest importers and the largest exporters of fish?
6. Suppose you were convinced that our fish stocks must be protected now so that they can regenerate or else they will disappear forever. How would you try to persuade people who can make a great deal of money by continuing to fish that they should stop fishing, or at least cut back greatly on the amount of fish they take?

4.3

THE VALUE OF THE WILDERNESS

Major Concepts

- Conflicts over wilderness areas
- Clear-cutting of forests
- Old growth forests

How we value and use our wilderness areas have led to a number of conflicts. Conservationists' pressure to keep and maintain natural wild areas raises many questions.

- Should all people be kept out of our wilderness areas, including scientists and caretakers?
- Should hikers and campers be allowed to walk only on selected paths in order to see and experience the wilderness?
- Should forest fires be deliberately set to maintain natural conditions?
- Should any logging or mining be permitted?

The demands for wood and wood products in today's world have also created serious conflicts over how we should use our wilderness resources. One of the major conflicts is over the methods logging companies use to harvest trees, in particular **clear-cutting**.

In clear-cutting, all trees in an area are cut down, and the tops and branches cut off. The trees are then trucked from the clear-cut area, and moved to sawmills and other wood-finishing industries. The brush is left behind to decay. Many forest companies claim that the effects of clear-cutting are no different than a forest fire. All

species are destroyed and the dominant species return. Many people outside the forest industry disagree. They argue that the impact of modern clear-cutting is sudden and dramatic. The loss of habitat is immediate, the damage to the ecosystem total.

Single-tree selection for cutting

Leaving a protected covering of shelter trees

Leaving seed-bearing trees standing

Clear-cutting all trees and replanting with seedlings

Figure 4.3.a Methods used to harvest trees

The Forest Industry, Improved Efficiency, and Sustainability

Logging companies today are generally working hard to practise sustainable forest activities. Ideally, when they leave a clear-cut area, tree planters move in to replant seedlings. The regeneration of the forest can also be done by reseeding. Many companies are trying both to replace the trees they cut down and to increase tree yields efficiently. Replacement trees are increasingly raised in nurseries and tree farms, and often are genetically improved. These trees can grow faster in the rigorous Canadian climate, reducing time to maturity from 80 or 100 years to 50 or 60 years. Fertilizers and insecticides also allow faster regrowth. All these improvements help make the forests sustainable. Some critics, however, argue that even with these improvements by the time a clear-cut area is reforested, the damage to the ecosystem has been done. As well, many critics argue that genetically altered trees are actually weaker when exposed to nature and that the wood quality is poor.

Figure 4.3.b Clear-cut forest

CASE STUDY   **Many Points of View**

Forester: With my chainsaw, I make enough money to live, to feed my family. The company keeps us employed.

Heli-logger pilot: If my machine doesn't break down, and the coastal weather co-operates and the crew gets the logs ready, I can make a return trip to the water with logs every two minutes.

Forest company manager: Our crews are fast and efficient. We have the wood to market in days. The clear-cutting is invisible because of a buffer zone. Our nurseries have trees ready to go and our planters have well-paid summer jobs.

Newspaper delivery person: If I can save up my pay, I can get a new bike, and with the tips...

A young couple: I think the cedar shakes on the roof of our new home look much better than shingles.

Old fly-fisherman: I can't wait to get back to the old trout stream and float my new line out over the water.

The problems with clear-cutting centre around the changes it creates in the soil and runoff water conditions. Tree leaves break the impact of falling rain, fallen leaves act as sponges to soak up water, and roots hold the soil in place. By the process of **transpiration** the trees send oxygen and water through their leaves back into the air. The forest provides homes and shelter for animals and birds. The streams are the habitat for fish and aquatic life.

Break the cycle by clear-cutting the forest and the change is immediate. The rain strikes directly on the ground and soil is swept away into rivers. If the site is mountainous, no life can grow on the exposed rock. There are no homes for wildlife. The silted streams become uninhabitable. In some tropical areas clay soil bakes into a type of pavement. The world loses its huge canopy of carbon-removing, oxygen-releasing leaves. **Global warming** is increased.

Figure 4.3.c "Scorched Earth, Clear-cut Logging on Native Sovereign Land, Shaman Coming to Fix." Shaman are brought in to heal the land after the forest has been logged by the clear-cut method.

Many supporters of forest wilderness want to save all **old-growth forests** (see Figure 2.6.d) as protected areas. They argue that these forests are places where the existing ecosystem will last and where cures for diseases may be discovered using plant varieties and animal species that we don't yet know about. As well, people can go to these forests for relaxation and revitalization. In short, supporters of saving all old-growth forests argue that forests such as those in Clayoquot Sound and Carmanagh

Valley in BC and Temagami and Algonquin Park in Ontario are places whose value extends far beyond the economic. Preserving old-growth forests is another area where the interests of tourists, fishers, recreational hunters, bird watchers, conservationists, and forest companies and workers collide. Many people, sometimes called "tree huggers" in the press, have chained themselves to trees to try to stop workers with chainsaws from felling old-growth trees.

The struggle between economic

Lawrence Paul Yuxweluptoun, National Gallery of Canada

Figure 4.3.d Helicopters lift valuable timber from remote forests.

benefits and maintaining the wilderness is not restricted to Canada. Forests are also under severe pressure globally. In some cases, like Nepal, the forests have been cleared from around Mount Everest to provide firewood. In other areas, like the rain forests of Brazil in the Amazon River basin, the trees are clear-cut for farmland or to harvest the valuable specialty woods such as teak and mahogany.

Figure 4.3.e Lands for Life regions. Nine of the areas set aside by the government: 1. Woodland Caribou (addition to existing provincial park); 2. St. Raphael wilderness area (includes old-growth red pine and calving sites for woodland caribou); 3. Nipigon Basin; 4. Great Lakes Heritage Coast; 5. Nagagamisis (combination of 2 existing parks + another 30 354 hectares); 6. Algoma Headwaters (contains towering 15-storey tall old-growth pine trees); 7. Spanish River; 8. Killarney (addition to existing provincial park); 9. Kawartha Highlands (expansion of existing park)

CASE STUDY — Lands for Life—Crown Lands in Ontario

Crown lands were deeded to the people of Ontario in perpetuity (forever). They cover 87% of the province. The Ontario government, through its Ministry of Natural Resources, developed a blueprint—Lands for Life—to oversee these lands and to allow all interested groups to present their suggestions for how the land should be used. For planning purposes, the government divided the lands into three regions (Figure 4.3.e below). Forest and mining companies, tourist businesses, hunters and fishermen, wildlife and conservation groups, and the people who live in the lands involved all brought their points of view—often conflicting views—to the discussions. In 1999, the Ontario government announced that it will create 378 new parks and wilderness reserves. In all, Lands for Life will create 60 new parks, 174 conservation reserves—some only a few hectares— and expand 44 parks. As a result, a total 9.5 million hectares of the province's lands will be protected. Logging, mining, and hydroelectric development will not be allowed in the parks and protected regions. Hunting and fishing will be allowed in the new parks. The government also set up a "living legacy trust" that will provide $21.5 million for forestry management, including research into improved harvesting practices. The trust will compensate the forestry industry for losses of existing logging areas and the building of new roads. The trust will also provide $7 million for fish and wildlife management. In addition, the province will spend $19 million in search of new mining opportunities over two years. And the Ontario Prospectors' Assistance Program will be doubled to $4 million to help prospectors in their search for new mineral deposits. Like many decisions involving differing interests, not all people are happy with the government's decisions. Conservationists praised the government's move to protect old-growth forests and expand the amount of protected area. Some, however, felt that the amount of land set aside was very small in contrast to the size of the areas involved. Aboriginal peoples claim many of these lands or the right to hunt and fish on them.

Boreal West Planning Region

Boreal East Planning Region

Great Lakes– St. Lawrence Planning Region

New Protected Areas

ONTARIO

Kenora
Dryden
Thunder Bay
Sault Ste. Marie
Kapuskasing
Timmins
Sudbury
North Bay
Ottawa
Toronto

0   200 km
Scale

Source: Ontario Ministry of Natural Resources

Figure 4.3.f A typical wilderness scene in Northern Ontario

| Redwood 111.43 m | Douglas fir 100.27 m | Sitka spruce 96 m | Giant sequoia 94.49 m | Western hemlock 79.55 m | Big-leaf maple 48.16 m | Average man 1.8 m |

Figure 4.3.g Old-growth forests illustrate the natural growth of trees to maturity. Old-growth forests produced these giant trees, six of the tallest types of trees found in North America. The Redwood is the tallest tree recorded in the world. Note the size of an average man against the size of these trees.

QUESTIONS & ACTIVITIES

1. Suppose you are responsible for maintaining our wilderness areas. How would you answer the questions in the opening paragraph? Give reasons for your answers.
2. Write a definition for clear-cutting.
3. Make a diagram to show four ways to harvest trees.
4. **a)** List five reasons why logging companies prefer to clear-cut.
   b) List five reasons why conservationists oppose clear-cutting.
5. Describe the forest problems in two other countries in the world. Locate them on a map of the world.
6. Read the Case Study on Ontario's Lands for Life. In your own words, write a summary of this government-sponsored plan.
7. Examine Figure 4.3.e. Do you live in one of the Lands for Life regions? If so, research any informa-

tion you can find on discussions of land use in your area. Prepare a report for your class. Put your information in chart form, listing what each group involved wanted to see happen. Are the groups happy with the government's decisions? If you do not live in a Lands for Life region, choose one of the regions and do the same research.
8. Read the statements from each person in the first Case Study who has an interest in the forest business.
   a) Write a sentence about each person to describe how they are connected to the forest business.
   b) In groups of two or three, brainstorm a list of people you know who work in an industry connected to wood or wood products. Hint: Newspapers and furniture stores count too.

SOIL DEPLETION AND EROSION

Major Concepts

- Soil is a valuable resource
- Many factors affect soil
- Soil is of global importance

Soil is a valuable resource. Section 1.9 introduced this key concept for understanding many geographic factors. The quality and care of soil is directly related to the food on our table. As is the case with our wilderness areas, how well we care for the soil is often affected by conflicts over how to use this resource. This section examines the care of our soil and the consequences of its misuse.

A number of factors affect soil's ability to grow plants, including **texture**, **structure**, **drainage**, **compaction**, **erosion**, **climate**, and **slope**. To maintain soil quality and plant growth, farmers and others must use good soil management practices. To prevent soil erosion, farmers use **contour ploughing** on hilly lands, rotate crops leaving stubble (like corn stalks) on fields, plant alternate fields, and install erosion control structures such as snow fences or tree shelter belts.

If soil has no plant cover or the soil has not been properly cared for, wind or water can quickly remove the topsoil, as happened during the Dust Bowl of the 1930s when strong winds blew for years. In tropical rain forests, cutting down trees for wood for homes, cooking, and special woods allows heavy rain to fall directly on the soil. Without the shelter of the leaf canopy or the sponge-like absorption of the roots, soils quickly wash away into streams and rivers.

Soil compaction is another problem of soil mismanagement. Continual use of the heavy farm machinery that makes farming so efficient can compact the soil, removing the air spaces and water channels from the soil and choking off root growth. Clay soils are particularly subject to compaction. Tropical soils are more easily compacted when the rain forest above them is destroyed.

City landscapes continue to spread and occupy fertile farmland. The use of land for homes, roads, parking lots, and factories means that the soil is no longer available for food production.

On a global level, **soil conservation** is an important factor in feeding the world's six billion people. Keeping soil in place, keeping it fertilized, and producing food is vital to preventing famine. Since many crops remove nutrients from the soil, replacing the nutrients is an important farming practice. In the past, animal manure was ploughed into the soil to keep it fertile. In some countries, **night soil**, or human waste, was worked

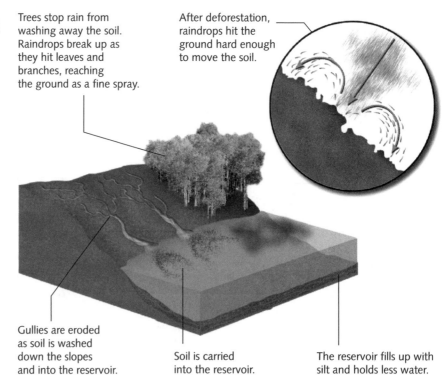

Trees stop rain from washing away the soil. Raindrops break up as they hit leaves and branches, reaching the ground as a fine spray.

After deforestation, raindrops hit the ground hard enough to move the soil.

Gullies are eroded as soil is washed down the slopes and into the reservoir.

Soil is carried into the reservoir.

The reservoir fills up with silt and holds less water.

Figure 4.4.a Deforestation from clear-cutting leads to soil erosion and silting of waterways and reservoirs. This diagram shows how heavy rainfall starts the destructive cycle.

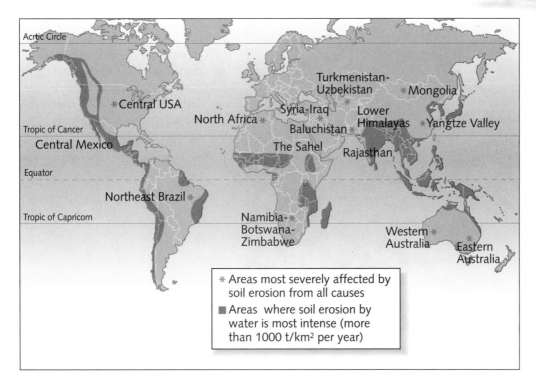

Figure 4.4.b Soil erosion around the world. Soil erosion by water is shown by one symbol. What other forces can cause soil erosion?

Map labels: Acrtic Circle, Tropic of Cancer, Equator, Tropic of Capricorn, Central USA, Central Mexico, North Africa, Northeast Brazil, Turkmenistan-Uzbekistan, Mongolia, Syria-Iraq, Baluchistan, The Sahel, Lower Himalayas, Yangtze Valley, Rajasthan, Namibia-Botswana-Zimbabwe, Western Australia, Eastern Australia

Legend:
* Areas most severely affected by soil erosion from all causes
■ Areas where soil erosion by water is most intense (more than 1000 t/km² per year)

into rice paddy soil. Today, chemical fertilizers are the more common method of keeping soils productive. Crop rotation alternates high nutrient-demanding crops like corn with fallow land to allow the fields to rest for a season. If crops are not rotated, the soil will become exhausted and unable to sustain healthy plants.

While fertilizers are valuable for maintaining soils, too much fertilizer can produce a chemical run-off with unwanted side effects, such as rapid weed growth in the fresh water.

Farmers of the world must be on guard for their soils constantly if we are to produce enough food for the world's citizens. Soils also need to be guarded against resource uses—such as cutting down rain forests and expanding cities—that destroy soils.

CASE STUDY — Holland Marsh

For 25 km from the south end of Lake Simcoe, an extensive post-glacial marsh covers about 10 000 ha of land. This marshy plain surrounds the Holland River. In the 1930s the marshes were drained with tiles, dams, and canals. Today Holland Marsh is the **market garden** of Ontario. The rich humus of the old marsh is ideal for fresh vegetables like onions, celery, spinach, carrots, potatoes, and more. Because of intensive use, however, the top level of soil is constantly diminished. Wind blows away the dry top layers and more fertilizers must be added to maintain the high level of production. The Marsh is also endangered by the insatiable hunger of the Greater Toronto Area for more land to house its peoples, expand its commerce, and develop more transportation routes.

Figure 4.4.c Low level air photo of intensive use by market garden farms on the Holland Marsh, upper right corner, with the Holland River running through it. The area on the bottom left is operated by Ducks Unlimited. Here this organization creates breeding and feeding areas for ducks.

Figure 4.4.d Salination can make farmlands useless because of the salt build-up. This illustration shows how crops are ruined when irrigation leads to salination, or the build-up of a salt crust in the top layer of the soil.

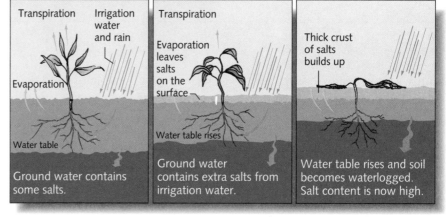

Transpiration Irrigation water and rain
Evaporation
Water table
Ground water contains some salts.

Transpiration
Evaporation leaves salts on the surface
Water table rises
Ground water contains extra salts from irrigation water.

Thick crust of salts builds up
Water table rises and soil becomes waterlogged. Salt content is now high.

QUESTIONS & ACTIVITIES

1. Make a chart to explain seven factors that affect the soil of a location.
2. Why is the growth of a city a problem for maintaining soil? Give several examples.
3. Use flow charts to describe three ways erosion of soil can happen.
4. Define these terms in your notes: soil compaction, soil conservation, night soil, crop rotation.
5. a) Explain how contour ploughing prevents soil erosion.
   b) Describe three other ways to help conserve the soil.

6. a) Using Figure 4.4.b. identify five areas of the world that have soil erosion problems.
   b) Research one of these areas and explain why it has soil erosion problems. Explain the effects of these problems on the people living in that region.
7. Make a copy of the diagrams in Figure 4.4.d. Write a paragraph to explain how putting water on a field (irrigation) can lead to a build up of salt in the soil (salination).

WETLANDS AND HABITAT LOSS

Major Concepts

- Wetlands are important ecosystems
- Habitat loss is ongoing
- Canada's Green Plan
- World sites under pressure

Canada is a huge area, yet habitat loss is a major problem as the demands of urban sprawl replace natural conditions. The wetlands discussed in this section were once regarded as waste lands, breeding insects, disease, and foul smelling gases. Today, people know that wetlands are some of the richest ecosystems and that they are vital to the food chain. Yet, they are still being destroyed. Already over two-thirds of the Great Lake's wetlands have been lost and the remaining third is threatened by pollution, drainage, and development.

Some terms used in wetland studies include **bog**, **marsh**, **swamp**, **coastal marsh**, **prairie slough**, **muskeg**, **river flood plain**, and **wetlands**.

As is the case with most of our other natural resources, conflicting needs are challenging the survival of many of Canada's remaining wetlands. The city of Toronto began as a small town on a swampy sand spit. Today it is bursting out of its Greater Toronto Area (GTA) and threatening to absorb the marshy gardens of the Holland Marsh. Along the way, almost all wetlands and swamps have been filled in and built over (see Figure 3.4.h).

The disappearance of wetlands results in the disappearance of the natural habitats for marine and animal life.

As governments become more aware of the immense value of the wetlands, more and more laws are being written to protect them. The plants that grow there play an important role in ecology. The common cattail is one of nature's best filters. Its rapid growth removes different kinds of materials from water and it breathes out oxygen and purified moisture. Plants keep the water in place, prevent runoff, and help build up the ground water supply.

The number of species found in wetlands is amazing. To be sure the mosquito is an annoying pest, but it is food to fish in the larval stage and to birds and the dragonflies in their flying stage. The prairie sloughs (pronounced "slews") or potholes are essential breeding grounds and rest stops for Canada Geese and thousands of ducks using the mid-western flyway.

▲ **Figure 4.5.a**   Wetland areas such as this one support a wide variety of plant and animal life.

Figure 4.5.b   This map illustrates ▶ the dramatic reduction of habitat. Pressures from human activities threaten the Grizzly bear population. About 10 000 to 13 000, or half of Canada's Grizzly bears, live in BC.

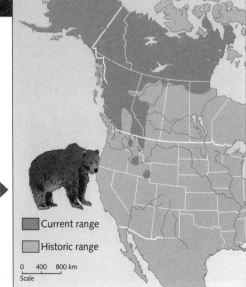

Current range

Historic range

0   400   800 km
Scale

FILE

Wetland Resources and Conflicting Interests

The effects on wetlands of conflicting resource needs are clearly illustrated by the Everglades and the delta of the Nile River. The Everglades are a huge expanse of saw grass wilderness in the southern tip of Florida. They are subject to fire, drought, and hurricanes naturally, but they have evolved an ecosystem to sustain life under these conditions. Florida has made most of the area a National Park to preserve this wilderness. In the past, Florida officials did not foresee the need to divert water from the Everglades to supply the demands of coastal cities and resorts such as Miami and Tampa Bay that expanded in part because of tourists coming to see the Everglades. Many people were unconcerned by this diversion of water because they see the Everglades primarily as a swamp filled with snakes and alligators. However, the ecosystem supports a huge array of wildlife and needs protection.

The Nile River delta has existed as a cradle of civilization since ancient Egypt began. The annual floods brought water and nutrients to the delta surrounding the mouth of the world's longest river. Today, 20 000 km of irrigation canals drain the river. The declining fresh water flow means that salt water from the Mediterranean Sea is rising inland and turning fields into salt pans. The ecosystem is drying out in the salty conditions.

Figure 4.5.d The Nile is the longest river in the world. The delta at the mouth of the river in the Mediterranean Sea has always provided fertile farmland. Dams and irrigation canals are creating serious habitat loss through salination today. ▼

With more than 20 000 km of irrigation canals sucking at the river, only 10% of the sediment entering the delta ever reaches the sea. Most of these channels were dug in the past 200 years.

At the Rosetta promontory, coastal erosion ate 352 ha of land (red) between 1984 and 1993; only 10% of the water and sediment has been deposited.

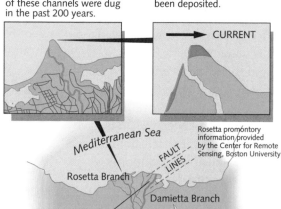

Rosetta promontory information provided by the Center for Remote Sensing, Boston University

The northeastern delta is rapidly sinking between two fault lines.

The Aswan High Dam traps 98% of the Nile's sediment.

Sediment is forming a new delta in southern Lake Nasser.

Figure 4.5.c Feluccas on Nile River at Aswan, Egypt

CASE STUDY — W3 Cold Creek Project

Wetlands, Woodlands, Wildlife are the W3 part of this Project's name. The Project is part of the Canada/Ontario Agricultural Green Plan. Also joining the team are the Ontario Federation of Anglers and Hunters and the Ontario Cattlemen's Association. The Project is intended to demonstrate that cattle herd production and health, water quality, and fish and wildlife habitat can all be improved at the same time. The W3 Project has ten demonstration sites to show that sustainable farm practices can also improve fish and wildlife habitat. Another interesting project includes planting a variety of trees to help re-establish the wild turkey in the Quinte region.

Figure 4.5.e The logo of W3 Cold Creek is to show that sustainable farm practices can improve fish and wildlife habitat.

Figure 4.5.f The logos of the five partners in W3 Cold Creek Project

Agriculture and Agri-Food Canada   Agriculture et Agroalimentaire Canada

QUESTIONS & ACTIVITIES

1. a) Write your own definition of "wetlands."
   b) Using the Glossary or a dictionary, make a chart to show eight types of wetlands. Use the headings: Term, Description, Example.
2. a) Discuss with your classmates examples of the kinds of wetlands found in your region.
   b) Draw a sketch map and locate these examples.
   c) What conclusions can you draw from the information on your map? Can you see any patterns?
3. In a diagram or flow chart, explain how the GTA and Golden Horseshoe areas have combined to destroy wetland habitat in their part of the Great Lakes basin. Refer to an atlas for the location of these areas.
4. a) Describe why wetlands are useful habitats for people.
   b) In diagram or chart form, give examples of how wetland plants help the environment.
   c) Give examples of how wetlands provide habitat for wildlife.
5. Read the case study on W3.
   a) What are the three Ws?
   b) What groups are in partnership?
   c) Describe the purpose of this program.
   d) Are there community groups in your area that are involved in projects designed to protect the environment? Make a chart listing the groups and the kinds of projects in which they are involved.
6. Explain how wetlands in the Florida Everglades are being affected by urban and tourist growth in Florida.
7. a) Explain how salination affects soil (review Figure 4.4.d).
   b) Report on how this process has changed the habitat of the Nile River delta in Egypt. Use diagrams or a flow chart to illustrate your report.

4.6

ENERGY SUSTAINABILITY

Major Concepts

- World energy production and consumption
- Energy "haves" and "have nots"
- Sustainable energy is necessary
- Pollution and conservation

The use of energy globally is not very balanced. Canada and the United States make up about 5% of the world's population yet they consume over 25% of the world's energy. In much of the world, people struggle to get enough energy to keep them warm and fed. The questions in this section and section 4.7 are:

- Can we in Canada meet our demands for energy without seriously depleting our energy sources or harming the environment?
- Can energy-poor countries around the world achieve the

energy required to reach a good quality of life without damaging other resources?

- Can the people of the world achieve a balance between the amount of energy they need, the amount of energy they have, and environmental concerns raised by energy projects?
- In short, can we reach a point where energy use in Canada and worldwide is **sustainable**?

Energy helps make Canadian life prosperous. Nearly 5% of all Canadian jobs are directly related to energy and 5% of our exports

are energy products. Electricity is available at the flick of a switch, our cars are fuelled on demand, homes and workplaces are warmed or cooled with a thermostat. Our comfort needs are satisfied.

Canada gets 75% of its energy from fossil fuels, all of which are non-renewable. We now have to start considering what will happen when these fuels are gone. Section 2.12 introduced us to the idea that, in fact, we need to consider replacing these fuels even before they are used up because they harm the environment. The burning or combustion of these fuels creates air pollution (acid rain from sulphur and nitrogen particles), thermal pollution or global warming (from carbon dioxide emissions), and urban pollution from ground level ozone.

Globally, the story is the same. While North America is responsible for a large part of the **greenhouse effect** (see section 5.2), energy consumption in Europe and Asia also contributes. The use of fossil fuels and their accompanying pollution will grow as China, Africa, and South America become more prosperous. Global warming from **greenhouse gases** is the subject of global research and international agreements to control emissions (see sections 5.2 and 8.2).

Electricity is a major type of energy use, but it also has an important impact on the environment. Large tracts of land are needed for generating stations and ecosystems are totally changed by the creation of reservoirs that accompany these stations. The disposal of nuclear waste is a huge

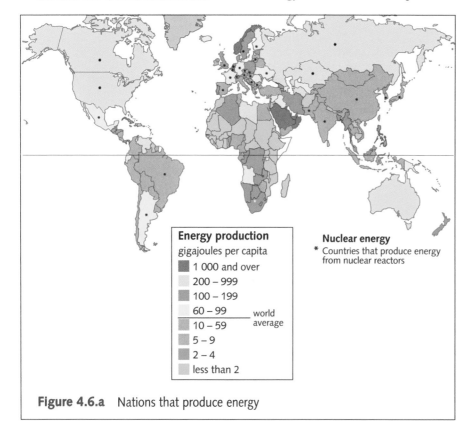

Energy production
gigajoules per capita

- 1 000 and over
- 200 – 999
- 100 – 199
- 60 – 99 — world average
- 10 – 59
- 5 – 9
- 2 – 4
- less than 2

Nuclear energy
* Countries that produce energy from nuclear reactors

Figure 4.6.a Nations that produce energy

problem with nuclear-powered electrical energy. Canada is a world leader in nuclear technology and sells Candu nuclear reactors around the world. China, Turkey, and South Korea are potential partners in the next millennium. As a result, the problem of nuclear waste will grow.

Energy demand is growing in Canada and the world. Solutions to the problems created by traditional methods of producing energy need to be found.

Higher prices have proven to have an effect on energy use. The oil restrictions during the Gulf War in the early 1990s brought price increases in petroleum products. Although consumers complained when the prices went up, usage did go down. **Alternative energy sources** like wood, solar power, biomass, geothermal, and hydrogen are in development (see sections 2.12 and 8.2).

Figure 4.6.c Domestic energy ▶ production by energy source. Canada is both a high producer and a high consumer of energy. Research and write definitions for "petajoules," "gigajoules," and "megawatts."

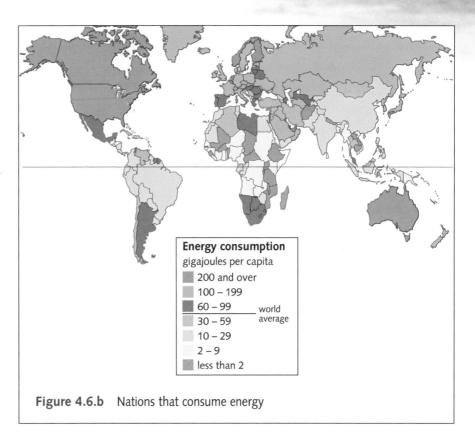

Energy consumption
gigajoules per capita
- 200 and over
- 100 – 199
- 60 – 99 ——— world average
- 30 – 59
- 10 – 29
- 2 – 9
- less than 2

Figure 4.6.b Nations that consume energy

	1993	1994	1995	1996	1997
	Petajoules				
Petroleum	4 556	4 829	5 033	5 283	5 449
Natural Gas	4 885	5 294	5 592	5 890	6 316
Hydroelectricity	1 153	1 175	1 190	1 214	1 242
Nuclear	1 064	1 221	1 108	1 155	956
Coal	1 651	1 735	1 799	1 817	1 855
Renewables and Other	500	541	589	612	504
Total	**12 827**	**13 825**	**14 854**	**15 367**	**16 321**

Source: National Energy Board

CASE STUDY — Electrical Energy in Ontario

Ontario has five coal-burning generating plants. While generating electrical power, they also produce sulphur dioxide (acid rain), nitrogen oxide (smog) and carbon dioxide (greenhouse gas associated with global warming). There is a movement to switch these generating plants from coal (which has to be imported) to natural gas. Natural gas burns more cleanly and arrives by Canadian pipelines. Ontario has nuclear energy sites but some were shut down in the mid-1990s for safety reasons. Nuclear energy helps reduce air pollution. However, issues of safety over handling and disposing of nuclear waste present major concerns.

Estimate made in 1997	
Crude Oil remaining established reserves millions cubic metres	1372
Natural Gas remaining established reserves billions cubic metres	1930
Coal remaining established reserves millions of tonnes	8623

Source: National Resources Canada

Figure 4.6.d Fossil fuel energy reserves in Canada, 1997

Province/Territory	In-Operation and Under Construction	Remaining Potential		
		Gross*	Identified**	Planning***
	(MW)			
Newfoundland	6 648	5 201	4 623	2 555
Prince Edward Island	0	0	0	0
Nova Scotia	390	8 499	8 499	0
New Brunswick	919	940	600	440
Quebec	32 480	66 286	34 844	6 437
Ontario	7 261	12 385	12 385	3 994
Manitoba	4 877	8 360	5 260	5 260
Saskatchewan	836	2 189	935	870
Alberta	854	18 813	9 762	1 833
British Columbia	11 277	33 137	18 168	10 164
Yukon	77	18 583	13 701	350
Northwest Territories	59	9 229	9 201	2 468
Canada	65 678	182 832	117 978	34 371

Gross Potential – The total gross resource that could be developed if there were no technical, economic, or environmental
 constraints (excludes sites already developed or under construction).
Identified Potential – Gross potential less sites that may not be developed for technical reasons.
Planning Potential – Identified potential less sites that may not be developed for environmental or economic reasons.
 The planning potential thus comprises all those sites that are considered to be likely candidates for future development.

Source: Canadian Electrical Utilities and Natural Resources Canada.

Figure 4.6.e Hydroelectric capacity in Canada, in megawatts, 1996. In Canada some provinces and territories have more hydroelectric capacity than others. Which three territories or provinces have the most and which three have the least capacity? Research and explain why this level of energy capacity is so for each group.

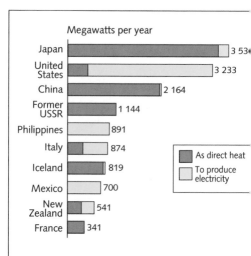

Figure 4.6.f Geothermal energy uses heat and steam from the Earth to generate power and direct heat to buildings. The graph shows ten nations that produce geothermal energy from natural sources.

QUESTIONS & ACTIVITIES

1. Compare Figure 4.6.a with Figure 4.6.b. What conclusions can you draw from your observations?
2. a) State Canada's population as a percentage of the world's. Illustrate your answer in a bar graph.
   b) State Canada's energy consumption as a percentage of the world's. Illustrate your answer in a pie graph.
   c) Explain how these two numbers indicate a high standard of living in Canada.
3. a) Why is Canada a good source for electrical energy?
   b) What are four problems with the generation of electricity?
4. Use diagrams to illustrate four problems with fossil fuel combustion as a source of energy.
5. Why does the selling of nuclear reactors to other countries bring Canada criticism about its potential connection to terrorists?
6. Read the case study on energy in Ontario.
   a) Write a summary of the pros and cons of using coal to provide electricity.
   b) Make a diagram to illustrate how coal creates electrical energy for people's use.
7. Use the information in Figure 4.6.c to create a graph of domestic energy production by energy source in Canada.
8. Reading, writing, and thinking about energy use around the world can sometimes create negative feelings about the future. Write a short essay explaining why the new global awareness about energy use will eventually be beneficial to humankind.

ENERGY MEGA PROJECTS

Major Concepts

- Energy mega projects affect the environment
- Fossil fuel projects
- Hydroelectric projects
- Win-win situations

M**ega projects** are really big construction projects for generating electricity or developing an energy resource. Because they are so big, they make large changes to the environment. In an ideal world, the impact of mega projects on the ecosystems would be balanced against the jobs created and the energy that will be supplied. This balance between protecting resources and using them is a **cost-benefit situation**. In such situations the views of many groups are taken into account. In a **win-win situation**, the ecosystem is protected, people get work, people are not seriously displaced, and a new flow of energy is ensured. This section examines four Canadian mega projects and their environmental impacts.

1. Alberta Tar Sands

The Alberta oil, or tar sands and the Hibernia oil fields are two fossil fuel energy mega projects. The **oil sands** cover 50 000 km^2 around Fort McMurray in Alberta. These fields contain more oil than Saudi Arabia, which has the richest fields in the world. People have known about the sands for many centuries, but it was not until the 1930s that technological developments made possible the first attempt to extract the oil. However, separating the useful petroleum from the **tar sands** is difficult and very expensive. The sands are covered with bitumen, a gummy form of crude oil. In the open-pit mining used on the oil sands, machines strip away all the ground cover and drag lines with huge buckets scoop up the oil-soaked sands. Steam and filters are used to separate the resource from the sand. Bitumen is processed on site to make a synthetic light crude oil (chemicals change the ratio of carbon to hydrogen) to be sent out by pipeline. The oil sand sites involve billions of dollars of investment and alter thousands of hectares of ecosystem.

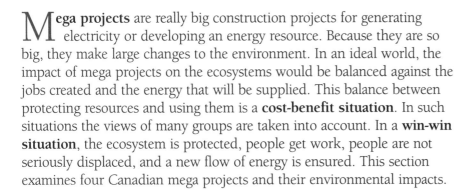

Figure 4.7.a Location of oil sands

2. Hibernia Oil Fields

Oil deposits have been discovered on the Grand Banks off Newfoundland. Getting to this oil, too, is very expensive. Floating drilling platforms had to be constructed and floated into place. They then had to be anchored against the forces of the sea so that the drill bit hits and drills in exactly the same spot. The rigs must stand up to the storms of the North Atlantic as well as the dangers of icebergs floating down "iceberg alley" from the Arctic. Helicopters and tugs have to carry supplies and equipment to crews who live on the rigs for weeks at a time. The extracted oil must be moved by ship or pipeline to refineries on land, and great care must be taken that no spills of oil are allowed to reach the ocean waters.

Figure 4.7.b Ocean-going tugs like this one have deep hulls that can carry supplies to the Hibernia oil rigs.

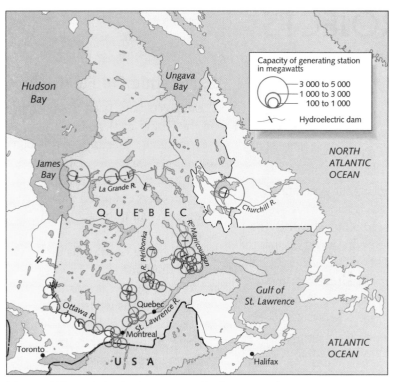

Figure 4.7.c Hydroelectric energy in Quebec. Natural waterways give Quebec huge potential for hydroelectric generation.

3. James Bay Project

Hydro projects also cost mega dollars and affect large amounts of land. In Quebec, the gigantic James Bay hydroelectric project in the early 1970s was very controversial. The initial phase was the La Grande Complex. The provincial government saw the development of the James Bay watershed in northern Quebec as an opportunity to develop energy to power Quebec and to solve the energy crisis then facing the northeastern United States. Selling energy to the United States would help solve the province's economic problems. As well 125 000 jobs would be created for Quebecers. Environmentalists, on the other hand, vigorously opposed the project. They argued that it would disrupt the ecosystem of a quarter of Quebec and seriously

affect the ecology of James Bay. Millions of nesting geese, caribou, and other animals would be permanently displaced, and the lifestyle of the self-supporting Cree destroyed.

Despite objections, the first phase of the project was put in place. Hydro-Quebec invested over $20 billion up to the early 1980s. Since 1971, La Grande has flooded about 10 000 km² by diverting and damming six waterways.

The disruption to the lives of the native Cree Indians, the destruction of ecosystems, and, in particular, the decline of demand for electricity, especially in the United States, have put further development of this project on hold.

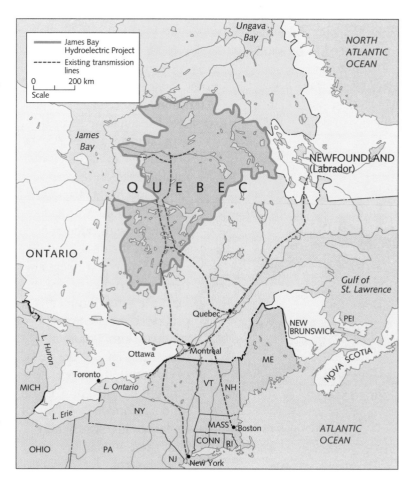

Figure 4.7.d Area covered by the James Bay hydroelectric project

4. Labrador/Churchill Falls Project

Labrador is adding to a mega project already built. For many years the Churchill Falls project has been producing enough power to heat and light 800 000 homes. The new project will add 30% more power to the existing site. Part of the existing project, the Smallwood Reservoir, collects water from a drainage basin larger than Nova Scotia. The Whitefish Falls sluice gate in the reservoir controls how much water flows from the reservoir into the Churchill Falls power station. The new project will use this water a second time at a new power station downstream.

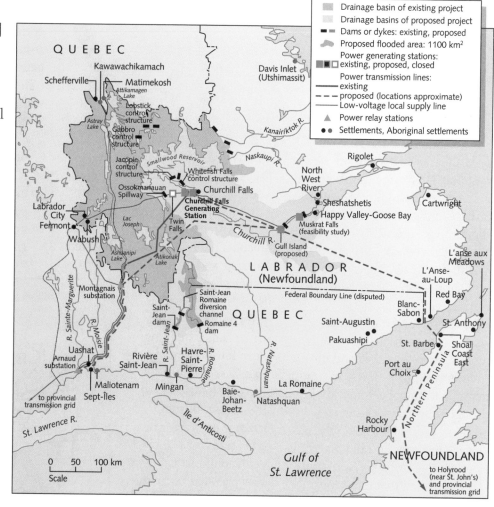

Figure 4.7.e The Lower Churchill power project, Labrador

QUESTIONS & ACTIVITIES

1. a) Draw the four mega projects on a blank map of Canada: Alberta oil sands, Hibernia oil fields, James Bay Project, Labrador/Churchill Falls Project.
   b) Use a legend and assign symbols to represent the type of energy at each project.

2. a) Describe the mining process of the oil sands.
   b) Why has it taken so long to develop this site?
   c) How do the oil reserves compare to the known world reserves?

   d) Describe how the oil is separated, refined, and transported to market.

3. What natural hazards occur in the Hibernia oil fields?

4. a) What three factors stopped further hydro development in the James Bay project of Quebec?
   b) In chart form or in a flow chart, prepare a cost-benefit summary of the James Bay project.

5. Why does the Labrador project have a better chance of being completed than the James Bay project?

HAZARDOUS WASTE MANAGEMENT

Major Concepts

- All waste is a problem
- Some wastes are dangerous
- Reduce, recycle, reuse
- Canada's Green Lane

Archeologists have declared that the Mayan society was very wasteful. They came to this conclusion after they dug up Mayan garbage and studied it for clues about the great civilization's disappearance. When the Mayans realized that their resources were in very short supply, it was too late to reduce, recycle, and reuse.

Waste is disposed of in many ways. Some methods have caused serious harm to people and the environment. The easiest and most traditional way of getting rid of waste has been by "throwing it away" or dumping it. But where is "away"? Swamps and old gravel pits were used as garbage dumps until it was discovered that hazardous liquids were leaking out and into water cycles. People did, and still do, throw things—out the car window, into fields, or into ditches. Waterways were easy dumping points. Raw human sewage and

industrial waste chemicals were discharged into flowing water, lakes, or ponds. The effects were soon obvious.

Today, landfill sites have to be lined with clay or non-porous rock to contain all the waste. Exhausted quarries and open-pit mines offer some sites for waste disposal, as do abandoned mines with shafts extending deep into solid rock (see Case Study). Incineration is a possible option. Burning garbage can create heat and steam for power-generating plants. However, the resulting air pollution is potentially a greater problem. Using heat to destroy hazardous chemicals is a possibility. One company owns a

portable incinerator that it takes around to different places to burn hazardous PCB chemicals.

These are some of the dangerous wastes we have to dispose of:

- **Nuclear waste**—All materials in contact with this generating process become contaminated by radiation. Mine sites buried deep in the solid Canadian Shield are possible storage sites. Dumping into deep ocean trenches is another possibility. The problem

Figure 4.8.a

is that materials stay contaminated for centuries.

- **Chemical waste**—Society uses thousands of chemicals. If chemicals escape in a concentrated form or a gaseous form, they can become serious health hazards. Recycling and reusing chemicals is one way to reduce the problem.

CASE STUDY — Adams Mine near Kirkland Lake, ON

An entrepreneur bought an abandoned mine, the Adams Iron mine, and wants Toronto's garbage. A sixty-car container train would transport about 4000 t of garbage from Toronto to the mine site every day of the year. The waste would be compacted and stuffed into the mine pits. The proposal is controversial. Many conservationists and other citizens are concerned about possible accidents to the train en route and worry that the waste might eventually leak out of the mine. Other people reject the idea of receiving garbage from others—NIMBY, "not in my back yard."

Name of Toxin	Uses	Source of Toxin	Effects of Toxin
Lead	Used in gasoline, paints, glazes, pipes, and roofing materials	Burning leaded fuels, incinerator emissions, boilers	Toxic effects on humans, fish and wildlife; can cause brain damage
Arsenic	Used in pesticides, smelters, glass production	Pesticide use, coal combustion, primary copper smelters	Poisonous to humans, fish and wildlife
Mercury	Used in batteries, paints, industrial instruments, and pulp and paper mills	Natural, coal combustion, municipal waste incineration, copper smelting, sewage incineration	Affects the nervous system and permanent damage can result; the brain may also be damaged
Benzopyrene (BaP)	Not used alone but is found as a by-product of burning fossil fuels	Combustion processes, such as wood burning, cigarette smoke, and coke oven emissions	Believed to be cause of high incidence of tumors in fish; carcinogen
Hexachlorobenzene	Used to control insects	Pesticide use, manufacture of chlorinated solvents	Linked to nerve and liver damage; suspected to cause birth defects

Figure 4.8.b Sources and effects of toxins. Toxins are harmful substances that get into the atmosphere.

- **Human waste**—Human sewage is loaded with dangerous bacteria. Discharging raw sewage into the water cycle can cause widespread illness. Treatment plants and septic systems must be used to protect societies.
- **Hospital waste**—Like sewage, hospital waste can be very dangerous. From obsolete drugs to contaminated fluids and diseased flesh, disposing of hospital waste is a risky business. Incineration is one method.
- **Marine waste**—This waste also comes in many forms. Ships discharging oily ballast, cities dumping garbage, and chemicals that wash away off the land are all hurting our oceans and marine life.

Recycling hazardous materials often seems difficult, but it is possible. Most cities now have hazardous waste collection sites and pick-up days. They are attempting to keep household hazardous waste such as paint, nail polish, radioactive smoke alarms, antifreeze, paint remover, flashlight batteries, and much more out of the ecosystem.

CASE STUDY   Dombind on Ontario roads

After a five-year trial, Ontario will phase out the use of Dombind. Dombind is a brown, syrupy waste product from the paper mills of Norampac (formerly Domtar). About one million litres per year have been given free to municipalities to put on gravel roads for dust control. Environmentalists worry that while the dioxin levels are low, it could get into water supplies. Citizens have complained about the smell and the black goo that gets on cars, shoes, and pets.

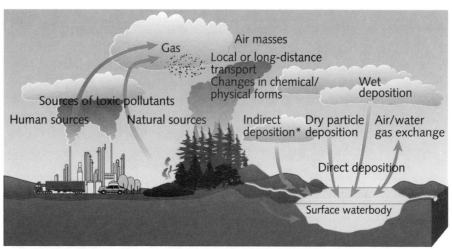

*Indirect deposition is direct deposition to land followed by runoff or seepage through groundwater to a surface waterbody.

Figure 4.8.c Airborne toxic cycle. Some toxins fall to Earth as rain and move in the water cycle. Some fall directly onto water bodies such as rivers, streams, and the Great Lakes.

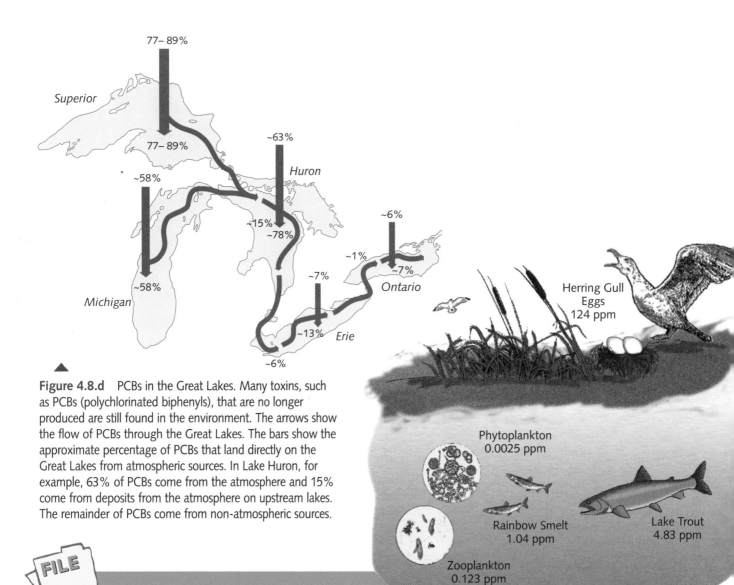

Figure 4.8.d PCBs in the Great Lakes. Many toxins, such as PCBs (polychlorinated biphenyls), that are no longer produced are still found in the environment. The arrows show the flow of PCBs through the Great Lakes. The bars show the approximate percentage of PCBs that land directly on the Great Lakes from atmospheric sources. In Lake Huron, for example, 63% of PCBs come from the atmosphere and 15% come from deposits from the atmosphere on upstream lakes. The remainder of PCBs come from non-atmospheric sources.

Figure 4.8.e Biomagnification of PCBs. **Biomagnification** is a process whereby toxins like PCBs are built up in quantity in the food chain. Each link in the chain retains the toxins of the things it eats. The amount of the toxins increases or magnifies in larger animals in the chain. Scavengers like gulls are also affected, sometimes developing reproductive problems or deformities.

FILE

FACT

Waste Exchange, a service on Canada's Green Lane

"One person's waste is another's raw material." Green Lane is an Environment Canada website that includes a section on Waste Exchanges in Canada. Through Waste Exchanges the government provides a "matching service" between waste generators and potential users of waste products. Interested companies direct their inquires through the Waste Exchange. Once two companies have been introduced, the role of the Exchange ends.

Examples:

- An oil refinery has 2000 barrels of phenol by-products waste. The refinery transfers it to a manufacturer of hard plastics because, for the manufacturer, the by-product is a resource.
- A solvent used to clean electrical contacts is contaminated by small amounts of grease that enter the solution. This "unclean" solvent becomes a resource for a paint manufacturer who needs 1000 L of solvent per month, and for whom small amounts of grease do not matter. http://www.doe.ca/

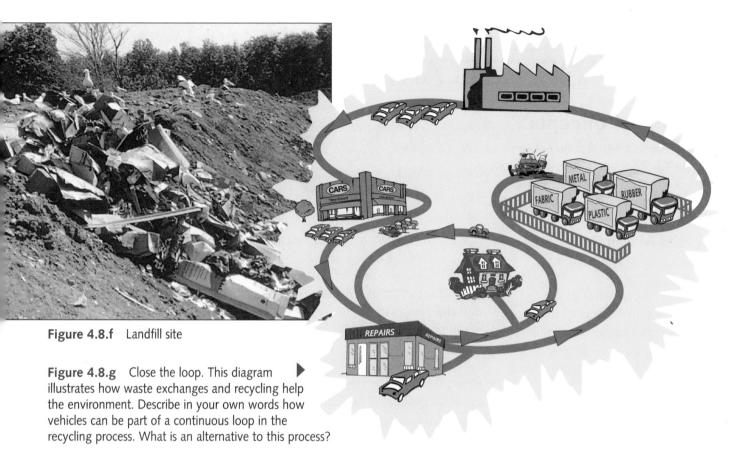

Figure 4.8.f Landfill site

Figure 4.8.g Close the loop. This diagram ▶
illustrates how waste exchanges and recycling help
the environment. Describe in your own words how
vehicles can be part of a continuous loop in the
recycling process. What is an alternative to this process?

QUESTIONS & ACTIVITIES ❓

1. **a)** What is an archeologist?
   b) Where did the Mayan people live?
   c) How does garbage reveal the lifestyle of old civi-lizations?
   d) Make a chart to illustrate what you think our garbage today would tell an archeologist digging up and examining our waste 100 years from now about our civilization.

2. **a)** What has been the traditional way to handle unwanted items and garbage?
   b) What were some disposal sites in the past?
   c) How have disposal sites changed today? Why have they changed?

3. Construct a chart to show types of hazardous wastes. Use these headings: Type of Waste, Description, Two Examples.

4. **a)** Do some research and make a second chart from Figure 4.8.b, about toxins, adding toxins that are no longer produced.
   b) If the toxins in a) are no longer produced, why do we have to worry about them and study their effects?

5. **a)** Make a sketch to show how biomagnification of PCBs happens in the food chain.
   b) Explain what biomagnification means.

6. Read the case study on the Adams mine site. Write an argumentative essay of three paragraphs. Defend the right to buy and import garbage or defend the right to reject the purchase and importing of garbage.

7. **a)** Research recycling programs in your area. Write an account of the programs to include: Blue box pick-ups, additional recycling plans, garbage dumps, waste disposal sites, waste exchange groups, and barter groups. Illustrate your account with flow charts.
   b) Devise a survey to find out who recycles and if they think recycling programs are successful in your community. Write a prediction for the future of recycling in your area.

4.9

THE AGGREGATE INDUSTRY AND LAND RECLAMATION

Major Concepts

- Sustainable resources
- Conflict resolution in land use
- Pits and quarries as economic resources
- Rehabilitation of land

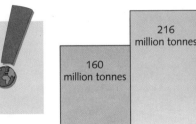

Source: Aggregate Producers' Association of Ontario

Figure 4.9.a Estimated annual aggregate consumption in Ontario

You have seen that as a nation's population grows, conflicts over how parcels of land should be used also grow. Some of the conflicts arise because of the need for resources to be sustained or made to last for future generations. The resolution of conflicting land use, the need for **sustainability** of resources, and how to reclaim land once a resource has been depleted can be examined through the **aggregate industry**. This industry works with rock fragments, stones, sand, and gravel that together are referred to as **aggregate**. The materials are dug, cut, or blasted out of the land creating **pits** or **quarries**.

When the glaciers finally retreated at the end of the ice age about 10 000 years ago, they left behind all kinds of material. **Glacial moraine**, for example, covers much of Ontario's farmland. As the ice melted, many melt water features called **eskers** were formed. These were rivers of water flowing inside the glaciers. They flowed on top of the frozen ground and were held in place by the ice walls of the glacier. When they were exposed after the glaciers melted, they showed up as raised, snake-like forms on the land and are composed of water-washed sand and gravel. These are the raw materials of the aggregate industry.

Aggregates are one of our nonrenewable natural resources. This means that that they need to be used wisely. It also means that pits and quarries eventually run out of the resource. The pits and quarries then stand as an open scar on the land. Public and private interests are often at odds over how land should be cleaned up or restored after an economic activity has finished. Most people today agree that just walking away and leaving the depleted area as had sometimes been done in the past is unsatisfactory. The aggregate industry has worked hard to reclaim the land it has used. In doing so, it has found that these parcels of land have post-mining uses that are as valuable as the original deposits.

Uses of Aggregate

- Over 400 t of aggregate are used in the construction of every house. Aggregate is used for foundations, concrete blocks, brick, mortar, shingles, steel, glass, and asphalt.
- Aggregate are used in the construction of every school. A small school uses 13 000 t in construction.
- An office tower uses hundreds of thousands of tonnes of aggregate.
- Roads and highways are the biggest user of aggregate in Ontario, accounting for 53% of annual consumption.
- The construction of 1 km of a six-lane expressway requires 37 600 t of aggregate.

Source: Aggregate Producers' Association of Ontario

STUDY Butchart Gardens

One of the most famous reclamation projects in Canada is Butchart Gardens on Vancouver Island. The limestone deposits on the Saanich Peninsula, about 30 km north of Victoria and just across the Strait of Juan de Fuca from Vancouver, were an excellent quality for cement. The growing cities in the population boom of the early 1900s created a huge demand.

As the quarry was excavated, the owners, the Butchart family, decided the deep pit would make a superb garden. The deepest part was below the water table and was transformed into a sunken garden lake, refreshed by deep, spring-fed waters. Plants like ivy were selected to grow on the steep cliffs to drape them with greenery. From this beginning, the property has been developed into a beautiful series of world-famous gardens. Today, a million visitors a year pass through this rehabilitated quarry to enjoy the scenic, quiet site of the old quarry.

Figure 4.9.b Scene from the earliest days in The Sunken Garden, around 1912

Figure 4.9.c The quarry transformed from a work site to The Sunken Gardens, around 1920

Figure 4.9.d The Sunken Garden today. Butchart Gardens is a major tourist attraction on Vancouver Island today, a very successful after-use or rehabilitation.

What happens to a pit or a quarry when it is depleted of aggregate?

Here are just a few examples:

- Housing developments
- Baseball diamonds
- Commercial/industrial uses
- Agriculture/forestry
- Fish and wildlife habitat
- Conservation area
- Parks/golf courses

Source: Aggregate Producers Association of Ontario

Figure 4.9.e Land uses on rehabilitated pits and quarries

Figure 4.9.f These four photos show rehabilitated quarries or pits.

QUESTIONS & ACTIVITIES

1. What does the aggregate industry produce?
2. a) When did the Ice Age end?
   b) Define and describe an esker. Use a diagram to help your description.
   c) What resource materials do eskers provide?
3. a) Where is Butchart Gardens?
   b) What type of rock was the deposit?
   c) What was the rock used for?
   d) Describe how the Butchart family transformed the old quarry into a tourist attraction and explain its current significance.
4. a) Make a table to show possible uses of rehabilitated pits and quarries.
   b) Why is rehabilitation preferable to abandoning old quarry and pit land?
5. a) Write a paragraph to describe how aggregates are an important part of your school's construction.
   b) Create a flow chart to show the movement of aggregate from the quarry to your school.
6. Find an example of a pit or quarry in your area.
   a) What is produced and how long will it last?
   b) What are the neighbouring land uses?
   c) What plans are in place for the pit or quarry after its resource has run out?
   d) Devise a plan to evaluate the future use options for the site.

RECREATION DEVELOPMENT IN SENSITIVE ENVIRONMENTS

Major Concepts

- Tourism's impact
- Significance of National and Provincial Parks
- Ecotourism

Figure 4.10.b Boardwalks allow visitors to discover Point Pelee without trampling on the fragile ecosystem. This is an example of a controlled "eco footprint."

Tourism is very important to Canada, generating over 25 billion dollars revenue each year. Canadians travel throughout the country in search of recreational activities. As well, visitors from other countries, especially the United States, tour Canada for their holidays. This section examines some recreational sites in Canada and around the world that are sensitive to overuse.

Our oldest national park, Banff, Alberta, illustrates the problems of conflicting resource use and pressure on sensitive recreational land in the mountains. Banff is a magnificent area. Hiking in summer, skiing in winter, a cultural centre,

an historic hotel, wildlife, and spectacular scenery all contribute to its beauty. People arrive in carloads and busloads to take advantage of what the park offers. Accommodations and services can barely keep up to the demand. Business people constantly pressure park officials to allow them to add more services such as accommodations, restaurants, and stores, while conservationists fight to keep the services and development restricted and contained to the town site in the park.

Because of the enormous numbers of people who visit the park, bears and mountain goats have become problems for park personnel.

People want to see the bears and take pictures, often forgetting that bears are powerful wild animals. Mountain goats and moose wander onto roads disrupting traffic and potentially causing accidents. Heli-skiing allows the adventurous to find the soft powdery slopes away

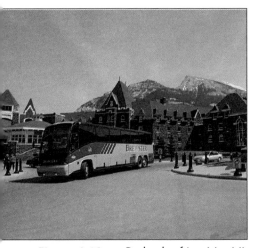

Figure 4.10.a Busloads of tourists visit Banff each year. Conflicts arise when the demands by visitors for services meet head-on with the restrictions on development by Parks Canada.

Figure 4.10.c Tourists travel to Churchill, Manitoba, on Hudson Bay to see polar bears roaming on the fragile tundra.

from the beaten path. Heavy snow brings avalanche danger to these skiers who want to ski away from groomed slopes. Finding a balance between maintaining the natural beauty of the park and the habitats of the wildlife that live there and satisfying the increasing numbers of people visiting the area is an ongoing struggle.

Point Pelee is the southernmost mainland tip of Canada. Jutting into Lake Erie out towards Pelee Island, this National Park is a sandspit with a large marsh area. Every year migrating birds and insects, like the monarch butterfly, use this fringe of land as a resting spot in their migration. The park contains one of the few examples of Carolina hardwood forests left in Canada.

Bird watchers and scientists know this is the place to see and study species. So do others who also want to swim, boat, and play along these shores of Lake Erie. Great Lakes cargo ships and trawlers navigate through narrow channels, while yachts, sailboats, and fishing boats enjoy the same area.

The park is laid out with trails and paths to allow visitors access to sites, especially the bird-watching sites. At the same time, they keep people from trampling the vegetation and away from the fragile marsh matte that is vital to migrating wildlife. Like Banff, in Point Pelee the struggle to balance people's search for recreational activities with keeping the ecosystem from being harmed is ongoing.

Figure 4.10.d The Niagara Escarpment. From Niagara where it creates the sensational Niagara Falls to Tobermory at the tip of the Bruce Peninsula where the cliffs overlook Georgian Bay, the limestone crests of the Niagara Escarpment create magnificent scenery.

FILE

FACT

Ecotourism is a growing form of recreational travel. People want to visit the exotic and unusual. They want to take an African safari, climb a high mountain, or swim with the fish in a coral reef. For some countries, ecotourism can bring economic relief. Ironically, it can also help save animals as tourism becomes more valuable and poachers are forced to stop killing potential attractions like elephants, tigers, rhinos, and eagles.

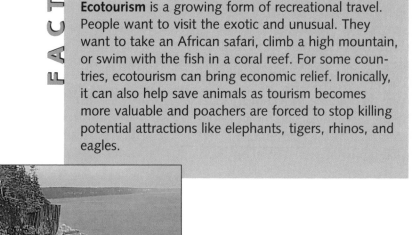

Photograph by Richard Armstrong

Figure 4.10.e View from part of the Bruce Trail, a natural walking trail along the Niagara escarpment.

CASE STUDY   Belize

Belize is a small, relatively poor country in Central America. Tourism is the fastest growing part of its economy. A tropical climate, beautiful beaches, coral reefs, and the interesting history of the Mayan people all draw visitors. The barrier reef in Belize is the second largest in the world and attracts scuba divers in increasing numbers.

With the help of British geographers, the country's ecosystems have been mapped. Nature reserves, wildlife parks, and conservation areas have been created by the government. The barrier reefs are now protected and a monkey sanctuary has been established. Belize wants to maintain its attractions in their natural state to support its ecotourism business. Yet, maintaining natural settings for tourists and the jobs tourism creates must be balanced against the needs of farmers for land and urban space for cities to grow.

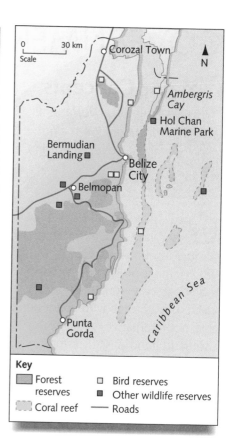

Key
- ▨ Forest reserves
- ▨ Coral reef
- ☐ Bird reserves
- ■ Other wildlife reserves
- — Roads

Figure 4.10.f Belize is a small country in Central America. Locate the country on your atlas of the region.

Figure 4.10.g Mayan temples are tourist attractions in Belize.

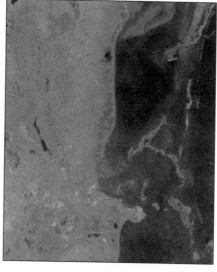

◀ **Figure 4.10.h** A satellite image of Belize shows the mainland coast, islands, and coral reefs. The Belize government and British geographers have used satellite images to map the country's vegetation.

QUESTIONS & ACTIVITIES

1. **a)** Describe how tourism contributes to the economy of Canada.
   b) What country sends the most tourists to Canada?
2. Using two sentences for each, describe three conflicts of resource use in Banff National Park.
3. **a)** List five ways people use the recreational facilities at Point Pelee National Park.
   b) What is unique about Point Pelee's location in Canada?
   c) What attracts naturalists to the park site?
   d) How are "eco-footprints" kept light in the park?
4. **a)** Write a definition for ecotourism.
   b) How does ecotourism help a country preserve scenic areas and wildlife?
5. Write a paragraph to describe how Belize is using ecotourism to develop its economy.
6. **a)** Select a region of the world that has ecotourism potential. Research this area and prepare a presentation. Use the Belize study as a model.
   b) Predict the conflicts that might arise when large numbers of tourists visit your region.
7. Create a Venn diagram with Banff at the centre to illustrate how six factors overlap at the site to make it a desirable site for a national park.

4.11

GOVERNMENT POLICIES

Major Concepts

- The role of governments
- Political decision making
- Levels of government in Canada

Governments at all levels play a vital role in determining how natural resources are used and the environment protected. We live in a democracy. Governments are elected by citizens who count on their representatives to make thoughtful and wise decisions. Elected officials, ideally, listen to all their constituents (the people who elected them) and follow the course of action that the majority wants. Unfortunately, life is never that simple!

Lobby groups attempt to convince elected officials that their concerns are more important than other points of view. Industries often support lobby groups, such as

Figure 4.11.b Elected members of the government must consider many factors in making decisions.

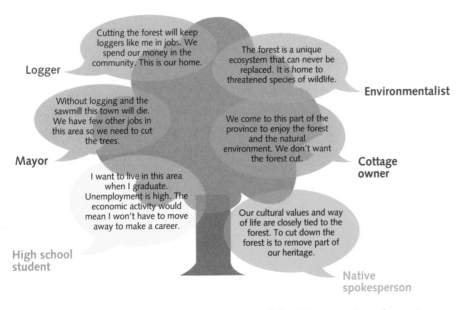

Figure 4.11.a Governments have to consider all the different points of view in making decisions.

the Canadian Pulp and Paper Association. This organization tries to educate politicians, the media, and the general public about issues its member companies consider important. Environmental organizations, including the World Wildlife Fund (see the Case Study in section 8.3), are also lobby groups. They try to convince the same people in society of the environmental perspective on issues. There are many other lobby groups representing a wide variety of perspectives. Individuals can also lobby politicians in order to influence decision making. In a democracy, all citizens have the right to make their views known to the people who represent them in government.

Levels of Government in Canada

Municipal government Your community is called a municipality. Cities, towns, townships, and counties are types of municipalities. Municipalities make by-laws to manage activities within their boundaries. They also provide services such as waste management, roads, parks, and recreational facilities.

Provincial and territorial government This level of government is responsible for much larger geographic areas. They pass laws concerning such things as pollution, highways, natural resources, and energy supply. Provincial parks and wilderness areas are administered by provincial governments.

Federal or national government This level of government ties all of Canada together. Decisions here affect the whole country. Some areas of responsibility are fisheries and oceans, the environment, immigration, and communications. The federal government must also deal with international issues.

Figure 4.11.d A variety of community facilities are run by municipalities.

Governments pass laws to put their ideas into practice. Laws both prohibit some actions and encourage others. A good example is the Montreal Protocol to restrict CFC use in Canada (see section 5.2). The Protocol both forces Canadians to stop using CFC and encourages them to use less environmentally harmful substances. In this way, governments play a very important role in protecting the environment and ensuring the careful use of natural resources.

Figure 4.11.c A provincial park ranger in Newfoundland surveys the park for any problems.

Figure 4.11.e The federal government is responsible for water and air quality throughout the country and for guarding our natural resources both on land and in the seas.

QUESTIONS & ACTIVITIES

1. Imagine that you have just written a book about how political decisions are made. Think up three titles that you would give your book. Explain your choices.

2. a) What is the purpose of a lobby group?
   b) What are some strategies that a lobby group might use to get their message across to elected government officials?

3. Suppose that you have just heard that the municipal government might build a landfill site near your home. Plan a campaign in which you get your neighbours to lobby your municipal government. Put at least three actions in your plan.

4. Political decision making in a democracy can be slow, and often many people are upset about the final decision. Think up another way that decisions could be made about natural resources and the environment. Compare the advantages and disadvantages of your approach and political decision making using a comparison chart with these headings:

Decision-making approach	Advantages	Disadvantages
Political decision making		
Your approach to decision making		

CHANGING PERSPECTIVES

Waste management or garbage is a serious issue in our consumer society. We buy a lot and we throw away a lot. Use the Inquiry Model on page 222 to plan and research a possible solution to the topic of garbage disposal in your community. You might start by investigating the success of an existing waste control project (such as a blue box program) in your school or community. You can also use "Perspectives on Research: Evaluation" on page 282 to help you. Whichever project you choose, prepare and make a presentation to the class (see "Perspectives on Research: Presentations" on page 260). Introduce them to the issue, describe your analysis and evaluation, then present your conclusions.

Perspectives on Research: Developing an Argument

Keep your mind open and develop a conclusion based on facts. Evaluate your sources. Are they reliable, accurate, and current? Separate facts from opinions. Has something been proven by valid testing? Is a statement a belief or an attitude? Can you identify any stereotypes, oversimplifications, or exaggerated statements, especially about people? Be wary of the use of a non-identified "they" quoted as an expert.

UNIT 5 INTERNATIONAL ASPECTS OF RESOURCE USE

Canada is closely linked to other countries. Many of our environmental and resource issues involve people in other nations. In this unit we analyze our connections and how they influence our use of resources.

COMPARING ECOLOGICAL FOOTPRINTS

Major Concepts

- Ecological footprints
- Damage can lead to extinction
- Ecosystems are inter-related

In the caption for Figure 4.10.b we referred to using boardwalks in Pelee Park to avoid trampling the fragile ecosystem as an example of a controlled "eco-footprint." This section examines the kinds of **footprints** our society may leave on the ecology of Earth. The footprint is a metaphor for the results of the inter-action of a society with its ecosystems. A society that lives in harmony with its environment is said to tread softly and leave a gentle mark—a gentle footprint—on nature.

Some recent studies have argued that some natural hazards have human **fingerprints** on them. In other words, some human activities have interfered with or changed ecosystems so severely that the activities have helped to create the natural hazard. Such changes are most likely to occur when people move onto and alter the flood plain of a river, increasing the likelihood of flooding.

We have examined many cases of modern industrial society in conflict with the natural world. The extraction of natural resources, oil exploration on the fragile tundra, and the loss of wetlands are examples.

We have also discussed the loss of forest land. The rain forests of the world are home to an enormous number of species of plants, animals, and birds, some of which have not been discovered yet. Some people argue that clear-cutting for a few select trees of valuable lumber is destroying the ecology. Heavy footprints are being made throughout the world.

Figure 5.1.a Dinosaurs left footprints on the Earth millions of years ago. Today, these fossil records remind us of their extinction and of our need to tread softly on our home planet.

Figure 5.1.b Human footprints match those of a bird in the sand. Tomorrow the footprints will be gone as the wind shifts the sands.

We have also seen evidence of how interconnected ecosystems are. The journey of PCBs in the air, to the water, to bird life is one example of this interconnectedness. The broad-ranging effects on wildlife habitats from one ecosystem to another created by of the loss of wetlands and forests is another.

Environmental assessment is a term planners use to refer to the study

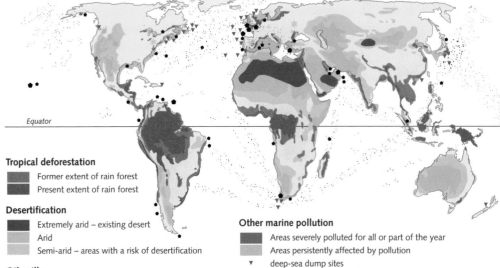

Tropical deforestation

- Former extent of rain forest
- Present extent of rain forest

Desertification

- Extremely arid – existing desert
- Arid
- Semi-arid – areas with a risk of desertification

Oil spills

- major oil spills – over 100 000 t
- major oil spills – less than 100 000 t
- Chronic oil slicks – pollution from routine tanker and other shipping operations

Other marine pollution

- Areas severely polluted for all or part of the year
- Areas persistently affected by pollution
- ▼ deep-sea dump sites

Nuclear accidents

- Major nuclear accidents causing damage to the environment and/or direct loss of human life

Equator

◀ **Figure 5.1.c** Heavy footprints: human-created damage to the world's environment. Desertification (land becoming desert), deforestation (loss of trees from the land), and pollution from a variety of sources form patterns on the Earth. Note that both oceans and continents are affected.

of the impact of human activity. Today, with the world shrinking through instant communication and rapid transportation, scientists and others are able to check changes to ecosystems throughout the world on a regular basis. We can also monitor how successfully we are working to achieve sustainable resources. Constant monitoring and action in response to the information gained by monitoring is necessary if we are to protect the Earth from heavy footprints. We also need to be aware as individuals of the tracks that we personally are leaving on the ecosystems we encounter.

Figure 5.1.d Societies can leave very different impressions on the land. The 49th parallel clearly marks the border between Montana's wheat fields in the United States (lower section) and the range lands of Alberta and Saskatchewan in Canada.

CASE STUDY Antarctica

Antarctica is a continent that surrounds the South Pole. A number of nations signed a treaty in 1961 making this uninhabited area a **world reserve** in order to preserve the area for peaceful purposes. The treaty prohibits military activity, nuclear testing, and disposal of radioactive waste. It encourages scientific research and international cooperation. Some of the studies have included the study of the ozone layer of the earth's atmosphere, whale behaviour, and penguin life. Eight nations have staked land claims here, but the treaty is holding. While many ecotourism trips to the area are in place, the tour operators are very careful to conduct the tours in such a way that only gentle footprints are left on the area.

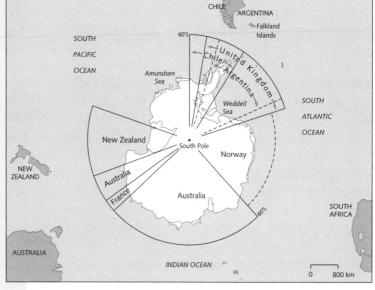

Figure 5.1.e Territorial claims in the Antarctic

QUESTIONS & ACTIVITIES

1. **a)** How does the footprint in stone symbolize the fate of dinosaurs?
   b) What is a metaphor?
   c) How do the terms "footprint" and "fingerprint" act as metaphors?
   d) Use diagrams or a flow chart to illustrate why it might be dangerous to live along populated riverbanks.
2. Describe the "footprint" problem in the rain forests of the world.

3. Which continent is a world reserve?
4. How has Antarctica become a model for world agreements designed to protect environments?
5. **a)** Construct a collage to show images of "human footprints" on the land.
   b) Create a new metaphor for human presence on Earth and write a story to describe your metaphor.
6. Create a series of webs illustrating what steps you can take to ensure that your footprints on the different ecosystems you encounter are gentle footprints.

INTERNATIONAL AGREEMENTS ON THE ENVIRONMENT

Major Concepts

- Pollution threatens the international community
- International Joint Commission
- Montreal Protocol on CFCs
- Trans-boundary movement of hazardous waste
- Rio Conference

The atmosphere is a global resource. Air circulates all around the planet. Polluting agents such as motor vehicles and industry put waste into the air. The world wind patterns then move those pollutants around the Earth. As a result, people everywhere are subject to air pollution. The glaciers in Greenland, the Canadian Rockies, and Antarctica all show traces of pollution from the inhabited parts of the earth.

Nations have increasingly recognized that pollution and other human-caused environmental hazards do not recognize national boundaries. As a result, they have begun to work together to solve the damage human activity is causing to the environment. The subject of world agreements and accords on the environment is lengthy and complex. Getting nations together, making resolutions, and putting the resolutions into action are major tasks. The United Nations leads the way in creating world agreements. The World Bank, the World Court, the Organization for Economic Co-operation and Development (OECD), World Wildlife Fund, and Greenpeace are other international agencies and groups with interests in reaching **environmental accords**. In this section, we will examine Canada's role in international agreements affecting the environment.

Canada and the United States have participated in a number of agreements designed to protect their mutual environments. In 1905 the International Waterways Commission was created to advise Canada and the United States about the Great Lakes. Four years later, the **International Joint Commission (IJC)** was created to resolve disputes over sharing this great international resource. The IJC is still in place today to monitor developments like the Great Lakes Water Quality Agreements of 1972 and 1978, the Great Lakes Charter of 1985, and the Great Lakes Toxic Substance Control Agreement of 1986. Work on Great Lakes and St. Lawrence River water quality continues today with eight states, Ontario, and Quebec participating.

The Canada-United States agreement on **Trans-boundary Movement of Hazardous Waste** came into effect in 1986. This agreement was designed to ensure that the movement of hazardous wastes across boundaries is done safely. The four major points of this agreement are:

- Each country must safely handle the waste in its own area.
- Proper notice must be given before moving materials.
- Proper documentation must describe and accompany the hazardous waste.
- The exporting country must permit re-entry of the waste if the importing country refuses it.

Canada, the United States, and other developed countries signed agreements to support the OECD resolution on Trans-frontier Movement of Waste, the United Nations Environment Program, and the resolutions of the London Dumping agreement.

The **Montreal Protocol** was finalized in 1987 and signed by 163 countries. The Protocol restricts the use of chlorofluorocarbons (CFCs). These refrigerants have been used in almost every air conditioner and refrigerator in the world. When the CFCs escape, they go into the atmosphere where they damage the **ozone layer**. There is now a worldwide phase-out of CFCs and other ozone-destroying chemicals. The reduction is expected to help the ozone layer recover over the next decades.

A groundbreaking conference on the environment was held in Rio De Janeiro in 1992. Now referred to as the **Rio Conference** or the **Rio Summit**, the conference focussed on developing international agreements that would protect the global environment and promote sustainable development.

The conference was followed by another treaty in 1997 in Kyoto, Japan. The **Kyoto Protocol** was designed to reduce world air pollution emissions by an average of 5% (from 1990 levels) by the period 2008 to 2012. Over 170 nations participated in the Kyoto Protocol. In 1998, a follow-up meeting was held in Buenos Aries in Brazil to keep up the work schedule.

Figure 5.2.a Headquarters of major world organizations involved in overseeing the state of the world's environment. ▶

The Hague: International Court of Justice
Geneva: World Health Organization (WHO)
Paris: United Nations Educational, Scientific, and Cultural Organization (UNESCO)

Organization for Economic Cooperation and Development (OECD)

Rome: Food and Agricultural Organization of the United Nations (FAO)

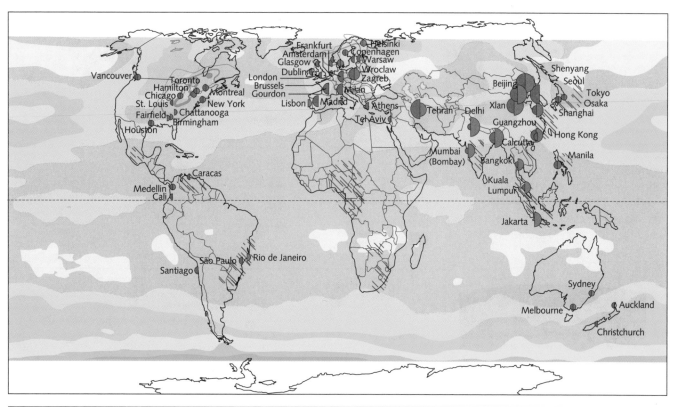

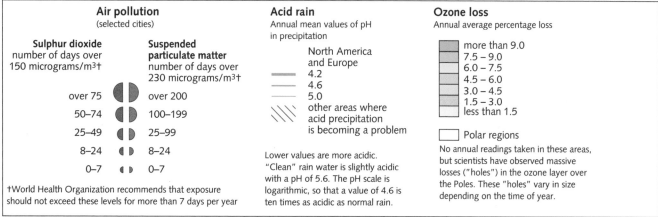

Air pollution
(selected cities)

Sulphur dioxide
number of days over
150 micrograms/m³†

Suspended particulate matter
number of days over
230 micrograms/m³†

over 75 — over 200
50–74 — 100–199
25–49 — 25–99
8–24 — 8–24
0–7 — 0–7

†World Health Organization recommends that exposure should not exceed these levels for more than 7 days per year

Acid rain
Annual mean values of pH
in precipitation

North America
and Europe
4.2
4.6
5.0
other areas where
acid precipitation
is becoming a problem

Lower values are more acidic. "Clean" rain water is slightly acidic with a pH of 5.6. The pH scale is logarithmic, so that a value of 4.6 is ten times as acidic as normal rain.

Ozone loss
Annual average percentage loss

more than 9.0
7.5 – 9.0
6.0 – 7.5
4.5 – 6.0
3.0 – 4.5
1.5 – 3.0
less than 1.5

Polar regions

No annual readings taken in these areas, but scientists have observed massive losses ("holes") in the ozone layer over the Poles. These "holes" vary in size depending on the time of year.

Figure 5.2.b The borderless enemy: worldwide atmospheric pollution

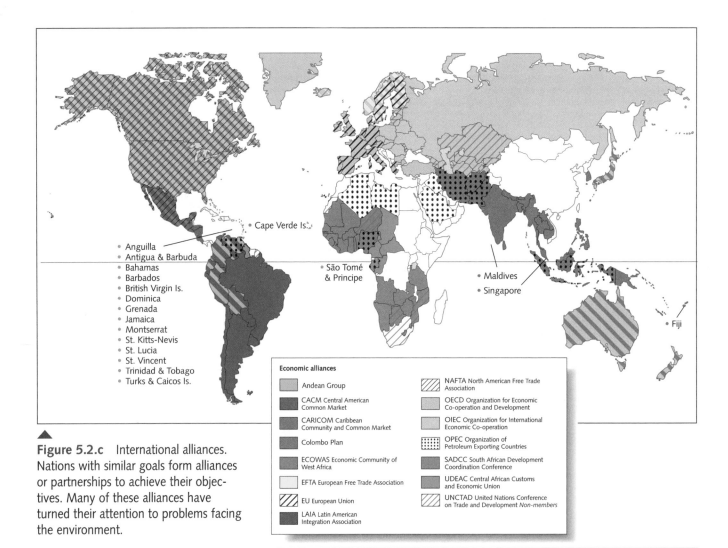

Figure 5.2.c International alliances. Nations with similar goals form alliances or partnerships to achieve their objectives. Many of these alliances have turned their attention to problems facing the environment.

Economic alliances

Andean Group

CACM Central American Common Market

CARICOM Caribbean Community and Common Market

Colombo Plan

ECOWAS Economic Community of West Africa

EFTA European Free Trade Association

EU European Union

LAIA Latin American Integration Association

NAFTA North American Free Trade Association

OECD Organization for Economic Co-operation and Development

OIEC Organization for International Economic Co-operation

OPEC Organization of Petroleum Exporting Countries

SADCC South African Development Coordination Conference

UDEAC Central African Customs and Economic Union

UNCTAD United Nations Conference on Trade and Development *Non-members*

- Anguilla
- Antigua & Barbuda
- Bahamas
- Barbados
- British Virgin Is.
- Dominica
- Grenada
- Jamaica
- Montserrat
- St. Kitts-Nevis
- St. Lucia
- St. Vincent
- Trinidad & Tobago
- Turks & Caicos Is.

- Cape Verde Is.
- São Tomé & Principe
- Maldives
- Singapore
- Fiji

Figure 5.2.d The **ozone layer** is a region of the upper atmosphere with a high concentration of ozone gas. This layer protects us from the ultraviolet rays of the sun.

Altitude in kilometres

Protective natural ozone layer

Supersonic aircraft

Limit of most clouds

Mountains

Damaging ground-level ozone

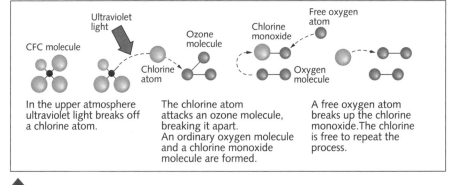

Figure 5.2.e
The destruction of ozone. Many scientists believe that emissions of ozone-depleting chemicals, especially CFCs, that escape into the atmosphere are responsible for the loss of ozone protection.

Ultraviolet light

CFC molecule

Chlorine atom

Ozone molecule

Chlorine monoxide

Free oxygen atom

Oxygen molecule

In the upper atmosphere ultraviolet light breaks off a chlorine atom.

The chlorine atom attacks an ozone molecule, breaking it apart. An ordinary oxygen molecule and a chlorine monoxide molecule are formed.

A free oxygen atom breaks up the chlorine monoxide. The chlorine is free to repeat the process.

Figure 5.2.f Global emissions of carbon dioxide per capita. Canada has 0.56% of the world's population but emits 2% of the world's carbon dioxide.

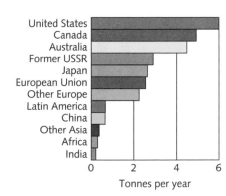

United States
Canada
Australia
Former USSR
Japan
European Union
Other Europe
Latin America
China
Other Asia
Africa
India

0   2   4   6
Tonnes per year

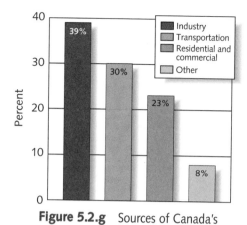

Figure 5.2.g Sources of Canada's carbon dioxide emissions

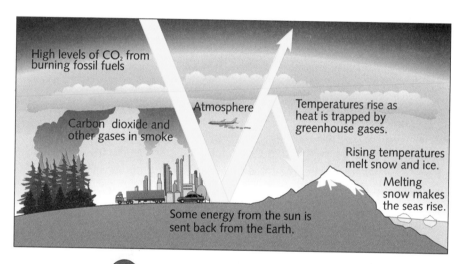

CFCs

Carbon Dioxide

Methane

Figure 5.2.i Where greenhouse gases come from. Note: Carbon dioxide makes up 80% of greenhouse gases.

Figure 5.2.h How pollution adds to the greenhouse effect and global warming. The greenhouse effect refers to the warming of the Earth's atmosphere that occurs when outgoing long-wave radiation is absorbed by water vapour and carbon dioxide. The way the atmosphere allows solar radiation in, but partly stops it from being lost again to space, is so similar to the way glass helps heat a greenhouse that the process is called the greenhouse effect.

QUESTIONS & ACTIVITIES

1. Use a sketch map of world wind patterns to show how prevailing winds create international pollution. Refer to Figure 1.7.c to get the wind patterns.
2. What does the pattern of atmospheric pollution in Figure 5.2.b suggest about the origins of worldwide pollution?
3. What are three obstacles to achieving successful agreements on the environment?
4. Identify five groups concerned with achieving agreements on world environmental issues.
5. **a)** What is the IJC?
   b) Describe three projects the IJC has been involved in.
   c) List the eight American states and two Canadian provinces sharing the Great Lakes-St. Lawrence system.

6. **a)** What is the name of the treaty that Canada and the United States signed on hazardous waste?
   b) What does it ensure?
   c) What are the four key points in this treaty?
7. **a)** What are CFCs and what are they used for?
   b) What problem is the use of CFCs responsible for?
   c) How will the Montreal Protocol help the problem created by the use of CFCs?
8. **a)** What was the purpose of the Rio Conference?
   b) Describe how the Kyoto Protocol follows up the work of the Rio Conference.
9. **a)** In your own words, explain the greenhouse effect.
   b) Use diagrams to suggest possible dangers of the greenhouse effect.

CANADA AND THE UNITED STATES: TRANSBORDER POLLUTION

Major Concepts

- Countries share continents
- Pollutants know no boundaries
- Air and water are eco-transporters

Canada shares the continent of North America with the United States and Mexico. As you saw in the previous section, pollutants recognize no borders. Whether in the atmosphere or in the water, polluting substances migrate according to natural forces. In this section, we examine some aspects of **transborder pollution**.

In Canada the prevailing winds are the southwesterlies. Because we are in the mid-latitude range, most of our weather systems come from the west or southwest. It is the weather from the southwest that causes most of the air quality problems experienced in the Great Lakes-St. Lawrence basin. This basin includes southern Ontario and the populated corridor from Montreal to Quebec City.

The problems created by weather from the southwest are most noticeable in the summer. As warm, humid, polluted air moves slowly from southwest to northeast, pollution is picked up from the heavily industrialized areas of the Ohio Valley. When this calm, stable air mass settles over southern Ontario and Quebec, air quality declines, acid rain increases, and people with breathing problems experience difficulty. Canada's National Air Pollution Surveillance Network, which monitors air quality across Canada, issues air quality warnings.

In extreme cases, industries are asked, or sometimes ordered, to shut down in order to reduce pollutants in the air. The effort to reduce pollutants would be helped if it was possible to reduce traffic, but doing so is difficult.

Fresh water is also a common resource on this continent. Part of the very long border shared by Canada and the United States includes the Great Lakes-St. Lawrence River system. Water can spread pollutants in the air (as rain), in surface water (lakes and rivers), and underground (wells and the water table). Over the years, the Great Lakes were polluted by industrial waste, sewage, and landfill leachates (polluted water seeping out of the landfill). The International Joint Commission continuously monitors the pollution of the lakes and urges both countries to take action to combat pollution in the lakes. Agencies like the Ohio State Sea Grant Education Program and the Ontario Ministry of Natural Resources promote education about the Great Lakes

to make people aware of the need to keep the Great Lakes healthy.

Transborder pollution can also occur with natural elements. Dutch Elm disease, carried to Canada from beyond its borders, has killed thousands of beautiful trees. The lamprey eel and the zebra mussel have invaded the Great Lakes causing death or deformations in fish already living in the lakes. Purple Loosestrife has invaded marshlands in Ontario, spreading rapidly and strangling other plant life in the marshes.

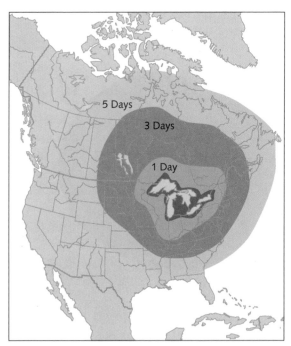

Source: EPA, *Great Waters Index*

Figure 5.3.a The Great Lakes "airshed." The bands indicate the approximate number of days for air pollution to reach the Great Lakes **watershed**.

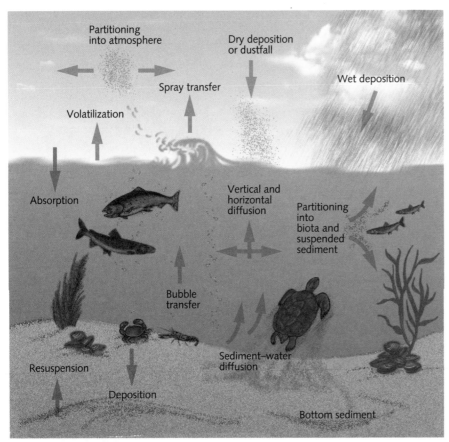

Partitioning into atmosphere

Dry deposition or dustfall

Wet deposition

Spray transfer

Volatilization

Absorption

Vertical and horizontal diffusion

Partitioning into biota and suspended sediment

Bubble transfer

Sediment–water diffusion

Resuspension

Deposition

Bottom sediment

Source: *The State of Canada's Environment*

Figure 5.3.b Movement pattern of toxic substances in the aquatic water environment

In December 1988, the tug *Ocean Service* accidentally rammed its barge the *Nestucca*. The hole in the barge allowed about 900 t of "Bunker C" oil to flow into the sea. The spill occurred off the coast of Washington State and currents swept the oil north to the tip of Vancouver Island. Over 40 000 shore birds died and long stretches of shoreline were contaminated by oil slicks.

The *Nestucca* spill was minor compared to the *Exxon Valdez* spill in 1989. This supertanker ran aground in the Gulf of Alaska and dumped forty-two million litres of crude oil into the Prince William Sound of Alaska. Over 100 000 birds were killed and 2500 km of shoreline were contaminated.

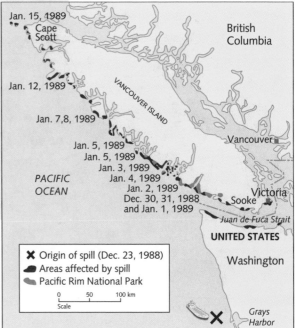

Jan. 15, 1989
Cape Scott

British Columbia

Jan. 12, 1989

VANCOUVER ISLAND

Jan. 7,8, 1989

Vancouver

Jan. 5, 1989
Jan. 5, 1989
Jan. 3, 1989
Jan. 4, 1989

PACIFIC OCEAN

Jan. 2, 1989
Dec. 30, 31, 1988
and Jan. 1, 1989

Victoria
Sooke

Juan de Fuca Strait

UNITED STATES

Washington

✖ Origin of spill (Dec. 23, 1988)
🖤 Areas affected by spill
🩶 Pacific Rim National Park

0   50   100 km
Scale

✖ Grays Harbor

Source: *The State of Canada's Environment*

Figure 5.3.c Thè *Nestucca* oil spill affected large areas of the coast of Vancouver Island.

◀ **Figure 5.3.e**
Extent of the
Exxon Valdez
oil spill

◀ **Figure 5.3.d**   When the *Exxon Valdez*
was wrecked on the Bligh Reef, the
resulting oil spill caused environmental
damage throughout the Gulf of Alaska,
especially as it washed ashore.

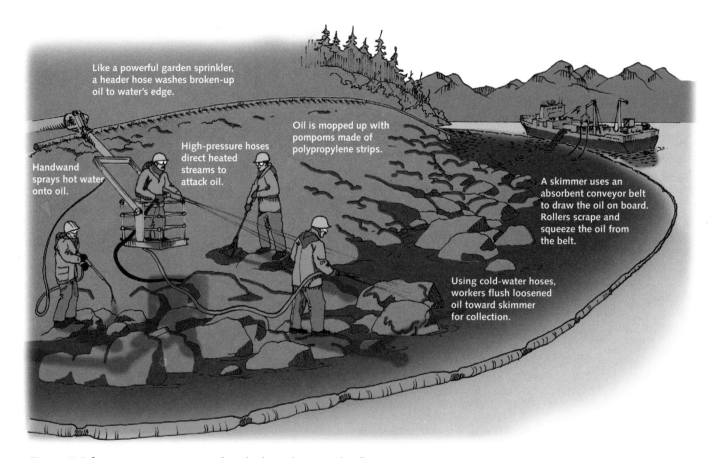

Figure 5.3.f   Experts use a variety of methods to clean up oil spills.

CASE STUDY   Ballard Fuel Cell

Pollution is fought in many ways. The **Ballard fuel cell** is an invention of a Niagara Falls geophysicist, Geoffrey Ballard. His goal was to replace the high-emission internal combustion engine with a cleaner source of power. The Ballard fuel cell produces energy from a chemical reaction between hydrogen and oxygen. The hydrogen comes from methanol. This fuel cell can help meet new government emission standards, reduce global warming, and make the cities of the world less polluted. (See also Case Study "Hydrogen Fuel Cells," page 266.)

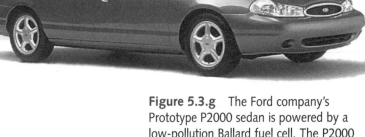

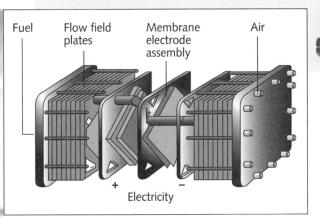

Figure 5.3.g The Ford company's Prototype P2000 sedan is powered by a low-pollution Ballard fuel cell. The P2000 is being developed to achieve a fuel efficiency of up to three times that of today's family car and extremely low levels of CO_2 emissions.

QUESTIONS & ACTIVITIES

1. **a)** What countries share the North American continent?

   b) Which continents have only one country?

2. **a)** What are the prevailing winds in most of Canada?

   b) Draw a sketch map to show where most of the pollution in central Canada originated and why.

3. Use diagrams to illustrate three ways that water can spread pollution.

4. Describe three other ways pollution can occur in the natural world.

5. Write an account of these two oil spills from the point of view of the following people:

   a) The *Nestucca* spill—as a press agent for the company

   b) The *Exxon Valdez* spill—as an environmentalist

6. Explain how the Ballard fuel cell will contribute to a healthier environment.

7. Research and report on an example of transborder pollution in the world. Include the following in your report:
   - a map of the region
   - sources of the pollutants
   - effects of the pollutants
   - future solutions to the problems

   If you have the appropriate computer software, do your report as a slide show.

STOPPING THE TRADE IN ENDANGERED SPECIES

Major Concepts

- Poaching endangered species
- Illegal trade in animal species
- Prevention of poaching and illegal trade

The estimated value of the illegal wildlife trade is about 1.5 billion dollars a year. **Poachers** capture or kill all kinds of wildlife, including endangered species. The fact that endangered animals are rare is an incentive for collectors to pay a great deal of money for the few animals that are left. Many wildlife species, including endangered species, are killed for certain parts of their bodies. The unwanted parts are simply discarded.

The following are some examples of the illegal trade in wildlife and reasons for that trade:

- Walrus are valued for ivory from the tusks.
- Night roosting robins are a delicacy in Cajun gumbo.
- Black bear gall bladders are sold as medicine.
- Rhinoceros horns are ground up for aphrodisiacs.
- Indian tigers are hunted for sport.
- Boa constrictor snakes are captured as household pets.
- Polar bears' white hides are sought by collectors.

The list of illegally hunted wildlife animals seems to grow daily.

Canada is a member of a number of international organizations that fight the illegal trade in endangered species. Canada supports the Convention in International Trade in Endangered Species (CITIES).

Figure 5.4.a Bighorn sheep are examples of some of the majestic animals that roam the mountains of Western Canada.

Figure 5.4.b The white fur hide of the polar bear is sought after by collectors.

CITIES regulates 48 000 species of plants and animals and has developed programs designed to fight poaching and the illegal trade of domestic and foreign wildlife. Canada is also a supporter of the Wild Animal and Plant Protection and Regulation of International and Interprovincial Trade Act (WAPPRIITA). **WAPPRIITA** protects Canadian and foreign species from illegal trade. It also protects Canadian ecosystems from the introduction of harmful species.

On the national level, Fish and Wildlife officers of the Canadian Wildlife Service and Park Rangers oversee large areas trying to protect animals from poachers. The wardens have to cover so much territory that it is difficult protect all wildlife. As well, poachers often have more money and better equipment than the wildlife officials. Penalties for wildlife crimes have been increasing in severity, ranging from fines to seizure of equipment and prison terms.

A second line of government defence and protection is at the border. It is illegal to import animals, pelts, and parts of animals

CASE STUDY · Hunting at What Price?

An Arizona businessman paid $627 370 to hunt for a Big Horn sheep in 1998. The fee was for a sheep-hunting tag issued by the Alberta government. The hunter and his guide trekked for two weeks in the mountains north of Jasper National Park. The hunter did not fire a shot. None of the heavy-horned rams he saw came close to the size of the existing big horn world record of 1911. The tag money goes to habitat conservation projects.

if they are under international protection laws. Canadian and American customs officials have removed thousands of items from this illegal trade at their borders. However, the trophies then reside in warehouses. The damage has already been done to the animals.

The conservation and protection story is discouraging in Canada. It is magnified in poorer countries. Many nations in Africa are trying to protect their wildlife. However, their citizens can make a great deal of money hunting highly prized big game and as a result poaching continues.

CASE STUDY — Horse of a Different Colour

A Canadian scientist, Amanda Vincent, is one of the leading conservationists in the world protecting the sea horse. Sea horses live in mangrove swamps, coral reefs, and estuaries. These tiny oddities of the ocean are endangered because collectors' search for more sea horses leads to overfishing. As well, much of the sea horse's habitat is being destroyed. Conservationists are trying to get sea horse habitats protected as sanctuaries.

Figure 5.4.c Professor Amanda Vincent is a Canadian who helped create Project Seahorse, an international organization to protect and preserve the sea horse in the wild.

Courtship
Sea horses have elaborate courtship rituals. Here, they entwine their tails and "promenade" through the water.

Fertilization
In mating, the female expels eggs into the male's pouch, where they are fertilized.

Birth
After 10 days, the babies emerge from the male's pouch.

Worldwide Distribution
Sea horses occupy shallow temperate coastal areas. The total range of species are indicated by the green offshore zones below.

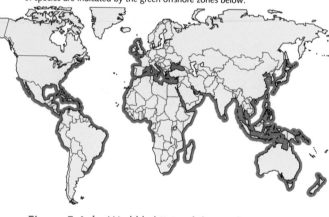

Figure 5.4.d World habitats of the sea horse. Overfishing and coastal pollution are destroying these habitats.

QUESTIONS & ACTIVITIES

1. Describe poaching in your own words.
2. List three types of officers in charge of protecting ecosystems for their country. To whom are they responsible?
3. a) Based on information in this section and your own knowledge, list at least five examples of trade in endangered species. You may want to review section 3.12.
   b) With the help of a group of classmates list five more examples.
4. a) How do customs officials help control the trade in endangered species?
   b) What are two international organizations that Canada belongs to in order to help control the trade in endangered species? Write a sentence to explain the activities of each organization.
5. Why is the problem of poaching greater in some countries than in others?
6. Is there a particular endangered species that you are interested in? Write your own brief "Case Study" of an endangered species.
7. Conservationists argue that it is essential that we save all species for the future. In chart form, indicate whether you support this argument and why you agree or don't agree.

THE ANTI-FUR CAMPAIGN

Major Concepts

- Canada's fur-trading heritage
- Anti-fur protesters
- Traditional Inuit economy

A new breed of terrorist fights for animals

Nunavut to export seals to China

La fourure, c'est la meilleure amie d'une femme contre le froid.

Animal rights activists shed coats, clothes in fur protest

Furriers fight for native heritage and livelihood – putting a face on trappers and hunters"

Seal Hunt ... Canadians! How much longer will you tolerate the annual mass slaughter of seals?

Figure 5.5.a Headlines

Figure 5.5.b Snow geese are at the centre of a controversy. The US plans to increase its annual hunt limit. Native groups in the Canadian North oppose this increase.

A number of groups in our society care strongly about the lives of animals and the conditions in which animals live. People in these groups are known as **animal rights activists**. They criticize any use of animals for product testing, particularly for use in beauty products. They also challenge using animals such as rats, dogs, and monkeys for medical research and testing. Their protests are increasingly the subject of media coverage and law making.

The emergence of anti-fur protest groups is fairly recent. The **anti-fur campaign** is particularly critical of the fashion industry. Protesters believe that neither exotic nor common animals (such as the Canadian seal) should be killed to be used in the fashion industry or even used at all.

The seal hunt has become a controversial event and is strongly protested by international anti-fur protest groups. The seals range from the Arctic Ocean to the Gulf of St. Lawrence. In the spring, seal pups are born on the sea ice. Their pure white coats camouflage them against the snow until they are mature enough to move into a more active sea life.

However, their white fur is highly prized and every year during the seal hunt, the pups are clubbed and skinned on the ice. Protesters have reacted to this form of killing, to the killing of the babies, to the use of their fur for fashion, and to the number of seals killed. They argue that the seals are being killed in such numbers that the species will eventually die out.

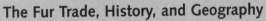

FILE

FACT

The Fur Trade, History, and Geography

The fur trade is at the heart of Canada's history and geography. Aboriginal peoples have lived in harmony with nature since the beginning of their history in Canada. They used furs and hides for shelter and clothing. Bones of the animals were used for tools, and glands provided medicine for cuts and injuries. After the arrival of European fur traders, beaver pelts became an important trade item. The pelts were used to make stylish hats for men in Europe. Much of Canada was explored by fur traders in search of these pelts.

Yet the fur industry supports a great deal of economic activity. As well as supporting the people directly working in the fur and fashion industries, Newfoundland fishers have traditionally supplemented their fishing income by collecting the pup fur in the annual seal hunt. Many people also argue that controlling the seal population in the annual hunt helps the return of the northern cod stock because seals eat the cod.

In an effort to balance the concerns of anti-fur protesters and those who participate in the seal hunt, Canada's Department of Fisheries and Oceans has established a **quota** system for the seal hunt and the hunters are required to kill humanely.

Figure 5.5.c The seal pup is hunted for its white fur. Its endearing face makes it an ideal symbol for anti-fur campaigners seeking public support for their cause.

CASE STUDY

Seals and a Traditional Way of LIfe

Inuit regard seals as a basic component of their economy and way of life. Inuit have always been hunters and the seal and other animals such as the caribou have always been part of their existence. They claim the right to maintain traditional ways despite protests. Some Inuit argue that if the fur trade was to be ended, the Inuit people would be displaced from nature and as a result would be pushed into poverty. Today, the Inuit not only kill and use seals for their own lives, they now have a market or demand from countries like China.

Figure 5.5.d The seal hunt is an important Inuit tradition. Hunting skills and knowledge are passed down from one generation to the next.

Figure 5.5.e The fashion industry uses a variety of furs. Fashion models are used to attract consumer attention.

QUESTIONS & ACTIVITIES

1. Write a general description of how animals have provided resources for people living in Canada during our history. Make a time line for Canada from 1500 to 2000. Mark every 50 years along the historical line graph. Show the stages of hunting and the anti-fur campaign.

2. a) What type of activities are animal rights activists trying to prevent and why?

   b) Why do protesters target the fashion industry?

3. a) Why is the traditional seal hunt important to the fishers of Atlantic Canada?

   b) What reasons do protesters use to argue against the seal hunt?

   c) Use diagrams or a flow chart to show how the seal hunt has formed part of the traditional Inuit economy.

   d) What new developments are creating more demand for seal products?

4. a) Organize and prepare for a debate in your class. Base your debate on the following statement: "Be it resolved that the fur industry in Canada is a necessary activity and traditional right in the Canadian economy." When debating be sure to define the terms you are using, such as "right" or "tradition."

FISHING DISAGREEMENTS

Major Concepts

- International agreements
- Offshore limits
- Supply versus demand
- Enforcement problems

Globally about 20% of dietary protein comes from fish (ranging from 75% in Japan to 4% in Argentina). Conflicting claims and interests have led to numerous international disagreements over fishing in the world's oceans. In all, about 40% of the oceans are involved in territorial claims. In many ways, the world's nations are facing a Wild West scene on the oceans. Laws are weak and there are few enforcers. And, as you saw in section 4.2, there is a great deal of money to be made fishing. The United Nations and other organizations have a full-time job trying to bring peace to the oceans and protect the fishing stocks.

The 370-km (200-nautical mile) offshore limit that Canada, like other nations, has placed on activi-

FACT FILE

Many experts predict that in ten years, the demand for fish and seafood will grow by one third. China, with over one billion people, is just starting to build up its fishing fleet.

ties in the waters off its shores is good in theory. But offshore limits are difficult to maintain in practice. There is no precise line in the water. On Canada's East Coast, part of the Grand Banks shelf extends beyond Canada's offshore limit and part of the Georges Bank is shared with the United States. Canada's attempts to control fishing within its offshore

limits on both the East and West Coasts in order to protect the declining cod and salmon stocks has brought Canada into dispute with Spain and the United States.

The Spanish fishing fleet, which had fished in the area for centuries, continued to fish for cod during the Canadian moratorium, and particularly during the cod's breeding season. The Spanish fishers also sometimes used the large-scale, fine-weave drift-nets that have been outlawed by the UN. Canada's Coast Guard intervened, boarding some fishing vessels, and exchanging some gunfire. The situation continues to be tense.

On the West Coast, salmon is under pressure all around the Pacific Rim. Canada and the US are trying to regulate salmon harvests as the adults return from the ocean to spawn. But US fishers and their state and national governments and the BC and Canadian governments strongly disagree on the amount of fish that can be caught and still leave the salmon stock in a sustainable position. Russian salmon fleets are also a factor in these waters. Some Asian markets prefer salmon caught at sea when the flesh has an oilier taste. Agreements have been reached to limit the catch to a narrow band in the mid-Pacific. Even with this agreement, Taiwanese squid boats with massive drift-nets have been caught poaching salmon in the mid-Pacific to sell to the lucrative Japanese market.

It is hoped that conservation measures and moratoriums will help fish stocks to rebuild. DNA studies, tagging programs, acoustic

CASE STUDY: The International Community and Fish Stocks

Since 1992 the UN has placed a ban on large-scale **drift-net fishing**. These nets, which often have fine weaves, catch much more fish than the particular fish being sought, including young stock. At the same time, the UN called for worldwide regulations and monitoring of fish catches. Canada also supports a global ocean observation system to keep fish harvests at a sustainable level. International agencies are mounting pressure to prevent any further dumping into the oceans of waste oil, human sewage, daily garbage, and toxic waste such as radioactive materials, all of which damage fish populations. As well, Canada is a member of the Northwest Atlantic Fisheries Organization (NAFO). NAFO is an agreement among Canada and the European community to guard against overfishing in North Atlantic waters.

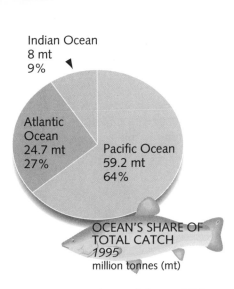

Indian Ocean
8 mt
9%

Atlantic
Ocean
24.7 mt
27%

Pacific Ocean
59.2 mt
64%

OCEAN'S SHARE OF
TOTAL CATCH
1995
million tonnes (mt)

Figure 5.6.a Shares of the total fish catch by oceans.

Falklands [islands off Argentina]: "Patrol boats chase Taiwanese squid boat, 4364 nautical miles from home."

New York City: "UN session on fisheries breaks without agreement."

New England: "Fishermen angry at proposed limits on Georges Bank fishing turn over cars and throw fish from a truck."

India: "Traditional fishermen are accused of burning commercial trawlers."

Norway: "Norwegian patrols cut the nets of three Icelandic trawlers fishing in Arctic waters claimed by Norway. Shots were exchanged."

Namibia: "Eighth Spanish trawler arrested in its waters."

Alaska: "Bristol Bay red king crab fishery shuts abruptly after a drastic decline in female crabs."

Japanese menu: "a two-bite portion of tuna sushi: price—$75.00 US"

Figure 5.6.c Headlines

or sound-wave monitoring from the surface, quotas, and net-size restrictions should all help sustainability. Aquaculture in fresh and salt water should improve the supply of fish and other seafood now in huge demand. However, as Figure 5.6.c shows, enforcing international fishing agreements, particularly in the face of the tremendous profits that can be made, remains extremely difficult.

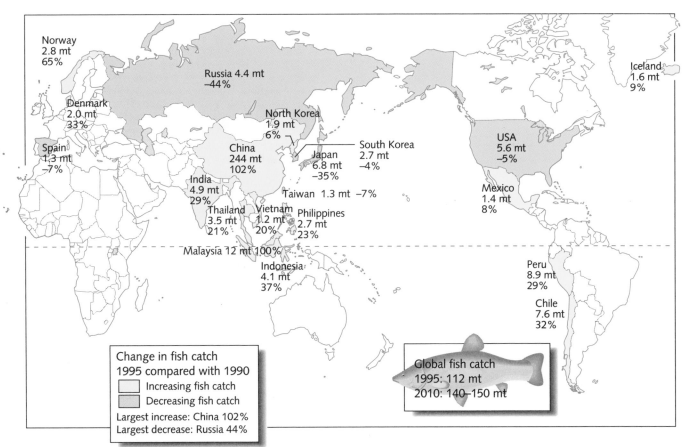

Change in fish catch
1995 compared with 1990
☐ Increasing fish catch
☐ Decreasing fish catch
Largest increase: China 102%
Largest decrease: Russia 44%

Global fish catch
1995: 112 mt
2010: 140–150 mt

Norway 2.8 mt 65%
Russia 4.4 mt −44%
Iceland 1.6 mt 9%
Denmark 2.0 mt 33%
North Korea 1.9 mt 6%
USA 5.6 mt −5%
Spain 1.3 mt −7%
China 244 mt 102%
Japan 6.8 mt −35%
South Korea 2.7 mt −4%
India 4.9 mt 29%
Taiwan 1.3 mt −7%
Mexico 1.4 mt 8%
Thailand 3.5 mt 21%
Vietnam 1.2 mt 20%
Philippines 2.7 mt 23%
Malaysia 12 mt 100%
Indonesia 4.1 mt 37%
Peru 8.9 mt 29%
Chile 7.6 mt 32%

Figure 5.6.b Estimated change in worldwide fish catch from 1995 to 2010. Create a bar graph to illustrate the percentage for each nation.

Figure 5.6.g Sushi, or raw fish, is considered a delicacy. Some kinds of fish and fish roe, or fish eggs, command extremely high prices at sushi bars. ▶

Figure 5.6.d In March 1995, then Canadian Minister of Fisheries Brian Tobin talked to reporters in New York City. He was standing in front of a large drift-net that Canadian officials seized from a Spanish fishing trawler.

Figure 5.6.e The Washington State-bound ferry *Malaspina* is blockaded for the third day by British Columbia fishers in Prince Rupert. The Canadians were protesting what they saw as salmon overfishing by American fishers.

Figure 5.6.f A traditional fish market restaurant serves up a variety of economical fish dishes.

QUESTIONS & ACTIVITIES ❓

1 **a)** What percentage of territorial offshore limits are under dispute?
   b) What actions has the United Nations started to protect fish?
   c) Look at a map of the East Coast, including the St. Lawrence River. What area off the coast of Newfoundland creates offshore limit issues with France? Why?
   d) What other human activities put stress on the fish population?
2. Name two disputed areas where Canada has claims against Spain and the United States.
3. Describe two claims disputes on the West Coast.
4. Use diagrams to illustrate how salmon stocks are under pressure in the Pacific Ocean.
5. **a)** Describe some conservation and moratorium measures being considered.
   b) How can they help?
6. Refer to Figure 5.6.c. Select one headline, or pick an example from a current news source, and write an account of the issue. Include:

a) statement of the problem
b) nations involved (include a map showing the locations of the countries)
c) location of problem (mark on your map)
d) possible solutions
e) possible methods to prevent a recurrence of the problem.
7. Research the Cod Wars between Canada and Spain in the mid-1990s. Draw a map to locate the areas under dispute. In a table, list the arguments put forward by each country.
8. Research the struggle between the Canadian and British Columbian governments and the Alaskan, Washington State, and US government over fishing in the Pacific and mainland rivers. Draw a map of the Alaska, BC, and Washington State coastline. Include the islands off the mainland. Using your map, describe the causes of the struggle between the Canadian fishers and the US fishers.

FAIR TRADE AND TRADE PROTECTION

Major Concepts
- Fair trade movements
- Trade protectionism
- Trade controversies

Canada is involved in many trade relationships throughout the world. This section examines two ideas that are connected to **trade patterns** and **morality**.

Fair trade is a movement to prevent resource-based trading partners from exploiting both human labour and the environment. In recent years, a number of Western companies have been in the headlines for unfair trade practices. Their subsidiary companies located in poor countries have been accused of exploiting workers in those countries. The exploited workers are usually poor women and children. The women and children are paid very low wages to manufacture clothing, footwear, or athletic equipment. Using local raw materials, workers often work in "sweat shops" or very poor working conditions. They receive few or no benefits.

Low production costs mean greater profits for the manufacturer. As well, the practice of hiring cheap local workers, not paying them any benefits, or caring about their working conditions benefits wealthier consumer societies because the price of the products created is low. World craft production also often falls into this category of unfair trade practices. Local artists and craft workers create beautiful pieces from local materials. These works are bought at very cheap prices by buyers who then

convert the works into profitable items in retail shops of Europe and North America.

Agencies like the International Labour Organization and the United Nations International Children's Emergency Fund (UNICEF) are working with nations like Canada and the United States to overcome the exploitation of workers in poor countries and to encourage the fair wages and working conditions that will help eliminate world poverty.

Trade protection focuses on situations within a country. It involves the passing of laws to protect parts of a nation's culture and economy from outside influences. Some nations feel they are under attack by powerful, private multi-national corporations. These corporations sometimes have larger revenues than the countries in which they operate (See Figure 8.4.c). Others

feel that small nations, and their culture, are in danger of being overpowered by larger neighbours.

Cultural issues that have led to conflict over trade protectionism between Canada and the United States include education, health, language, and the arts. A particularly controversial issue in the nineties arose over split-run magazines. Split-run magazines are American magazines that split the

Figure 5.7.a Children are exploited by being forced to work long hours for low wages.

Figure 5.7.b In 1995, twelve-year-old Canadian Craig Kielburger launched an international anti-child labour organization, Free the Children, after he heard reports about the murder of a boy working in a Pakistani carpet factory. In this 1996 photo, Kielburger talks to a 10-year-old street vendor in New Delhi. He was on a seven-week children's crusade that would take him to Bangladesh, Thailand, Nepal, India, and Pakistan.

run of the magazine into American and Canadian editions. Often, the "Canadian" edition has one or two articles on Canadian issues; the rest of the magazine is basically the same as the American edition. The American publications have already paid for the cost of producing the US editions through advertising from the US market. Thus the Canadian editions of the US magazines are able to charge Canadian advertisers much lower rates than wholly Canadian magazines can offer for the same advertisements. In 1999 the Canadian government sought to bring in a law that would eliminate what the Canadian government saw as an unfair trade practice that seriously threatened the survival of Canadian-produced magazines and that, therefore, threatened Canadian culture. The US government saw the proposed Canadian law as a restriction on free trade, not a cultural survival issue. Both governments threatened trade sanctions.

Trade controversy occurs between countries in other resource sectors as well. Timber, pulp and paper, agricultural products, and fresh water are regularly in the news and on government agendas for discussion. A practice called "dumping" brings howls of protest. If a nation has a surplus of a product, it may try to sell the product below normal price in another market. Such dumping makes it difficult for local producers to sell their products at a reasonable price to make a profit and earn a living. Usually tariffs or taxes are imposed on the import of cheap items to bring the price up to market rates but this action goes against the philosophy of free trade.

Figure 5.7.c Craft markets are outlets for beautiful handmade items.

Newsstand display

US magazines and other foreign periodicals take up the vast majority of display space on Canadian newsstands...

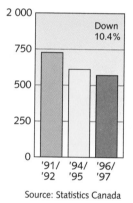

Canadian magazines 20%

US and foreign periodicals 80%

Readership

...but half the magazines bought in Canada – through subscriptions and newsstand sales – are Canadian publications.

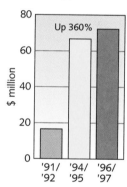

Canadian magazines 50%

US and foreign periodicals 50%

Figure 5.7.d Canada's magazine industry

Figure 5.7.f Women in less developed countries often work in "sweatshop" conditions. Poor light and air quality, high heat, low wages, and long hours often contribute to almost inhuman working conditions.

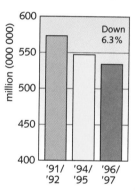

Number of periodicals

2 000

750 — Down 10.4%

500

250

0

'91/ '94/ '96/
'92 '95 '97

Operating profits

80

$ million

60 — Up 360%

40

20

0

'91/ '94/ '96/
'92 '95 '97

Total annual circulation

600

million (000 000)

550 — Down 6.3%

500

450

400

'91/ '94/ '96/
'92 '95 '97

Source: Statistics Canada

Figure 5.7.e Periodical publishing in Canada. The bar graphs show the number of periodicals (magazines), the operating profits, and the circulation numbers from 1991 to 1997.

QUESTIONS & ACTIVITIES

1. Write definitions for the following items:
   a) fair trade
   b) trade protection
2. a) Describe how some workers have been exploited in their working conditions.
   b) How do low production costs benefit wealthier consumer nations?
3. a) What is UNICEF?
   b) Create a list of eight or nine ways to improve working conditions to achieve Fair Trade.
   c) Can you suggest other ways to work for fair trade practices? What can you personally do?
4. Why do some cultures feel they need trade protection laws?

5. Describe in your own words some cultural items Canada feels it needs to protect against free trade.
6. a) Research and describe what "dumping" means in world trade.
   b) What are tariffs?
   c) How are tariffs used to restrict trade practices?
7. Research in more detail a product or company that has been involved in controversial fair trade practices. Write a one-page argumentative essay to defend or attack the practices employed in your research case.
8. Research the Tobin currency trading tax. Write a brief paragraph explaining what the Tobin tax is and how it is intended to reinforce fair trade.

Countries around the world have different ways of looking at environmental issues. As a result, they often create different kinds of eco-footprints. Work with a partner to select a nation and investigate environmental concerns in that country. Write a series of 5 headlines to reflect the types of footprints that may be left in that country. Figures 5.5.a, page 186, and 5.6.h, page 189, are examples of actual headlines. They will give you an idea of how to write headlines.

Perspectives in Research: Questionnaires and Surveys

People take polls to get a sample of opinions. Questionnaires and survey forms are two ways to collect the data. These are forms of primary (original source) information. Target audiences are selected groups of people who are asked to complete the questionnaire or survey. The questions can be oral (asked directly to the people being surveyed) or written answers given by the people being surveyed. Questions should be clearly worded and have a short answer. The answers must be counted and analyzed. The results can be shown as graphs.

Questions can also be designed to provide for a range of answers, e.g., from excellent to poor, 1 through 4, where 1 represents one extreme and 4 is the other. For example, "very good" (1), "good" (2), "poor" (3), "very poor" (4).

When you are preparing your questionnaire or survey you may want to review "Perspectives on Research: Questions" on page 88.

UNIT 6   CHANGING CANADA: AN URBAN NATION

The focus for this unit is the change that takes place in human systems as Canada grows and matures. As an urban nation, we face both opportunities and challenges that must be addressed as we plan for the future.

URBAN GROWTH IN CANADA

Major Concepts

- Urbanization in Canada and the world
- Census Metropolitan Areas (CMAs)
- Core and periphery

Throughout the twentieth century, people continued to shift from living in the **rural** countryside to living in **urban** parts of the country. Most people moved seeking greater economic opportunities. These opportunities occurred as a result of the rapid development of industries in larger centres. As industries demanded more workers, unemployed, and underemployed farmers migrated to jobs and cities. The effect of this population shift has been a dramatic rise in importance of urban areas, and a marked reduction in importance of rural areas. In spite of popular Canadian images, Canadians today are largely urban dwellers.

The process of **urbanization** has been fastest in urban places of over 100 000 people. By 1996, cities of

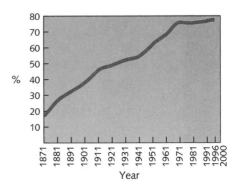

Figure 6.1.c The percentage of the population living in urban areas, 1871-1996

this size accounted for 62% of the total population, with the three largest cities (Toronto, Montreal, and Vancouver) housing 33% of Canadians.

Census Metropolitan Areas (CMAs) are geographical areas created by Statistics Canada. They contain core or built-up urban areas that have populations of 100 000 or more. CMAs include municipalities completely or partly inside the urbanized core as well as any surrounding **suburban** and rural areas that have

CMAs	1951		1996	
	Population ('000)	% of Can. Pop.	Population ('000)	% of Can. Pop.
Toronto	1117.5	8.0	4263.8	14.8
Montreal	1395.4	10.0	3326.5	11.5
Vancouver	530.7	3.8	1831.7	6.3
Ottawa–Hull	281.9	2.0	1010.5	3.5
Edmonton	173.1	1.2	862.6	3.0
Calgary	139.1	1.0	821.6	2.8
Quebec	274.8	2.0	671.9	2.3
Winnipeg	354.1	2.5	667.2	2.3
Hamilton	259.7	1.9	624.4	2.2

Figure 6.1.a Population in the top nine CMAs, 1951 and 1996

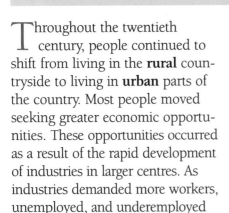

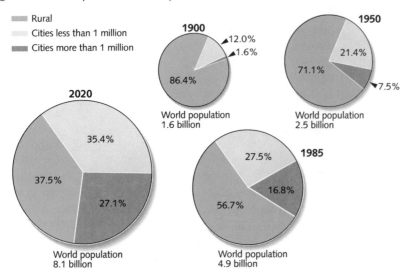

Rural
Cities less than 1 million
Cities more than 1 million

1900
12.0%
1.6%
86.4%
World population 1.6 billion

1950
21.4%
71.1%
7.5%
World population 2.5 billion

2020
35.4%
37.5%
27.1%
World population 8.1 billion

1985
27.5%
16.8%
56.7%
World population 4.9 billion

Figure 6.1.b Global patterns of urbanization

jobs   entertainment
educational opportunities   excitement
services
anonymity

crime   crowded streets
no one cares
high prices for housing   no privacy
few parking spaces

Figure 6.1.d People have different views about urbanization.

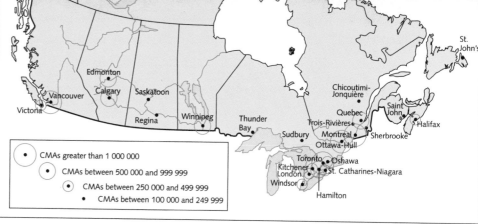

strong economic and social links to the cities. At the time of the 1996 Census, there were 25 CMAs.

The concentration of large urban areas in southern Ontario and Quebec has led people to refer to this region as the "**core**," or heartland, of the country. Economic activities in the core tend to be relatively "high tech," pay higher wages, and have greater investment than anywhere else. All the area outside of this core is known as the "**periphery**," or hinterland. The resources needed to maintain the core frequently come from the periph-

Figure 6.1.e Populations of Census Metropolitan Areas in 1996

ery, such as the minerals, forest products, and farm output from Canada's West, North, and East.

Urbanization has had a profound impact on our land use and our resources. One result of increasing urbanization is urban sprawl. As suburbs are developed trees are cut down, fertile fields are paved over, and streams are diverted into culverts. These developments interrupt the way the areas worked naturally. Wildlife loses its habitats and the amount of available farmland is decreased.

QUESTIONS & ACTIVITIES

1. Define the term "urbanization."
2. Here are a variety of factors that contribute to the process of urbanization. In one or two sentences, explain how each item is connected to the movement of people to the cities.
   a) Manufacturing plants are established in towns.
   b) Farmers buy more tractors.
   c) The railway system expands to more places in the country.
   d) A greater percentage of people finish high school.
3. a) Refer to Figure 6.1.c. During which time period was urbanization most rapid in Canada?
   b) When was the process of urbanization largely complete?
   c) In the country of Singapore, 100% of the population is classified as urban. Explain why Canada will never reach the 100% urban mark.
4. Use Figure 6.1.a to calculate the rate of population change for the 9 CMAs. Make a chart with four columns with these headings: CMAs, Population Change 1951-1996, Percent Population Change, Rank of Population Change.
   a) List the 9 CMAs in the first column.
   b) Calculate the absolute change in population by subtracting the 1951 population from the 1996 population for each CMA. Show the differences in the second column.

   c) Calculate the percentage change for each CMA by dividing the population change values in column 2 by the 1951 population figures. Multiply the answer by 100 to convert it to a percentage. Put these percentages in the third column.
   d) In the fourth column, rank the CMAs by the percentage change figures in the third column. The highest percentage is ranked 1, the second highest 2, and so on.
   e) Which places had the fastest rates of population growth? Where are they located in Canada? Which places had the slowest growth? Where are they located?
5. What is your view of large urban areas such as Toronto or Montreal? Make a list of 10 words or phrases that describe your feeling about big cities.
6. Does Canada have a true core and periphery? Use the map in Figure 6.1.e as evidence to answer this question.
7. a) Global patterns of urbanization are shown in Figure 6.1.b. Explain how the graphs were constructed using the data. Why are the circles different sizes?
   b) What patterns do the graphs show about world urbanization?

CHANGING ECONOMIC STRUCTURE

Major Concepts

- Economic structure in Canada
- Primary, secondary, tertiary, and quarternary industries
- Global economic trends

Economic structure refers to the arrangement or inter-relationships of all economic activities involved in producing, distributing, and consuming wealth. The economic activities that traditionally make up a country's (or a community's) economic structure can be divided into three broad sectors or categories—**primary**, **secondary**, and **tertiary**, (see Figure 6.2.a). The balance among these three sectors determines a country's particular economic structure. This balance is influenced by the country's physical geography, natural resources, and economic activities. In developed countries, the balance tends to include strong tertiary industries.

Canada's first economic activities were centred on using and developing natural resources (primary industries). However, we have not remained a resource-based country. The industrial revolution that began in Europe during the 1700s soon spread to North America. Manufacturing (secondary industries) was a vital part of the country's economy by the second half of the 1800s. Throughout the twentieth century, businesses expanded to offer services (tertiary industries) to the growing Canadian population. The economy is now very diverse and includes strong primary, secondary, and tertiary sectors. A fourth sector of service has been added today called **quarternary** industries. This sector includes decision makers such as stock brokers and accountants.

Economic change does not happen on its own. It is the result of a complex web of decisions and forces that act on a country. These forces can be categorized in this way:

a) global trends—broad developments that affect every nation, such as world wars and the increasing use of computer technology

b) world economy—economic patterns that affect the movement of capital and the development of wealth, including worldwide booms or recessions and trade patterns

c) national policies—decisions made within the country that encourage or discourage change; these might include government controls on businesses and trade agreements

d) business decisions—changes initiated by companies as they grow and develop, such as the adoption of new technologies, investment, and location decisions.

The complexity of these forces means that some countries have developed differently than others. Even within countries, economic

Primary Industries
(agriculture, fishing, forestry, mining, fur trapping)

Secondary Industries
(manufacturing, construction)

Tertiary Industries
(transportation, communications and other utilities, trade, finance, insurance and real estate, services, public administration)

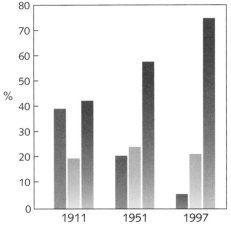

Figure 6.2.a Change in employment in Canada. These changes reflect changes in Canada's economic structure.

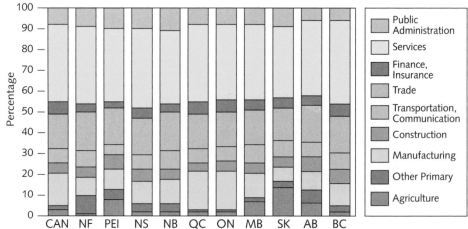

Figure 6.2.b Percentage employment by industry, 1997

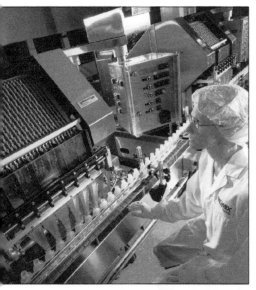

Figure 6.2.c Canadian businesses have become increasingly high-tech, employing workers using sophisticated manufacturing technology.

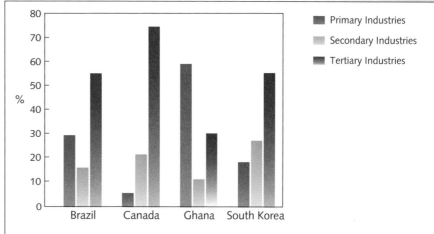

Figure 6.2.d Canada's economic structure compared to other countries around the world

change varies from place to place. The various parts of Canada have different economic structures as a result of the distinct forces in each region (Figure 6.2.b).

Employment

When the Second World War ended in 1945, the service sector employed 4 out of 10 Canadian workers. Today this sector employs 7 out of 10 people in the work force.

Five decades ago, construction and manufacturing provided jobs for 1 in 3 Canadians. Now they provide 1 in 5.

QUESTIONS & ACTIVITIES

1. Define these terms: primary industries, secondary industries, tertiary industries, quarternary industries.

2. Four different forces that affect the economic structure of a country are identified on the previous page. Offer one current Canadian example for each of these four forces and explain how it affects our economic structure.

3. **a)** Using Figure 6.2.a, describe the changes that have taken place in the economic structure of Canada.

   b) Suggest some reasons to explain why these changes have taken place.

   c) In what ways might the changing economic structure affect Canadian towns and cities?

4. **a)** List five skills of workers that would have been valued by employers in 1911 (Figure 6.2.a). Make a list to show those most valued in 1997

(Figure 6.2.b).

   b) In what ways would the different skills demanded by employers affect the education and training of workers?

5. Use Figure 6.2.b to identify the regional differences in economic structure in Canada. Compare the Atlantic region, Quebec, Ontario, and the West to the Canadian average and record your observations in your notebook.

6. **a)** Canada is a developed country and its economic structure is quite different from developing countries. Using the bar graphs in Figure 6.2.d, rank the four countries from most economically developed to least economically developed.

   b) Using an atlas, world almanac, or encyclopedia, identify the economic structure of five other countries and rank them according to their levels of development. What conclusions can you draw?

MIGRATION WITHIN CANADA

Major Concepts

- Internal migration patterns over time
- Net migration
- Divergence bar graphs

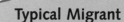

Typical Migrant

What are the characteristics of a typical migrant?
- 25 - 34 years old
- university education
- unmarried

As economic conditions in Canada changed over the years, the areas where economic opportunities were greatest have also changed. While agriculture was predominant, the rural areas, especially in the West, offered opportunities and a future for young people. As manufacturing became more important, the better job possibilities were in the factories of the developing manufacturing cities, typically located in central Canada. The growth in services in recent decades is seen best in the largest cities in Alberta and British Columbia.

Declining economic opportunities in one area of the country make people look for opportunities elsewhere. This movement of population from one part of a country to another is called **internal migration**. Internal migration creates distinct patterns within the country.

Figure 6.3.b Changing economic times!

Province of Origin				Province of Destination						
	NF	PEI	NS	NB	QC	ON	MB	SK	AB	BC
Newfoundland		305	2 629	848	351	7 890	434	111	2 747	2 350
Prince Edward Is.	230		470	560	43	773	60	38	179	240
Nova Scotia	1 577	830		2 897	946	7 976	590	300	2 773	3 080
New Brunswick	687	540	2 683		2 444	4 874	332	216	1 494	1 433
Quebec	287	99	1 137	2 593		27 522	708	438	2 131	6 157
Ontario	5 360	1 077	8 115	4 960	19 153		6 348	2 581	13 668	28 093
Manitoba	97	117	442	323	528	6 346		3 216	5 636	5 602
Saskatchewan	63	33	337	138	387	2 498	3 522		11 625	5 243
Alberta	1 222	288	1 912	1 245	1 564	10 368	4 071	11 027		27 332
British Columbia	930	155	2 450	911	2 482	15 418	4 256	4 974	24 326	

Figure 6.3.a Internal migrants of Canada, 1995-96

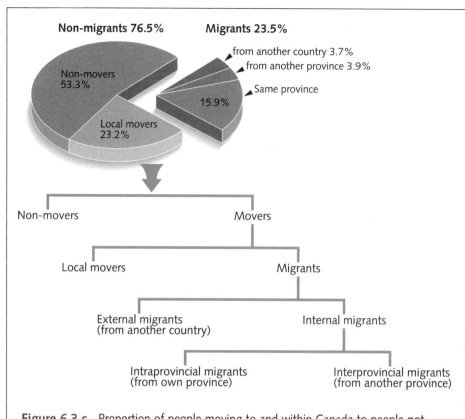

Figure 6.3.c Proportion of people moving to and within Canada to people not moving

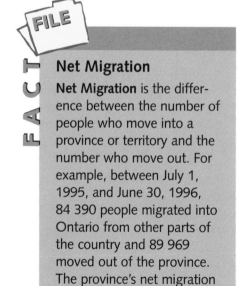
FACT

Net Migration

Net Migration is the difference between the number of people who move into a province or territory and the number who move out. For example, between July 1, 1995, and June 30, 1996, 84 390 people migrated into Ontario from other parts of the country and 89 969 moved out of the province. The province's net migration for the year was -5579.

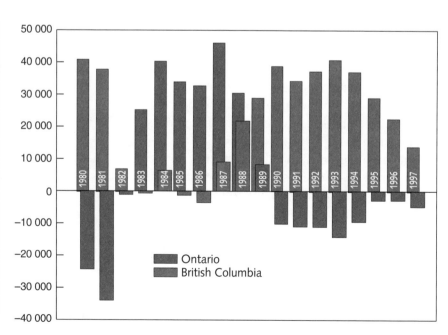

Figure 6.3.d A divergence bar graph comparing net migration totals for Ontario and British Columbia, 1980-1997

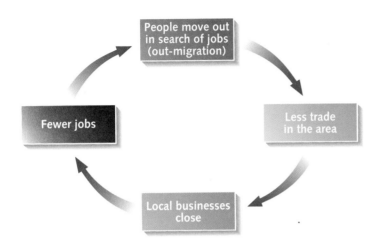

Figure 6.3.e This figure shows the effects of out-migration from an area of declining opportunities.

QUESTIONS & ACTIVITIES

1. a) Besides economic opportunities, what might be three other reasons why people would migrate within Canada?

   b) What might be some reasons why people would not migrate to a new location at some point in their lives?

2. Sketch a diagram to show the shift in locations of job opportunities in Canada as the economy shifted from agriculture, to manufacturing, to services.

3. Examine Figure 6.3.e.

   a) In your own words, explain what this flow diagram shows.

   b) Suppose you were a government official in a province experiencing out-migration. What are three things you would recommend be done to avoid the problems that come from high rates of out-migration?

   c) In your notes, make another flow diagram showing the impact on jobs when people migrate into an area of increasing job opportunities.

   d) What might be some disadvantages of rapid in-migration to a part of the country?

4. Figure 6.3.a identifies the major flows of migrants from province to province for one year. The left column shows the provinces people left. Read across the top and down to determine the number who moved to each of the other provinces. For example, of those who left Newfoundland, 305 people went to Prince Edward Island, 2629 moved to Nova Scotia, and so on.

   a) How many people moved from New Brunswick to Quebec? How many moved from Manitoba to Saskatchewan?

   b) Identify the three largest movements of migrants from the table. List the provinces of origin and the provinces of destination.

   c) Explain why some cells in the table are blank.

   d) On an outline map of Canada, use arrows to show the two largest flows of migrants out of each province. Colour the largest flows in red and the second largest in green. Describe the patterns that your map shows.

5. The first Fact File gives three characteristics of a typical migrant. Give reasons why each of these characteristics would apply to migrants.

6. a) The divergence bar graph in Figure 6.3.d compares net migration for Ontario and British Columbia. Describe the pattern in the graph.

   b) How would you explain the fact that when BC's net migration is positive, Ontario's net migration tends to be negative, and vice versa?

7. Are you likely to become an internal migrant? Make up an advantages and disadvantages chart for you moving to another part of Canada. What is your conclusion?

CITIES AND TECHNOLOGICAL CHANGE

Major Concepts

- Changing urban forms
- Technological change
- Urban growth

Manufacturing grew throughout much of the 1900s, leading to a steady growth of towns and cities as more and more workers were needed for the manufacturing industries located there. With the rise in services in the past few decades, cities expanded even more in size and importance. Many Canadian cities were forced to deal with rapidly growing populations because of **in-migration**, immigration, and relatively high birth rates. Fortunately, technology was

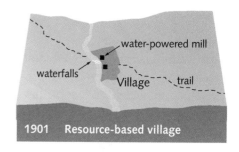

1901   Resource-based village

	Resources focus	Manufacturing focus	Services focus	Information focus
Major activities	Extracting natural resources (farming, forestry, etc.)	Manufacturing products to meet consumers' demand	Providing services to meet consumers' needs	Communicating using electronic media
Location of activities	**Dispersed**, where resources are located	Centralized, where conditions are suitable	Variable, depending on where services are needed	Dispersed, where people choose to live
Urban patterns	Scattered, some small **clustering**	Massive clustering	Combinations, to meet different needs	Dispersed, some small clustering
Urban forms	Resource-based, single-industry towns	Large cities with factories on transportation routes	Large cities with well-connected suburbs	Smaller cities and towns offering amenities

Figure 6.4.a The phases of development of urban areas

> *Decentralizing technology encourages the far-flung growth of large cities, but it also has the opposite effect. It makes new, smaller cities competitive.... Small cities are now able to offer the same multiplexes, the same national chains and the same franchises.... Small cities often offer more responsive—and responsible—governments and a stronger sense of community. Listings of 'The best places to live' are headed not by big cities, but by relatively small cities like Kingston, ON, or Sherbrooke, QC, or Victoria, BC.*

Witold Rybczynski,
Maclean's, 1998

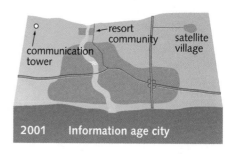

1981   Service-focused city

2001   Information age city

Figure 6.4.b The evolution of urban forms over time

changing too. Innovations in urban transportation, building design, water and sewage services, and communications were adopted by cities in an effort to keep the urban areas functioning. In cities, change, for better or worse, is now a fact of life.

As well as helping cities function, technological innovations have changed the need that people have for cities as workplaces. In Canada's early days, communities served a small population connected to a mill or mine site. Later, manufacturing demanded large concentrations of workers in centres where conditions were best for factories. The service focus in the second half of the twentieth century saw the development of extended urban areas with large suburbs. The newest phase of technological development—the Information Age—does not demand large urban areas. Using electronic means, people can do their jobs in places quite remote from their co-workers. Urban concentrations will become less necessary as people will be able to work and live just about anywhere they want.

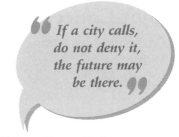

If a city calls, do not deny it, the future may be there.

Christine Turner Curtis,
Montreal Remembered, 1952

Technological Innovations	Impacts on Cities, People, and the Environment
1. Improvements in public transit, such as subways and light rapid transit lines, increase the speed of people moving within cities.	People are able to move farther away from their places of employment, often the centre of the cities, encouraging growth along the transit lines.
2. Expressways are constructed to move automobiles rapidly from outside the cities to the centres of the cities and to industrial areas within the cities.	Along the expressway routes, suburbs grow quickly, expanding the outer edges of the cities.
3. Use of reinforced concrete and steel in the construction of large buildings means that they can be built much higher than before.	Cities expand upwards with the construction of skyscrapers in the central areas of the cities.
4. The **infrastructure** of cities–such as sewers, water lines and power grids–are updated and expanded to meet the greater demands of urban dwellers.	Population densities rise as more people are able to be accommodated within the city and its suburbs.

Figure 6.4.c Impacts of technological innovation on cities

Figure 6.4.d Edmonton is an example of a city that has grown upwards as well as outwards.

Figure 6.4.e Large cities usually build their "people movers" (and other infrastructures) underground, such as Montreal's Metro.

QUESTIONS & ACTIVITIES ?

1. Identify three factors that led to the growth of cities in Canada during the twentieth century.
2. **a)** Figures 6.4.a and 6.4.b identify different forms that urban areas have taken. What might be the advantages and disadvantages of living in scattered resource-based communities?
   b) What might be some advantages and disadvantages of living in large service-focused urban areas?
3. For each of the following technological innovations, identify ways that cities have been changed, or will be changed:
   a) computerized traffic signals at major intersections
   b) subterranean or elevated pedestrian walkways
   c) widespread use of the Internet
   d) highly effective waste reduction and recycling programs
4. Use the photograph in Figure 6.4.d to sketch a profile of Edmonton to show the vertical nature of the city. Mark on large buildings that are obvious in the photograph. In words, describe the vertical nature of the city.
5. Examine Figure 6.4.f.
   a) What does this graph tell you about transit and automobile use in Canada since 1950?
   b) Why do you suppose this trend is occurring? Give two reasons.

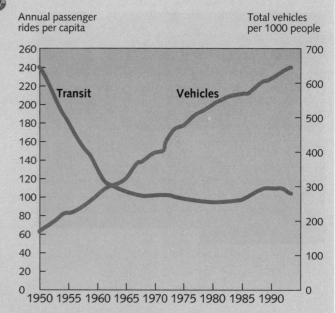

Source: Canadian Urban Transit Association and Statistics Canada

Figure 6.4.f Vehicle ownership and transit ridership

   c) What impact will this trend have on cities?
   d) In your opinion, is this trend good or bad for cities? Explain your answer.
6. The role and importance of the city has changed over the years. Speculate on the role of cities twenty years from now.

FUNCTIONS OF URBAN AREAS

Major Concepts

- Urban functions
- Basic and non-basic activities
- Distinctive urban functions

Urban functions are those economic activities that exist in a town or city that provide employment to the inhabitants. A paper mill is a function based on extracting raw materials. A town with a manufacturing function would have one or several factories that employ workers from the town. Tourism is an example of a service function. While there are specialized towns, where one function is far more important than all others, most urban places are multifunctional, with a variety of economic activities. The particular mixes of urban functions help to give communities their character or uniqueness.

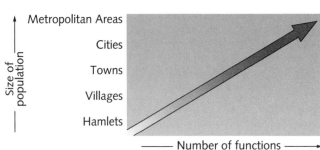

Figure 6.5.b
The number of functions in urban areas increases with population.

Stelco

View of Hamilton from Sam Lawrence Park

Hamilton City Hall

Copps Coliseum

Figure 6.5.a Examples of urban functions in Hamilton, Ontario

DEFINITIONS

Economic activities in an urban place can be categorized into two groups.

a) **Basic activities** produce goods or services to be sold outside of the community. These activities bring money into the community and are often called "town-forming activities." Without these activities, the town has no reason to exist. An example would be a mine that exports its output.

b) **Non-basic activities** are designed to serve the people who live in the community and are called "town-serving activities." They circulate money within the town, but do not generate any additional wealth. An example of a non-basic activity would be a hair dressing salon that only serves residents of the community.

CMA	Function	CMA	Function
Toronto	Manufacturing	Victoria	Public Administration
Montreal	Manufacturing	Windsor	Manufacturing
Vancouver	Trade	Oshawa	Manufacturing
Ottawa-Hull	Public Administration	Saskatoon	Community Service
Edmonton	Transportation	Regina	Community Service
Calgary	Community Service	St. John's	Public Administration
Winnipeg	Manufacturing	Chicoutimi-Jonquière	Manufacturing
Quebec	Public Administration		
Hamilton	Manufacturing	Sudbury	Public Administration
St. Catharines-Niagara	Manufacturing	Sherbrooke	Manufacturing
		Trois Rivières	Manufacturing
London	Manufacturing	Thunder Bay	Manufacturing
Kitchener	Manufacturing	Saint John	Manufacturing
Halifax	Public Administration		

Figure 6.5.c   These are the important and distinctive functions of Canada's CMAs.

QUESTIONS & ACTIVITIES

1. Make a list of 10 urban functions that you have used in the past several weeks. Organize your list into functions that are basic and non-basic to your location.

2. Using Figure 6.5.b and your own experience, add at least two more urban functions to the list that has been started for each of the following categories:
Manufacturing—auto parts manufacturer
Construction—architectural firm
Retail trade—department store
Finance and insurance—stock brokerage
Transportation and communications—cable TV station
Personal services—dry cleaners
Public administration—parks department

3. a) Figure 6.5.b tells us that as the population of an urban area increases so does the number of urban functions in the urban area. Give two reasons that might explain why this is the case.
b) Here is the way that one urban function—health care services—varies with the size of an urban area:
Metropolitan area—several hospitals, a variety of specialty clinics, many pharmacies
Cities—one large hospital, several specialty clinics, some pharmacies

Towns—one small hospital or medical clinic, no specialty clinics, several pharmacies
Villages—no hospital, family doctors, one pharmacy
Hamlet—no health care services
Complete the same type of service listing by size of urban area for automotive services and recreation services. Find newspaper articles to support your listings.

4. a) Use the data in Figure 6.5.d to produce a proportional circles map for locations of corporate headquarters in Canada. A scale that might be appropriate for the circles is 100 head offices = 1 cm radius.

Figure 6.5.d
Top ten locations of largest corporate headquarters in Canada, 1998

Toronto, ON	338	Winnipeg, MB	25
Calgary, AB	194	Edmonton, AB	24
Vancouver, BC	152	Markham, ON	23
Montreal, QC	136	Ottawa, ON	21
Mississauga, ON	56	Brampton, ON	9

b) In words, describe the pattern that the map reveals.
c) What explanations can you suggest that would explain the pattern you identified?

URBAN DENSITIES

Major Concepts

- Central Business District
- Population density pattern
- Change in population density

Before Canada became an urban nation, when towns were quite small, people who lived in urban areas wanted to be close to the downtown part of the community, to be near to the shops and services it offered. The downtown area—known as the **Central Business District** or **CBD**—had the highest population density in the community. As transportation improved, people who could afford the commuting costs moved away from the congestion, noise, crime, and pollution of the CBD to the quieter outskirts of the community. In the later half of the twentieth century the move to the suburbs continued this pattern. The movement of people resulted in the population density curve shown in Figure 6.6.a. This pattern is one we would expect to find around small to medium-sized cities.

As cities grow to become large metropolitan areas, this population density pattern changes. Job opportunities are no longer found only in the CBD. The new suburbs create their own economic activities, and jobs are distributed throughout the whole area. In these cases, the population density patterns reveal a density peak near the CBD and secondary density peaks at key transportation hubs across the whole metropolitan area (Figure 6.6.d).

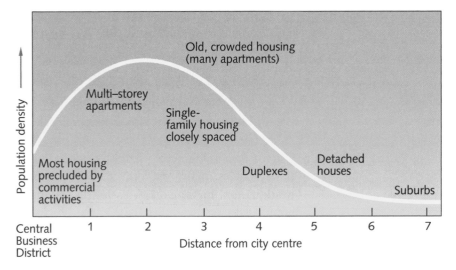

Figure 6.6.a A generalized population density curve for a small to medium-sized city

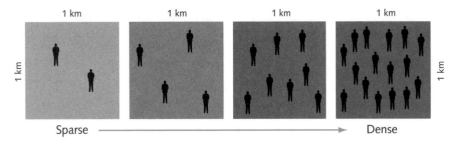

Figure 6.6.b Population density is calculated by dividing the population by the area of a place.

Figure 6.6.c Large metropolitan areas such as Toronto develop a pattern of regional peaks in population densities.

CMA	Population	Area (sq. km)	Population Density
Calgary, AB	821 628	5 083	161.6
Chicoutimi-Jonquière, QC	160 454	1 723	93.1
Edmonton, AB	862 597	9 537	90.5
Halifax, NS	332 518	2 503	132.8
Hamilton, ON	624 369	1 359	459.4
Kitchener, ON	382 940	824	464.7
London, ON	398 616	2 105	189.4
Montreal, QC	3 326 510	4 024	826.7
Oshawa, ON	268 773	894	300.6
Ottawa-Hull, ON/QC	1 010 498	5 686	177.7
Quebec, QC	671 889	3 150	213.3
Regina, SK	193 652	3 422	56.6
St. Catharines–Niagara, ON	372 406	1 400	266.0
Saint John, NB	125 705	3 509	35.8
St.John's, NF	174 051	790	220.3
Saskatoon, SK	219 056	5 322	41.2
Sherbrooke, QC	147 384	980	150.4
Sudbury, ON	160 488	2 612	61.4
Thunder Bay, ON	125 562	2 295	54.7
Toronto, ON	4 263 757	5 568	765.8
Trois–Rivières, QC	139 956	872	160.5
Vancouver, BC	1 831 665	2 821	649.2
Victoria, BC	304 287	633	480.7
Windsor, ON	278 685	862	323.3
Winnipeg, MB	667 209	4 078	163.6

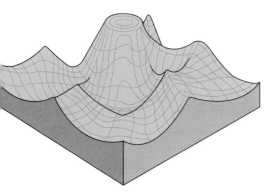

Figure 6.6.d Theoretical population densities in a large metropolitan area

Figure 6.6.e Population densities of ▶ Canada's CMAs, 1996

QUESTIONS & ACTIVITIES ❓

1. Why is the population density of Central Business Districts less than in nearby areas of the city?

2. a) Transportation costs seem to have an impact on population densities in cities. Explain why this is the case.

   b) Suggest two other factors that may have an impact on urban population densities and explain how they will influence densities.

3. a) Think about your own community and communities with which you are familiar. Name some places that have high population densities. Identify some areas that have low population densities.

   b) Are any parts of your community currently experiencing changes in population density? Describe where these places are and identify reasons for the changes.

4. Make a sketch of the area included in the photograph in Figure 6.6.c. Mark on significant features such as transportation routes and high rise buildings that are visible. Shade any residential or commercial areas of the city using colours for high, medium, and low densities. (Base your decisions on the heights of the buildings shown in the photograph.)

5. a) Are there any patterns in the population density figures for Canada's CMAs (Figure 6.6.e)? Answer this question by organizing the data in visual ways. Start by drawing two parallel 10 cm lines on a sheet of notepaper and labelling them evenly from 0 to 1000 persons/km^2 (1 cm = 100 persons/km^2). On the first line put dots to show the population densities for all the CMAs in the core area of Canada (see page 197). These are the cities from Windsor, Ontario, to Quebec City, Quebec. On the second line, do the same for those CMAs in the periphery. Label the two lines. Describe the pattern that you reveal.

   b) Try using the same organizing technique in two other ways to try to find patterns in population densities. You might, for example, compare densities by categorizing the CMAs by population or by area or even by latitude. Use your imagination!

6. What effect does population density have on people who live in urban places? Answer this question considering aspects such as ability to travel within the city, freedom, personal security, opportunities, etc.

URBAN LAND USES

Major Concepts
- Types of land uses
- Location costs
- Shape and pattern

Why is it that, in urban areas, similar activities are often located near one another? For example, in the centre of a town or city you will find businesses, while homes are located in other areas, often closer to the edges of the urban area. One way we can explain this grouping of activities is by looking at the competition for land in urban areas. (Another way is by looking at zoning by-laws—see section 6.8.)

Many commercial businesses need to be in locations that their customers can easily reach, such as on major streets or in the centre of the community. If these businesses choose locations that are not accessible, then they may fail to be successful. That is why they are willing to pay high rent costs in order to be in the best possible locations: these are their **location costs**. Industries also have location needs, such as good transportation connections or flat

land. However, since there may be a variety of locations in a city that meet their needs, they don't have to pay the same high location costs as commercial activities. Housing generally cannot absorb high land costs. Housing occupies areas that have little advantage for commercial

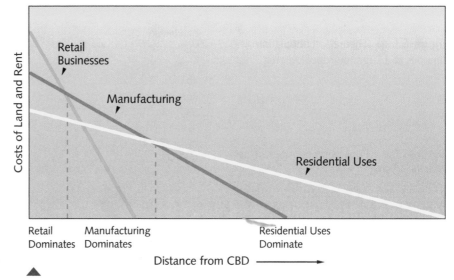

Figure 6.7.b The competition for land means those with the greatest ability to pay are located in the most accessible locations.

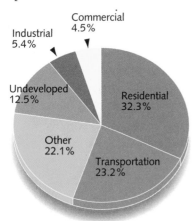

Figure 6.7.a Land uses in a typical urban area

Land use	Purposes	Subdivisions of land uses
Residential	Where people live	Single-family homes · Multi-family homes (townhouses and duplexes) Apartments and condos
Industrial	Factories and industries	Light industrial uses, often located in industrial parks Heavy industry, such as steel mills or auto assembly plants
Commercial	Places that sell goods and services	Single shops, such as corner stores CBD locations Strip plazas, usually along major streets Shopping malls
Transportation	Land used to provide facilities to move goods and people	Roadways Railways, and their stations Airports Harbour and port facilities
Other	To meet the various other needs of people in urban areas	Public administration uses, such as city hall and libraries Recreational areas Institutions, including religious places and schools Health care facilities

Figure 6.7.c Types of land uses in urban areas

or industrial uses, so there is little competition from these uses and land costs are lower. Figure 6.7.b shows the relationship between ability to pay for the land and the location of urban activities. Because of their different needs for locations, and their abilities to pay location costs, land uses tend to group together in urban areas.

West Edmonton Mall

Central Business District

Variety store

Strip plaza

Figure 6.7.d Because of their different needs, businesses are found in a variety of locations in urban areas.

City	Per capita transit trips
Montreal	146.9
Toronto	132.3
Ottawa-Hull	103.6
Vancouver	89.0
Calgary	81.8
Winnipeg	76.4
Saskatoon	68.5
Quebec	68.0
Victoria	63.9
Halifax	59.8

Figure 6.7.e Canadian use of public transit, 1995

Figure 6.7.g This air photograph is of a part of North Vancouver. The Lions Gate Bridge is shown in the photo.

curvilinear pattern

expressway

rectangular grid pattern

Figure 6.7.f Interpreting shape and patterns

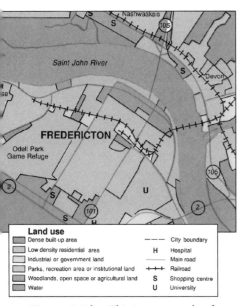

Figure 6.7.h This is an example of a simple land use map of Fredericton, New Brunswick. You can create a similar map for the area near your school or your home.

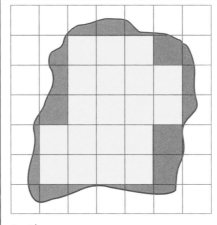

A grid square over an area on a map

Figure 6.7.i Measuring area on maps

Determining the area of rectangular areas on a map is simply a matter of multiplying length times width. Calculating the area of irregularly shaped spaces is more difficult, but can be done using this procedure:
1. On a photocopy of the map, draw a 1cm x 1 cm grid over the area you wish to calculate.
2. Count and record the number of full squares.
3. Look at the part squares. Estimate the number of full squares that could be made from all the part squares put together. Record this number of full squares.
4. Use the map scale to determine the area of a 1 cm x 1 cm grid square. Multiply this area by the number of squares you calculated to get the area of the place.

QUESTIONS & ACTIVITIES

1. For each of the following types of land use, list three characteristics that would be desired in a location and two characteristics that would be considered undesirable:
   a) residential
   b) industrial
   c) commercial
2. Explain why commercial activities can afford high location costs while residential uses cannot.
3. a) Identify at least one location in your own community that fits each of the categories in Figure 6.7.a.
   b) The data in Figure 6.7.a is for a typical urban area in Canada. How does your community compare to this typical situation? Identify ways that your community land use resembles the typical situation and ways that it is different.
4. Figure 6.7.d illustrates the four commercial land uses identified in Figure 6.7.c. Find pictures to illustrate the types of land uses identified as residential or transportation. Prepare a display with appropriate headings.

5. According to Figure 6.7.e, there is quite a range in public transit use across the country.
   a) Brainstorm a list of at least 7 factors that would affect the rate of public transit use in an urban area.
   b) Suggest reasons why Montreal, Toronto, and Ottawa-Hull have the highest rates of public transit use. Use a map to support your suggestions.
   c) What connection might there be between some urban land uses and rates of public transit use?
6. a) Figure 6.7.f shows a part of North Vancouver that includes residential land uses. Compare the residential area north of the expressway with the residential area to the south of it. Consider the following characteristics in your comparison:
      i.   pattern of streets
      ii. density of housing
      iii. parks and other recreational facilities
      iv. access to shopping malls
   b) What do the results of your comparison tell you about North Vancouver?
   c) Which of these two parts of the city would be considered more exclusive or prestigious? Explain your answer.

LAND USE CONFLICTS

Major Concepts

- Land use conflicts
- Official plans
- Zoning by-laws

Incompatible uses near one another

Excessive traffic on city streets

Derelict buildings and structures

Land left vacant for long periods of time

Overuse of sewers and water supplies

Safety and security problems

High rates of pedestrian/vehicle accidents

Figure 6.8.c Examples of land use conflicts

With all the different land uses in urban areas, conflicts over how to use particular pieces of land sometimes occur. Often these **land use conflicts** happen because of uses that are incompatible with other nearby uses. A good example would be a decision to use a particular piece of land as a landfill site for garbage, with all of its sights, sounds and smells, upwind of a residential area. The presence of the landfill would mean the residents could not enjoy their homes to the fullest, and their complaints would no doubt put pressure on the landfill operator.

Authorities in urban areas try to reduce the chances of land use conflicts by establishing **official plans** and **zoning by-laws**. The official plan is written after consulting with the people in the community and takes into account their wishes and the economic, physical, and social conditions of the community. The plan sets out policies for future land uses such as where commercial development can take place and where new homes can be built. The zoning by-laws are the regulations that put the plan into effect. They specify what uses can be made of the land in different areas or zones and under what conditions development can take place. A zoning by-law for a residential area, for example, might specify lot sizes, building heights, how far back the residence must be from the street, parking requirements, and so forth. Applications for a particular land use that do not meet the zoning by-laws are rejected. In some cases, the zoning by-laws may be changed. In these ways, official plans and zoning by-laws reduce the likelihood of land use conflicts.

Figure 6.8.a Residential areas near busy traffic arteries is an example of land use conflict.

Figure 6.8.b Getting a zoning by-law amended usually involves notifying the public, so that people might have an opportunity to express their opinions on the change.

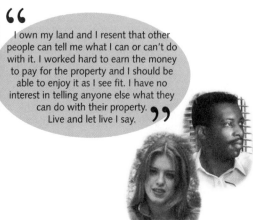

" I own my land and I resent that other people can tell me what I can or can't do with it. I worked hard to earn the money to pay for the property and I should be able to enjoy it as I see fit. I have no interest in telling anyone else what they can do with their property. Live and let live I say. "

" We all have to cooperate to make the best community that we can. Sometimes people use their property in ways that harm other people's use of their property. Zoning by-laws might restrict some people's ability to use their land, but in the end, the community is better, so everyone benefits. "

Figure 6.8.d Different views on land use planning and zoning by-laws

A **non-conforming land use** is a use that does not comply with a zoning by-law but is allowed because it existed before the official plan and zoning by-laws were written.

Zoning by-law amendments or changes are sometimes made to allow development that does not meet the by-law. In this case, builders ask the city council to change or amend the by-law. The change may be allowed if the amendment still meets, or conforms to, the policies set out in the official plan.

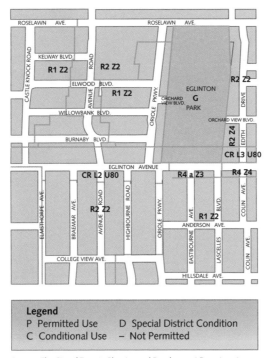

	R.1	R.1A	R.1F	R.2	R.3	R.4	R.4A
Residential							
One Family Dwelling	–	–	–	P	P	P	P
Detached Dwelling	P	P	P	P	P	P	P
Semi–Detached	–	–	D	P	P	P	P
Duplex	–	C	D	P	P	P	P
Double Duplex	–	D	D	P	P	P	P
Triplex	–	–	–	P	P	P	P
Double Triplex	–	–	–	P	P	P	P
Row House	–	–	–	P	P	P	P
Apartment House	–	D	–	C	C	C	C
Converted Dwelling	–	C	C	C	C	C	C
Boarding & Lodging House	C	C	C	C	C	C	C
Converted Boarding & Lodging House	–	–	–	C	C	C	C
Non–Residential							
Nursing Home	–	–	–	–	C	C	C
Residential Care Facility	C	C	C	C	C	C	C
Private Home Day Care	P	P	P	P	P	P	P
Day Nursery	C	C	C	C	C	C	C
Professional Office	–	–	–	–	–	–	P
Doctor/Dentist Office	C	C	C	C	C	D	P
Administrative Office Building	–	–	–	–	–	–	P
Retail Store	–	–	–	D	–	–	–
Parking Station	–	C	–	C	C	C	C
Commercial Use	–	–	–	–	D	–	–

Zoning Districts

Legend
P Permitted Use D Special District Condition
C Conditional Use – Not Permitted

Source: The City of Toronto Planning and Development Department

Figure 6.8.e Part of a zoning map for Toronto.

QUESTIONS & ACTIVITIES

1. List three examples of land use conflicts that could be found in your local area.
2. Explain the difference between an official plan and a zoning by-law. Give examples to support your explanation.
3. Make an advantages/disadvantages chart on the use of zoning by-laws. You should be able to identify at least five items on each list.
4. A developer has requested a zoning by-law change in order to build a strip plaza in a residential area. Already a convenience store, a video rental place, a donut shop and a dentist have agreed to open up in the plaza. The land is currently zoned for town-houses and low-rise apartments and there are approximately 200 families within a ten-minute walk of the plaza. A four-lane street runs past the site. You are on the planning committee for the town and must accept or reject the request.
   a) Brainstorm a list of all the factors you would want to consider in making your decision.
   b) What are the positive points about the proposal?
   c) What are the negative points about the proposal?
   d) Will you vote to accept or reject the proposal? Explain your decision.
5. a) Refer to the zoning map in Figure 6.8.e. What is the dominant zoning designation in this part of Toronto?
   b) How do you account for the irregularly shaped boundary lines between land use designations?
   c) What are the important differences between the R.1, R.2 and R.4A land use designations?
   d) If you were a landowner in a part of the area designated as R.3, what uses would be permitted on your land? What are some uses that would not be permitted?
6. From your own experience and understanding do you think that official plans and zoning by-laws are good and should be used by a city? Explain your answer in an expository paragraph.

URBAN POVERTY

Major Concepts

- Urban poverty and low-income families
- Poverty cycle
- Poverty line

Poverty is largely an urban problem. In Canada, 7 out of every 10 **low-income families** live in urban areas with populations of 100 000 or more. In Canada, the poor are usually seniors, single-female parents and their children, or adults living alone.

While people with low incomes may be distributed throughout the whole city, in larger communities they are often concentrated in areas next to the CBD. It is here that the housing stock is the oldest. The houses have generally been sold by those people who can afford to leave the area and commute into the centre of the city or other business centres from the newer suburbs. At the same time, commercial uses have not yet expanded outwards from the CBD to convert the land the houses stand on into retail and office uses. Owners of buildings in this area usually divide the houses into smaller rental units. Since the landowners anticipate selling the land for commercial use in the future, rarely will they make any improvements to their houses in the area. As a result, properties become run down or dilapidated.

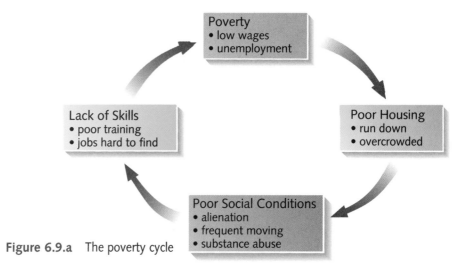

Figure 6.9.a The poverty cycle

Family size	Population of Community of Residence				
	Fewer than 30 000	30 999 – 99 999	100 000 – 499 999	500 000 +	Rural
1	$13 796	$14 827	$14 931	$17 409	$12 030
2	$17 245	$18 534	$18 664	$21 760	$15 038
3	$21 448	$23 050	$23 213	$27 063	$18 703
4	$25 964	$27 903	$28 098	$32 759	$22 639
5	$29 023	$31 191	$31 409	$36 618	$25 307
6	$32 081	$34 478	$34 720	$40 479	$27 975
7+	$35 140	$37 766	$38 032	$43 339	$30 643

Figure 6.9.b The "poverty line" by community size and family size, 1997. The table shows the minimum income levels families must make in these communities in order to live at or above the **poverty line**. For example, a family of four living in a community of less than 30 000 people is considered to live below the poverty line if the family income is under $25 964. People are generally considered to live below the poverty line when they earn less than 50% to 56% of the income of the average family living in their community. People living below the poverty line usually have only enough money to pay for the bare minimum of food, clothing, and housing.

	1994	1995	1996
All people	17.1	17.8	17.9
Children under 18 years	19.5	21.0	21.1
People 65 years and older	19.3	18.7	20.8
Unattached individuals	40.6	39.3	40.2

Figure 6.9.c Poverty rates in Canada, 1994–1996. Poverty rates refer to the percentage of the population with low incomes.

Only those families with few other options—those with low incomes—rent these homes. In some cities in recent years, middle-class and upper-middle-class people have moved back into city cores. They buy inexpensive houses there and then remodel them. As a result, poor people in these cities are being forced out of these areas and have more difficulty finding living accommodation they can afford.

Over 80% of one-parent families are headed by single mothers.

The rate of poverty among seniors varies considerably. Just 3% of seniors living in Saskatoon, Regina, and Oshawa live in poverty, but about 20% of seniors living in Winnipeg, Montreal, and Quebec City have low incomes. The difference is related to the costs of living in these places and the seniors' pension plans.

Poverty rates in Quebec are high compared to the rest of Canada. Four of the six Canadian cities with the highest poverty rates are in Quebec.

Figure 6.9.d Food banks have become part of the reality of urban poverty.

CMA	Poverty Rate, 1995	Poverty Rate, 1990	Population, 1996
Montreal	27.3	22.2	3 326 510
Trois–Rivières	23.4	20.3	139 956
Vancouver	23.3	17.9	1 831 665
Winnipeg	23.0	20.7	667 209
Sherbrooke	22.8	19.9	147 384
Quebec	22.8	18.7	671 889
Saskatoon	21.4	18.9	219 056
Edmonton	21.3	19.4	862 597
Toronto	21.1	15.0	4 263 757
Chicoutimi–Jonquière	20.7	15.9	160 454
Saint John	20.0	17.3	125 705
Calgary	19.8	17.7	821 628
St. John's	19.5	16.3	174 051
Hamilton	19.0	15.5	624 360
Ottawa–Hull	18.9	14.6	1 010 498
Halifax	17.8	14.1	332 518
Regina	17.6	15.9	193 652
Sudbury	17.3	13.5	160 488
London	17.3	13.6	398 616
St. Catharines-Niagara	16.1	12.8	372 406
Windsor	15.7	14.6	278 685
Victoria	15.4	13.5	304 287
Kitchener	14.6	11.7	382 940
Thunder Bay	14.5	12.1	125 562
Oshawa	12.4	9.2	268 773

Figure 6.9.e Poverty rates and population by CMA

Figure 6.9.f Street people—people who literally live on the streets—are a visible sign of urban poverty.

Photograph by Ivaan Kotulsky

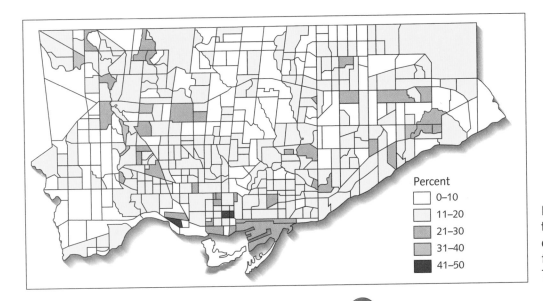

Percent
- ☐ 0–10
- ☐ 11–20
- ▨ 21–30
- ▨ 31–40
- ■ 41–50

Figure 6.9.g The location of single-parent mothers as a percentage of all families, 1991 Metropolitan Toronto census tracts

QUESTIONS & ACTIVITIES

1. Explain why, in urban areas, people who have low incomes have tended to move into the central or older parts of cities.

2. Suggest some reasons why the following groups of people have high rates of poverty:
   - people over 65
   - single-parent families headed by females
   - adults living alone

3. What might be some ways the poverty cycle could be broken? Suggest three ideas using Figure 6.9.a.

4. Figure 6.9.b gives the income levels required to be considered above the poverty line.
   a) Explain why families need to earn more money to live in larger cities than in smaller ones.
   b) Suggest reasons why a family would need less income to live in a rural area than in cities of any size.

5. Figure 6.9.c shows that the overall rate of poverty in Canada rose from 1994 to 1996. Calculate how many additional people joined the ranks of the poor between 1994 and 1996 if the population of the country was 29 255 600 in 1994 and 29 969 200 in 1996.

6. a) The photographs in Figure 6.9.d and Figure 6.9.f show two ways that people who live below the poverty line attempt to deal with low incomes. Identify the coping strategies used in the two photos.
   b) Give three other coping strategies that people might use in responding to urban poverty.

7. a) Refer to Figure 6.9.e. How do you account for the fact that Montreal has a poverty rate more than double that of Oshawa?
   b) Looking at the data in the table, does there seem to be a relationship between the sizes of urban areas and poverty rates?
   c) Test the relationship between the population of CMAs and poverty rates by constructing a scattergraph using the data. Draw a graph with the horizontal axis displaying 1995 poverty rates. Start labelling the line at 12.0 % and continue to 28.0 %. The CMA population figures will go on the vertical axis (the data is for 1996, but it will work for our analysis). Label this axis of your graph from 0 to 5 million people. Locate a dot at the spot that corresponds to the poverty rate and population for each CMA. For example, the dot for Montreal will be plotted on the graph where 27.3 % and 3 326 510 people intersect. Look for patterns or correlations in the dots when all are plotted on your scattergraph.
   d) What might be other factors that would cause the rates of low income people to vary across the CMAs? List and explain at least 3 factors.

8. a) Figure 6.9.g displays the percentage of single-parent mothers by census tracts in Metropolitan Toronto in 1991. Describe in words the distribution the map displays.
   b) In what ways might municipal officials use a map like this one to plan social programs and services for single-parent families?

CHANGING URBAN AREAS: TORONTO'S RAILWAY LANDS

Major Concepts

- Railway lands in urban areas
- Crown corporation
- Urban redevelopment

Technology plays a big role in determining how land is used in cities. In the last several decades of the nineteenth century and the first half of the twentieth century, railways were important movers of products and people. Most cities with railways at their centres had impressive train stations and railway-owned hotels as a focus point. Toronto was no exception. Much of the waterfront was given over to the railways. Large areas of the harbour were filled in to create room for the railways and the industries they generated. Union Station remains a glorious reminder of the age of the railways. However, improvements in road and air travel greatly reduced the importance of railways in the second half of the twentieth century. Changing travel patterns meant that railway tracks and equipment were no longer needed in the centre of cities. In fact, these facilities often blocked new development. Only the land continued to be valuable.

Recognizing that the underused railway lands were prime areas for development, Toronto began to find new uses for "The Railway

Figure 6.10.a Union Station was constructed between 1913 and 1927. This photograph demonstrates the grand style and importance given to the railways during the first half of the twentieth century.

Figure 6.10.b Toronto's railway corridor in 1955. Notice the extent of the land occupied by the railways, the industrial development of the port area, and the Toronto Islands in the background.

Lands." About 81 ha of land between Front Street and the Gardiner Expressway were made available for development in the 1980s. The SkyDome Stadium was built on part of the redeveloped railway lands. A positive advantage of this **redevelopment** of the railway lands was that the development allowed the downtown part of the city to reconnect with the waterfront and the islands of Toronto Harbour. By the middle of the 1990s, the Canada Lands Company, a **Crown corporation** acting on behalf of the government which owned much of the as-yet unused land, aggressively looked for purchasers or tenants for their CityPlace development. They planned an area of mixed residen-

...our marketing program... builds on the existing tourist/entertainment related activities which the area has become known for. With the CN Tower and the SkyDome already located on these lands, and with neighbours such as the Metropolitan Toronto Convention Centre, North America's second largest theatre district, and Harbourfront, the entertainment and tourist orientation of the neighbourhood is clear.

Roman Winnicki,
Vice President,
Canada Lands Company, 1996

tial uses, offices, and tourist and recreational facilities. In 1997, TrizecHahn Corporation and Grand Adex Properties purchased much of the railway lands and were given permission to complete a $2 billion project that would house 10 000 people and create 2000 permanent jobs on a 20 ha block of railway lands.

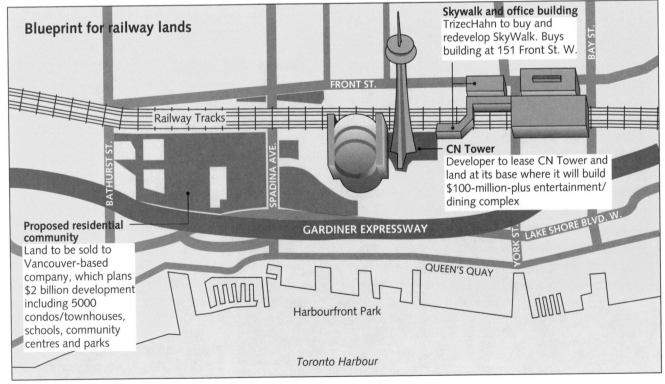

Blueprint for railway lands

Skywalk and office building
TrizecHahn to buy and redevelop SkyWalk. Buys building at 151 Front St. W.

BAY ST.

FRONT ST.

Railway Tracks

BATHURST ST.

SPADINA AVE.

CN Tower
Developer to lease CN Tower and land at its base where it will build $100-million-plus entertainment/ dining complex

GARDINER EXPRESSWAY

YORK ST.

LAKE SHORE BLVD. W.

Proposed residential community
Land to be sold to Vancouver-based company, which plans $2 billion development including 5000 condos/townhouses, schools, community centres and parks

QUEEN'S QUAY

Harbourfront Park

Toronto Harbour

Source: Canada Lands Co.

Figure 6.10.c The TrizecHahn redevelopment plan for the Toronto Railway Lands, 1997

Figure 6.10.d   The Railway Lands in Toronto's CBD in 1998

QUESTIONS & ACTIVITIES

1. Explain why railway lands in Canadian cities have been targeted for redevelopment in recent years.
2. Why are railway lands considered prime real estate for residential, commercial and recreational uses, especially in Toronto's CBD?
3. Use Figure 6.10.b to identify these railway facilities that existed in 1955 when the air photograph was taken:
   - Union Station
   - loading platforms
   - roundhouses
   - repair yards and other maintenance facilities
   - grain elevators
4. a) The redevelopment plan in Figure 6.10.c includes residential options such as townhouses and condominiums. Why do you suppose these uses are included in an area that is known for its recreational and tourist facilities?
   b) Would you choose to live in this area? Explain your answer.

5. a) Figure 6.10.d shows the same area as Figure 6.10.b. What railway facilities are apparent in this photograph, taken in 1998?
   b) Make a sketch map of the area shown in Figure 6.10.d. Mark on your sketch map the railway facilities that still exist and all recent development on the Railway Lands. Label as many of the new developments as you can. Also, shade in those areas that have yet to be redeveloped but have clearly lost their railway functions.
   c) Label buildings and land uses that have been added since 1998.
6. Do you think the new uses of the Railway Lands have been good or bad for Toronto? Explain your answer in a well-written paragraph.
7. Suppose you were given an opportunity to redevelop Toronto's Railway Lands. What uses would you suggest for this area? Explain your choices.

Many local businesses in your area are success stories. What makes them successful? With a partner select one of these businesses and develop a list of reasons why you think the business is successful. Arrange an interview with the owner or manager and see if your reasons for success match those of the owner/manager. Make a report of your findings to the class. Include zoning, parking, access, services, financing, customers/market, and other factors.

Design a business plan of your own to open and operate a business in your neighbourhood. Use a variety of media to describe your business plan to your classmates. Make sure you describe where you want to locate your business and why. Be sure to check zoning regulations. Make a community map and put on the proposed locations of all the businesses developed by your class.

Perspectives on Research: The Inquiry Model

The basic inquiry model builds in strategies to help you do good research. Use a variety of resources to search out the best alternative answer to your research question.

The Basic Inquiry Model

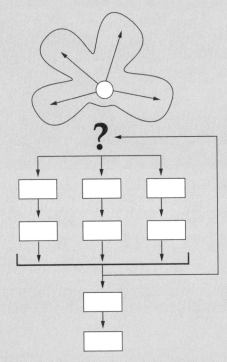

Question
The researcher develops a suitable question around which he or she will develop a study.

Data
The researcher collects information on each alternative or possible solution to the question.

Synthesis
The researcher arrives at a conclusion by deciding, on the basis of the information collected, which of the alternatives gives the best answer or solution to the question.

UNIT 7 CHANGING CANADA: A PART OF THE GLOBAL COMMUNITY

Our history and geography make us important members of the global community. Our ties to other countries, and the obligations and opportunities that come from them, are the subject of Unit 7.

IMMIGRATION: POST-SECOND WORLD WAR

Major Concepts

- Push and pull factors in immigration
- Immigration patterns
- Multiculturalism

FILE

FACT

Immigration

Most immigrants obtain Canadian citizenship as soon as they are eligible, within three or four years of coming to Canada. By 1996, of all immigrants eligible to become Canadian citizens, 83% had done so.

Between 1991 and 1996, 1 403 170 people immigrated to Canada, but 227 612 people **emigrated** or left Canada to live in other countries.

Since the 1950s, the number of people who have immigrated to Canada has made up 15% to 17% of the total population. By 1996, about 5 million people, or 17.4% of all Canadians had moved to this country. The largest single percentage came from the United Kingdom, a group that made up about 13% of all immigrants.

The number of people who immigrated (came to Canada) in any given year has varied widely, depending on world situations and conditions in Canada. When people decide to leave their homelands, we talk about "**push factors.**" Push factors include war and violence, lack of jobs, overcrowding, poor housing, or restricted freedoms. People who have decided to leave their homelands can go to many destinations. They are attracted, or pulled, to Canada by the conditions in this country. "**Pull factors**" are such things as peace, jobs, freedom, good housing, and safe environments. Canada ranks very high on the United Nations' quality of life indicators. It is an attractive place to live for most people seeking a new life.

Many changes can be seen clearly in the patterns of where immigrants originated on their way to Canada. Before 1961, 90% of the

Place of birth	Period of immigration				
	Before 1961	1961–1970	1971–1980	1981–1990	1991–1996
Southern Europe	21.6	31.0	13.2	5.3	5.0
United Kingdom	25.2	21.3	13.3	5.8	2.4
Northern and Western Europe	26.9	11.5	6.0	4.4	3.1
Eastern Europe	16.6	5.2	3.2	10.2	8.5
Eastern Asia	1.9	4.9	10.5	15.8	24.3
Southeast Asia	0.2	1.8	11.2	14.9	11.4
Southern Asia	0.4	3.7	8.1	9.1	13.5
West-Central Asia & Middle East	0.5	1.9	3.1	7.1	7.9
Central and South America	0.6	2.2	6.8	9.7	7.3
Caribbean	0.8	5.7	9.6	6.6	5.5
United States	4.3	6.4	7.4	4.2	2.8
Africa	0.5	3.3	5.8	5.9	7.3
Oceania and Other	0.4	1.2	1.5	0.9	1.0

Note: Oceania includes Australia, New Zealand and the island nations of the southern Pacific Ocean.

▲ **Figure 7.1.b** Immigrants by place of birth, 1996 (percentages)

Year	Number of Immigrants
1946	71 719
1951	194 391
1956	164 857
1961	71 689
1966	194 743
1971	121 900
1976	149 429
1981	128 618
1986	99 219
1991	232 020
1996	226 074
1997	216 044

Figure 7.1.a Immigration to Canada for selected years, 1946-1997

Figure 7.1.c This scene is typical of many Canadian high schools.

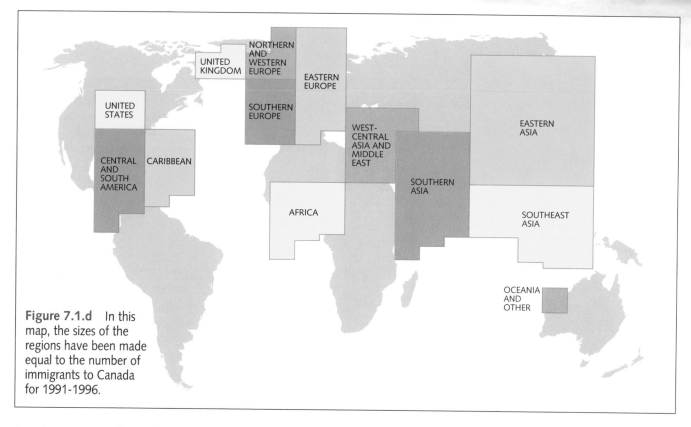

Figure 7.1.d In this map, the sizes of the regions have been made equal to the number of immigrants to Canada for 1991-1996.

immigrants were from the United Kingdom and Europe. Since 1991, Asia has become the origin of 70% of immigrants. These changes have made Canada a **multicultural** nation with citizens from all over the globe. The blend of cultures, races, and peoples often puts Canada in a leadership role for promoting world peace and harmony.

Country of Origin	Number	%
Total	441 035	100.0
Hong Kong	48 535	11.0
Sri Lanka	36 735	8.3
People's Republic of China	35 330	8.0
Philippines	33 210	7.5
India	33 185	7.5
Poland	18 605	4.2
Jamaica	16 780	3.8
Guyana	13 195	3.0
Vietnam	12 290	2.8
Trinidad and Tobago	11 375	2.6

Figure 7.1.f Immigration to Toronto, 1991-1996

Country of Origin	Number	%
Total	134 535	100.0
Haiti	9 995	7.4
Lebanon	9 610	7.1
France	7 540	5.6
People's Republic of China	6 650	4.9
Romania	5 225	3.9
Sri Lanka	4 675	3.5
Philippines	4 640	3.4
India	4 380	3.3
Vietnam	4 135	3.1
Morocco	3 820	2.8

Figure 7.1.e In larger cities, the proportion of immigrants is higher than in other parts of Canada. Here crowds in Toronto gather to celebrate the city's Caribana festival.

Figure 7.1.g Immigration to Montreal, 1991-1996

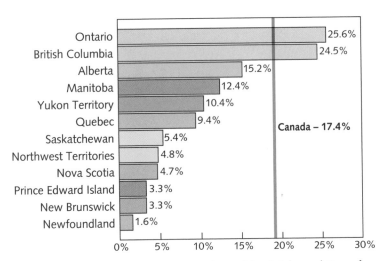

Figure 7.1.h Immigrants as a percentage of the total population of provinces and territories, 1996

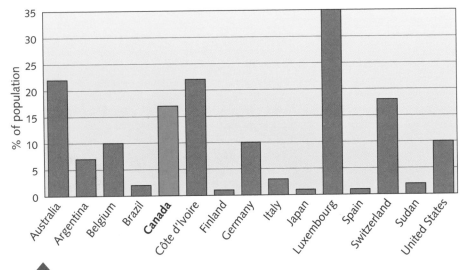

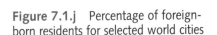

Figure 7.1.i Foreign-born population as a percentage of total population for selected countries

Figure 7.1.j Percentage of foreign-born residents for selected world cities

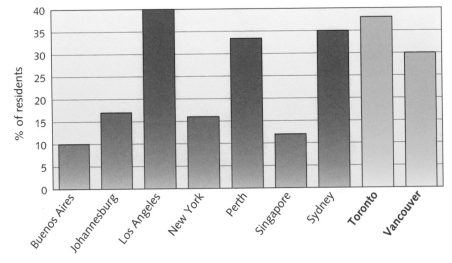

FILE

Benefits of High Immigration

- Many different foods are available in ethnic restaurants.
- Canadians learn about other cultures and ways of life.
- Immigrants bring money and other wealth with them to Canada.
- People bring knowledge and skills that are used in the work force.
- Canada has stronger ties to other countries through family connections.
- Immigrants cause our population to grow more rapidly, creating jobs.
- The country gets a reputation for being generous and welcoming.

QUESTIONS & ACTIVITIES ❓

1. Explain how push-and-pull factors make Canada a popular choice for immigrants from around the world.
2. Think about the things you value and want in your life. Make a list of five push factors that might encourage you to move out of Canada. Now, make a list of five pull factors that are encouraging you to remain in Canada. Looking at your lists, are you likely ever to seriously consider leaving Canada? Explain your answer.
3. Examine the second Fact File. Write each item in your notebook, putting the items in order from the greatest benefit to Canada to the least. When you are finished, compare your list to others in the class and defend any differences in ranking in your lists.
4. Look for three historical events that might help to explain why immigration rates to Canada have varied so widely, as Figure 7.1.a illustrates.
5. a) Using Figure 7.1.b, identify the peak decades of immigration from these parts of the world:
   i. Europe
   ii. Asia
   iii. the Americas
   iv. other parts of the world
   b) Use the "Before 1961" and "1991-1996" columns to make a divergence bar graph for immigration to Canada. Begin by subtracting the "Before 1961" percentages from the "1991-1996" percentages. If the first value is greater than the second (in other words, if immigration has slowed down), you will have a negative sign. Draw these axes in your notebook and plot and label a bar for each geographic area. Use the heading Change in Immigration, Before 1961 Compared to 1991-96

(percent)

-25 -20 -15 -10 -5 0 5 10 15 20 25

6. Figure 7.1.d gives a visual indication of immigration to Canada. Why do you suppose the Caribbean region is the source of many immigrants when its population is much smaller than other places, such as Central and South America or the United States?
7. Compare Figures 7.1.f and 7.1.g.
   a) What are the differences in the immigration rates for Montreal and Toronto?
   b) What are some similarities in the two lists?
   c) What reasons can you give to try to explain the similarities and the differences between the immigration rates of the two cities?
8. What might be some advantages for immigrants who decide to move to the largest cities of Canada? What might be some disadvantages for these immigrants?
9. In the 1990s, immigrants to Canada tended to settle in Ontario and British Columbia, as Figure 7.1.h indicates.
   a) Give reasons to explain why Ontario and British Columbia become home to over half of Canada's immigrants.
   b) Why do you suppose the Atlantic provinces become home to a relatively small share of the total numbers of immigrants? Give three reasons.
10. According to Figure 7.1.i, how does Canada rank in comparison to the other countries shown in the graph? How do you account for this rank?
11. Using Figure 7.1.j to help form an opinion, do you think that large cities in developing countries would have more or fewer foreign-born residents than large cities in developed countries like Canada? Explain your answer.

CULTURAL DIVERSITY

Major Concepts

- Cultural mosaic
- Diversity of population
- Mother tongue

When the Second World War ended in 1945, most Canadians could trace their ancestry to our two "founding" nations. They were either of French stock, or had ancestors who originated from the British Isles. Of course, other groups were here, including Aboriginal peoples, former slaves who had arrived via the Underground Railway, Asian people who had laboured to build the transcontinental railway, and Eastern Europeans who had settled the West and broken the rich prairie sod with their ploughs. However, these groups were relatively small compared to our two founding groups. Immigration after the Second World War, however, began to shift cultural influences away from the French and the British towards a more diverse pattern. By the end of the century, Canada had become a mosaic of many different groups of people and cultures with broad and interesting designs.

We have virtually no monuments to the multicultural nature of Canada, to salute those who came here seeking a fresh and better future—which, when you think about it, includes just about all Canadians.

Peter C. Newman, columnist

Figure 7.2.a Recent immigrants to Canada

DEFINITIONS

A **mosaic** is a picture or design made up of small pieces of stone, glass, etc., of different colours.

According to the **Employment Equity Act**, **visible minority persons** are those who are non-Caucasian in race or non-white in colour. Aboriginal peoples are not included in the visible minority population.

Mother tongue is the language you learn first. Some people learn several languages as young children and they are considered to have multiple mother tongues.

Canada	11.2
Newfoundland	0.7
Prince Edward Island	1.1
Nova Scotia	3.5
New Brunswick	1.1
Quebec	6.2
Ontario	15.8
Manitoba	7.0
Saskatchewan	2.8
Alberta	10.1
British Columbia	17.9
Yukon Territory	3.3
Northwest Territories	2.6

Figure 7.2.b Visible minorities in Canada, 1996 (percentage of total population)

CMA	Total Population	Visible Minorities (%)
Toronto	4 232 905	31.6
Vancouver	1 813 935	31.1
Calgary	815 985	15.6
Edmonton	854 225	13.5
Montreal	3 287 645	12.2
Ottawa-Hull	1 000 940	11.5
Winnipeg	660 055	11.1
Windsor	275 745	10.0
Kitchener	379 350	8.9
Hamilton	617 815	7.9
London	393 900	7.7
Victoria	300 030	7.6
Halifax	329 750	6.8
Oshawa	266 585	6.0
Regina	191 485	5.4
Saskatoon	216 445	5.2
St. Catharines-Niagara	367 790	3.7
Thunder Bay	124 325	2.2
Sherbrooke	144 570	2.1
Saint John	124 215	2.1
Sudbury	158 935	1.8
Quebec	663 885	1.5
St. John's	172 090	1.4
Trois-Rivières	137 700	0.9
Chicoutimi-Jonquière	158 860	0.4

Figure 7.2.c Visible minority population by CMA, 1996

	Vancouver	Toronto	Montreal
Total Visible Minorities	564 605	1 338 100	401 420
Black	16 400	274 935	122 320
South Asian	120 140	329 840	46 165
Chinese	279 040	335 185	46 115
Korean	17 085	28 555	3 505
Japanese	21 880	17 055	2 310
Southeast Asian	20 370	46 510	37 600
Filipino	40 715	99 115	14 385
Arab/West Asian	18 155	72 160	73 950
Latin American	13 830	61 655	46 705
Other and multiple	16 990	73 090	8 365

Figure 7.2.d   Visible minority populations for Vancouver, Toronto, and Montreal, 1996

	English	French	Multiple	Other
Canada	**59.2**	**23.3**	**1.4**	**16.1**
Newfoundland	98.5	0.4	0.1	1.0
Prince Edward Island	93.9	4.2	0.3	1.6
Nova Scotia	94.0	3.9	0.5	2.8
New Brunswick	64.9	32.9	0.9	1.4
Quebec	8.3	80.9	1.4	9.3
Ontario	72.3	4.5	1.6	21.6
Manitoba	73.9	4.3	1.7	20.1
Saskatchewan	83.7	2.0	1.4	13.0
Alberta	80.9	2.0	1.3	15.9
British Columbia	75.5	1.4	1.4	21.7
Yukon Territory	86.2	3.6	1.4	8.8
Northwest Territories	55.9	2.1	1.6	40.4

Note: "Multiple" includes those whose mother tongues were English and French or English and/or French and a non-official language.

Figure 7.2.e   Mother tongue, 1996 (percentages).

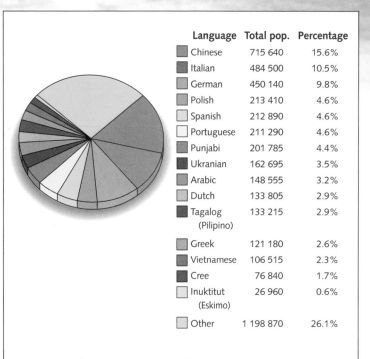

Language	Total pop.	Percentage
Chinese	715 640	15.6%
Italian	484 500	10.5%
German	450 140	9.8%
Polish	213 410	4.6%
Spanish	212 890	4.6%
Portuguese	211 290	4.6%
Punjabi	201 785	4.4%
Ukranian	162 695	3.5%
Arabic	148 555	3.2%
Dutch	133 805	2.9%
Tagalog (Pilipino)	133 215	2.9%
Greek	121 180	2.6%
Vietnamese	106 515	2.3%
Cree	76 840	1.7%
Inuktitut (Eskimo)	26 960	0.6%
Other	1 198 870	26.1%

Figure 7.2.f   The largest non-official languages in Canada, 1996 (as a percentage of population whose mother tongue is not French or English)

QUESTIONS & ACTIVITIES

1. Canada's cultural make-up began to change dramatically after the Second World War. Suggest three reasons to explain why this was the case.

2. **a)** Examine Figure 7.2.a. What problems might a family of a visible minority face when they arrive in Canada?

   b) In what ways might the presence of a larger number of visible minorities have changed Canadian society in the second half of this century? Give three ideas.

3. **a)** Using Figure 7.2.b, list those provinces that have more than the national average number of visible minorities, and those that have less.

   b) Explain why only two provinces had higher than the national average of visible minorities in 1996 while eight provinces and the territories have less than the national average.

   c) What significance might the pattern discussed in a) and b) have for the country?

4. Create a scattergraph to analyze the data given in Figure 7.2.c. On the horizontal axis of your scattergraph label the population of the CMAs, from zero to 4.5 million. On the vertical axis, show the percentage of visible minorities, labelling from zero to 32%. Plot a dot for each CMA. For example, for Toronto, you would put a dot where 4.2 million and 31.6% visible minorities intersect. When you are finished, your scattergraph will have all 25 CMAs plotted. What does your scattergraph tell you about where visible minorities are concentrated in Canada?

5. **a)** Figure 7.2.d is a comparison of the visible minorities in Vancouver, Toronto, and Montreal. Study the table carefully and choose one important difference among the three cities. Show the difference in a visual way, such as a graph or an illustration.

   b) Offer an explanation for the differences you see in the pattern of visible minorities in the three cities.

6. Explain why mother tongue is a good way to look at the cultural diversity of Canada.

7. **a)** Identify three interesting observations about the mother tongues of the people of Canada using Figure 7.2.e.

   b) Using the data in Figure 7.2.e, which province or territory seems to be the most culturally diverse in Canada? Which is the least culturally diverse?

CULTURAL LINKAGES

Major Concepts

- Ethnic origins of Canadians
- Non-Christian religions
- Travellers to Canada

Very few of us in this country share the same past, but all of us can share the same future. Especially if we refuse to permit the past to poison that future.

Romeo LaBlanc,
Governor General
of Canada, 1995

The culturally diverse immigrants who arrived in the second half of the twentieth century changed the nature of Canadian society in some very visible ways. The transformation was not sudden, nor is it yet complete.

We can see differences in the ethnic origins of Canadians in the religions that they practise. We can also see these differences in the backgrounds of travellers who come to Canada to visit friends and relatives.

DEFINITIONS

"**Ethnic origins**" refers to the cultural background of a person, in other words, the characteristics, customs, and languages of a person's ancestors. It reflects the roots of a person, not his/her place of birth, citizenship, or nationality. In the 1996 census, people were allowed to name up to four ethnic groups.

"Canadian" was one of the examples that was provided.

Single Origins	18 303 625	Multiple Origins	10 224 500
British Isles	3 267 525	British plus	6 459 160
French	2 683 840	French plus	1 167 045
Other European	3 742 895	Canadian plus	579 045
Arab	188 430	British, French, plus	920 945
Southwest Asian	697 015	Other multiple origins	1 098 295
East and Southeast Asian	1 271 450		
African	137 315		
Pacific Islands	5 765		
Latin American	118 635		
Caribbean	305 290		
Aboriginal	477 635		
Canadian	5 326 995		
Other single origins	80 845		

Figure 7.3.a The ethnic origins of Canadians, 1996

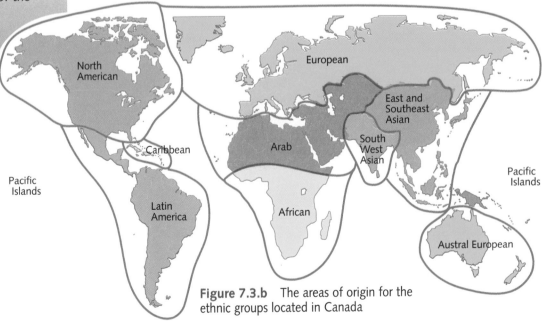

Figure 7.3.b The areas of origin for the ethnic groups located in Canada

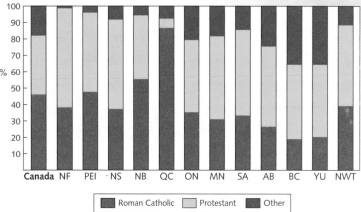

Figure 7.3.d Religious composition of Canada, 1991.*
*This data was not collected in the 1996 census.

Roman Catholic | Protestant | Other

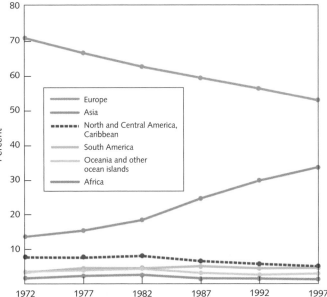

Europe
Asia
North and Central America, Caribbean
South America
Oceania and other ocean islands
Africa

Figure 7.3.c Non-resident travellers entering Canada (other than from the US), 1972-1997

	World	Canada
Christian	33.1	83.4
Roman Catholic	18.8	45.7
Protestant	11.2	36.3
Eastern Orthodox	3.1	1.5
Eastern Non-Christian	37.8	4.0
Islam	17.7	1.0
Hindu	13.4	0.6
Buddhist	5.7	0.7
Other	1.0	1.9
Para-religious groups	8.2	0.2
No religion	20.8	12.4

Figure 7.3.e Religious composition of Canada and the World (percentages), 1996. The earliest Europeans to settle in the northern half of North America were almost all Christians, and Christianity has continued to be the largest religion in Canada. In recent years, Eastern non-Christian beliefs have established themselves and are growing in size.

QUESTIONS & ACTIVITIES

1. List five ways that cultural differences may be seen in a community or a neighbourhood.
2. Using your dictionary and other reference sources, define and distinguish among the following terms:
   a) ethnic origin
   b) racial group
   c) visible minority
   d) nationality
3. Notice in Figure 7.3.a that some ethnic groups have a clear geographic connection (for example, the French are related to France) while others have none (Arab and Aboriginal do not imply a specific place). Suggest three reasons to explain these differences.
4. a) What is your ethnic origin? Would you fit best into the single or multiple origin categories? Explain.
   b) What are the ethnic characteristics of a "Canadian"?
   c) In what ways might a person of Canadian ethnic origin be different from persons of other ethnic origins?

5. Using Figure 7.3.e, explain why Christians make up such a large part of the religious composition of Canada, compared to the rest of the world.
6. Examine Figure 7.3.d. Find three facts or patterns that you would consider interesting or unique in the graphs. For each one, suggest an explanation for how the pattern came to be.
7. Figure 7.3.d suggests that there are some quite large variations in religion across the country. In what ways might these differences affect the way people would get along in communities? Within the country of Canada?
8. a) Non-resident travellers are often people vacationing in places to visit relatives or friends. In what ways have travel patterns to Canada changed since 1972 (see Figure 7.3.c)? What do these changes suggest about the cultural composition of the population of Canada? Explain your answer.
   b) How do you think these changes would affect the tourist industry?

CANADA'S FOUR PERSPECTIVES

Major Concepts

- Geographic perspective
- Map projection
- International relationships

The many heritages of the people who make up Canada help link this country to the rest of the world. We are connected in a host of other ways as well. Imports and exports, participation in international organizations (such as the United Nations), travel and tourism, and Canada's long history of peacekeeping, all help link us to the rest of the world.

Canada's physical size and location help shape what international roles Canada plays. Canada borders on three of the world's oceans. As a result, we are affected by the forces and influences that originate anywhere around or on these oceans. And, since Canada occupies a large part of the continent of North America, we are greatly influenced by what goes on in this continent and hemisphere. Our site and situation, in short, explain why Canadians view the world from four distinct perspectives:

- looking westward, as a Pacific nation, inspired by the peoples of Asia and the south Pacific;
- looking eastward, as an Atlantic nation, influenced by Europe, Africa, and the Middle East;

- looking southward, as an American nation, to our neighbours in North America, Central America, and South America;
- looking northward, as a polar nation, interacting with the people of the circumpolar region.

These different perspectives sometimes cause Canadians difficulties. Depending on where we live and our experiences, we may see the world in quite different ways than Canadians who live in other parts of Canada and whose experiences are different from ours. At the same time, these different perspectives enable us to learn more about people and cultures and to become uniquely global citizens who play important international roles.

Our Pacific Perspective

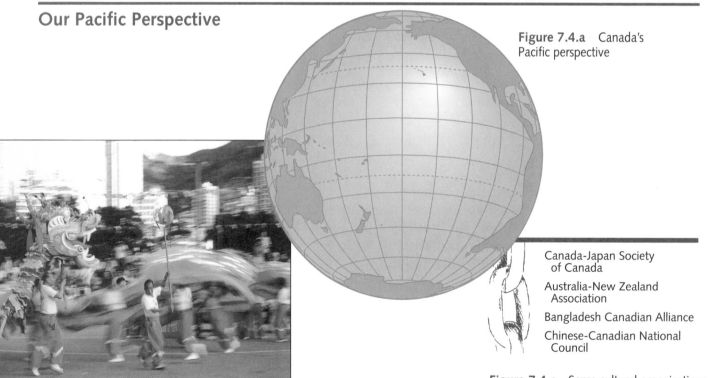

Figure 7.4.a Canada's Pacific perspective

Canada-Japan Society of Canada

Australia-New Zealand Association

Bangladesh Canadian Alliance

Chinese-Canadian National Council

Figure 7.4.b A familiar scene from Asian celebrations

Figure 7.4.c Some cultural organizations that link Canada to the Pacific region

Our Atlantic Perspective

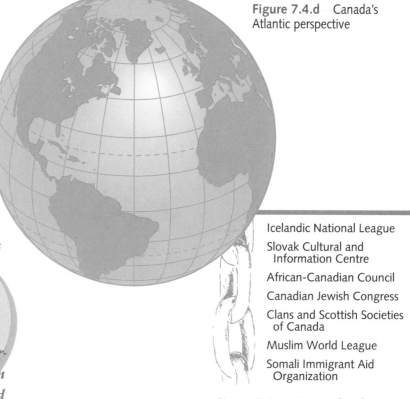

Figure 7.4.d Canada's Atlantic perspective

> ❝ *I saw the urgent need for ongoing support to help Palestinians improve their living conditions. It is also imperative that we continue to support activities that will help to build a lasting peace in the region, since peace and development are intertwined. Peace is a necessary condition for poverty reduction, yet poverty and lack of opportunity are often the root causes of conflict.* ❞

Diane Marleau,
Minister for International Cooperation,
November 1998

Icelandic National League

Slovak Cultural and Information Centre

African-Canadian Council

Canadian Jewish Congress

Clans and Scottish Societies of Canada

Muslim World League

Somali Immigrant Aid Organization

Figure 7.4.e Some cultural organizations that link Canada to the Atlantic region

Figure 7.4.f Canada was a founding member of the North Atlantic Treaty Organization (NATO) in 1949. These soldiers are part of Canada's NATO forces stationed in Germany.

Our American Perspective

Figure 7.4.g Canada's American perspective

Caribbean Cultural Committee

Latin American Working Group

Canadian Foundation for the Americas

Figure 7.4.h Some cultural organizations that link Canada to its American neighbours

66 It is important for our continuing growth that the countries of the Americas press forward with the negotiations towards a Free Trade Area of the Americas. The reduction of trade barriers throughout the hemisphere will bolster all of our economies and strengthen our hemispheric community. 99

Sergio Marchi,
International Trade Minister, December 1998

Figure 7.4.i RCMP officers helped to train local police in Haiti in 1996, as part of a United Nations program in that country.

Our Circumpolar Perspective

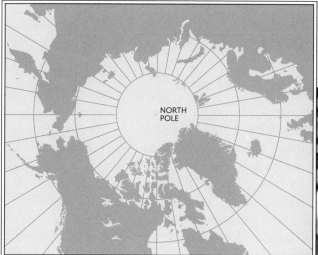

Figure 7.4.j North circumpolar projection

Canadian-Nordic Society
Canadian Circumpolar Institute
Inuit Circumpolar Conference
Arctic Council

Figure 7.4.k Some cultural organizations that link Canada with circumpolar countries

Figure 7.4.l "Knuckle" is a popular event at the international Arctic Winter Games.

QUESTIONS & ACTIVITIES

1. Select one of the four perspectives illustrated in Figures 7.4.a, 7.4.d, 7.4.g, and 7.4.j. Trace it into your notebook. Explain how the perspective illustrated has an influence on Canada's worldviews.
2. For each of the four perspectives, make a list of the products or services that Canadians use that originate in these other parts of the world.
3. Of the four perspectives, which do you feel you are most influenced by? Give some reasons to explain why you feel this way.
4. Do you agree that having oceans for borders opens us to more forces or influences than land borders do? Explain your answer.
5. a) For each of the four perspectives, name five countries that are important in that perspective.

b) Rank the four perspectives (1 = strongest, 4 = weakest) for each of these characteristics:
   i. cultural influences on Canada
   ii. political influences on Canada
   iii. economic influences
   iv. potential for conflict or violence
   v. sources of immigrants to Canada over the next 25 years
   vi. destinations for Canadian tourists

c) In the nineteenth century, European and Atlantic forces dominated the Canadian outlook. The twentieth century saw the growing influence on Canada of the impressive power of the United States. What perspective will be most important in the twenty-first century? Give three reasons for your choice.

CANADA'S TRADE PARTNERS

Major Concepts

- International trade
- Imports and exports
- Trade mission

The trade of goods and services is an important part of the relationship between Canada and other countries. "**Trade**" means the sale or **export** of our goods or services to another country and the purchase or **import** of their goods or services to Canada. Because we are one of the top trading nations in the world, we rely heavily on our international relationships.

Canada's trading, both importing and exporting, is mainly with the United States. In fact, the trade between Canada and the United States represents the largest trading partnership in the world. Throughout the 1990s, trade with the United States continued to grow in spite of efforts on the part of Canadian business and government to find other markets for our goods and services. Our closeness to this large and powerful economy is a great advantage for Canada's industries, and our natural resources are in great demand in the factories to the south. At the same time, our dependence on US markets and trade makes Canada extremely vulnerable to the ups and downs of the American economy and to changes in American politics.

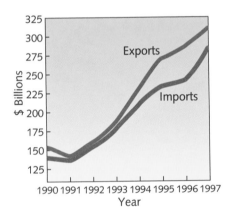

Figure 7.5.a Canada's **total** imports and exports of goods, 1990-1997 (billions of dollars)

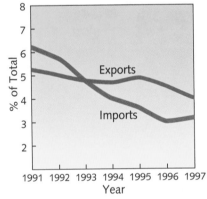

Figure 7.5.c Imports and exports of goods to and from **Japan**, 1991-1997 (percentage of total imports and exports)

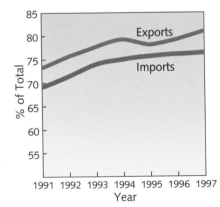

Figure 7.5.b Imports and exports of goods to and from the **United States**, 1991-1997 (percentage of total imports and exports)

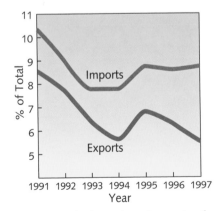

Figure 7.5.d Imports and exports of goods to and from the **European Union**, 1991-1997 (percentage of total imports and exports)

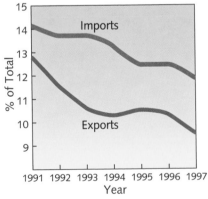

Figure 7.5.e Imports and exports of goods to and from all **other** countries, 1991-1997 (percentage of total imports and exports)

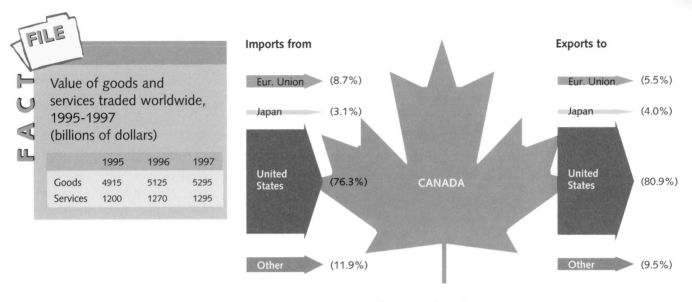

Value of goods and services traded worldwide, 1995-1997 (billions of dollars)

	1995	1996	1997
Goods	4915	5125	5295
Services	1200	1270	1295

Imports from

Eur. Union (8.7%)

Japan (3.1%)

United States (76.3%)

CANADA

Other (11.9%)

Exports to

Eur. Union (5.5%)

Japan (4.0%)

United States (80.9%)

Other (9.5%)

Figure 7.5.f Imports and exports of goods, 1997

Rank 1990	Rank 1997	Importers	Value ($ billions)	% Share
1	1	United States	1 339.8	16.1
2	2	Germany	657.8	7.9
3	3	Japan	504.2	6.0
5	4	United Kingdom	457.7	5.5
3	5	France	397.5	4.8
12	6	Hong Kong, China	310.9	3.7
6	7	Italy	310.8	3.7
10	8	Canada	299.4	3.6
7	9	Netherlands	263.8	3.2
9	10	Belgium-Luxembourg	231.7	2.8
13	11	South Korea	215.4	2.6
	12	China	212.1	2.5
15	13	Singapore	197.2	2.4
11	14	Spain	182.8	2.2

Figure 7.5.g World importers of goods and services, 1990 and 1997 (value in billions of dollars)

Rank 1990	Rank 1997	Exporters	Value ($ billions)	% Share
2	1	United States	1 026.4	12.6
1	2	Germany	762.4	9.4
3	3	Japan	627.4	7.7
4	4	France	428.8	5.3
5	5	United Kingdom	417.3	5.1
6	6	Italy	355.9	4.4
8	7	Canada	319.4	3.9
7	8	Netherlands	288.3	3.5
11	9	Hong Kong, China	280.2	3.4
15	10	China	272.2	3.3
9	11	Belgium-Luxembourg	249.7	3.1
13	12	South Korea	203.5	2.5
	13	Singapore	186.2	2.3
12	14	Taiwan	181.6	2.2
	15	Mexico	164.5	2.0

Figure 7.5.h World exporters of goods and services, 1990 and 1997 (value in billions of dollars)

January 19

5:00 a.m. leaves Ottawa

1:20 p.m. arrives Port of Spain, Trinidad and Tobago

3:15 meets the prime minister

4:15 ceremonial signing of contracts

January 20

7:20 a.m. leaves Port of Spain

3:00 p.m. arrives Montevideo, Uruguay

4:30 meeting with president

6:15 meeting with president-elect

8:30 dinner with president

11:00 leaves Montevideo

January 21

12:30 a.m. arrives in Buenos Aires, Argentina (no official duties)

January 22

(no official duties)

January 23

11:20 a.m. lays wreath at monument

11:45 meeting with president

1:00 p.m. speech to business people

3:00 contract signing ceremony

7:00 gala at presidential palace

9:00 state dinner

January 24

10:20 a.m. visit to city hall

11:00 meeting with president

1:00 p.m. reception for diplomats

6:00 leaves Buenos Aires

10:10 arrives in Santiago, Chile

January 25

10:00 a.m. lays wreath at monument

10:30 meeting with president

12:30 p.m. contract signing ceremony

1:00 lunch with business group

3:30 visit to industrial site

6:00 reception at presidential palace

January 26

9:30 a.m. meeting with government officials

10:30 meeting with president and contract signing

3:00 p.m. leaves Santiago

8:20 arrives in Brasillia, Brazil

January 27

10:00 a.m. meeting with president

12:00 contract signing ceremony

3:30 p.m. meeting with government officials

4:00 meeting with legal officials

8:30 dinner with president

January 28

8:30 a.m. leaves Brasillia

10:10 arrives Rio de Janeiro

10:30 visits Canadian corporation

12:30 p.m. lunch with business group

2:00 contract signing ceremony

3:30 visits Brazilian wheat mill

8:00 dinner with governor

January 29

11:00 a.m. leaves Rio de Janeiro

2:30 p.m. arrives in San José, Costa Rica

8:00 dinner with president

January 30

9:00 a.m. cuts ribbon on new Canadian government office

10:00 opens new Canadian factory

11:00 meets with Central American leaders

12:30 p.m. lunch with leaders

4:00 leaves San José

10:25 arrives in Ottawa

◀ **Figure 7.5.i** In order to find new markets for their products and new sources of goods, governments and interested business people travel together on **trade missions** to countries they hope will provide new markets. This was Prime Minister Chrétien's travel itinerary while on a trade mission to open new markets in Latin and Central America in 1995. The mission was called Team Canada.

Figure 7.5.j The prime minister's route

Figure 7.5.k Prime Minister Chrétien in Trinidad

QUESTIONS & ACTIVITIES

1. Define these terms: trade, imports, exports.
2. What three reasons could explain why the United States is Canada's largest trading partner?
3. **a)** What is meant by a "trade surplus"?
   b) Explain why countries want to have a trade surplus.
   c) According to Figures 7.5.b to 7.5.e, with which countries does Canada have a trade surplus? With which countries does Canada have a trade deficit?
4. In general, what has been happening with Canada's trade with:
   a) the United States
   b) Japan
   c) the European Union
   d) other countries.
5. **a)** Figure 7.5.f shows the dominance of the United States in Canada's trade picture. Suggest some advantages and disadvantages of being confined largely to one trading partner.
   b) What are some things that the Canadian government could do to try to reduce our trade dependence on the United States?

6. **a)** On an outline map of the world, outline in red those countries that are the world's top importers using Figure 7.5.g as your source of information. Shade in yellow all those countries that are the world's top exporters, from Figure 7.5.h. Describe the patterns on your map.
   b) When you have finished your map, investigate why you get the patterns you do.
7. Figures 7.5.i and 7.5.j give details about Prime Minister Chrétien's trade mission to Central and South America in 1995.
   a) Why might this part of the world have been targeted for a trade mission?
   b) Of what value to a trade mission would there be in laying wreaths and having dinner with the president? (Figure 7.5.i)
   c) If you had been making up the prime minister's itinerary, what kinds of activities related to establishing trade relations would you have set up for him to do? Explain why you would select these things.

TRADE PRODUCTS

Major Concepts

- Competitive advantage
- International trade
- Commodity groupings

Part of Canada's imports are products that we cannot produce ourselves. Fruits and vegetables that grow in warmer climates must be imported. We have also come to expect a constant supply of fresh produce year round, so that we import the perishable foods that we do grow when our foods are out of season.

However, the majority of goods we import are bought because they can be made cheaper or better somewhere else. Because the Canadian market is comparatively small, it would not make good business sense for Canadian companies to try to produce all the consumer goods and services that Canadians might desire. A better strategy is to produce, for other countries, products in which Canadian businesses have real strengths. These strength's give us a **competitive advantage** in trade areas.

Canadian businesses have a competitive advantage in some key sectors of the economy. First of all, Canada's natural resource industries use the forests, minerals, oceans, and soils to produce goods to sell around the world. Second, a highly educated and technically skilled labour force gives Canada a competitive advantage in the manufacturing of complicated machinery and goods, such as automobiles and auto parts. A third area where Canadians have strength is in telecommunications. Canadians are known around the world for designing and running telephone systems and were the first to use satellites for relaying phone signals. (Some have argued that having to overcome the great distances here in Canada has forced Canadians to be inventive in communications.)

Labour costs are lower in developing countries. (Sports shoes are made in Asian countries where wages are much lower.)

Materials are not available or are too expensive in Canada. (Mexico produces glass products bought by Canadians.)

Why are goods and services imported into Canada?

Canada's climate is not suitable for some products. (By weight, bananas are the best selling fruit in Canada, even though we can't grow them.)

Canadian corporations have not developed the required expertise. (Precision lens for optical equipment is often imported from Europe, particularly Switzerland.)

Figure 7.6.a Reasons for international trade

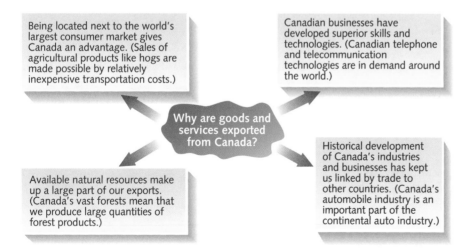

Being located next to the world's largest consumer market gives Canada an advantage. (Sales of agricultural products like hogs are made possible by relatively inexpensive transportation costs.)

Canadian businesses have developed superior skills and technologies. (Canadian telephone and telecommunication technologies are in demand around the world.)

Why are goods and services exported from Canada?

Available natural resources make up a large part of our exports. (Canada's vast forests mean that we produce large quantities of forest products.)

Historical development of Canada's industries and businesses has kept us linked by trade to other countries. (Canada's automobile industry is an important part of the continental auto industry.)

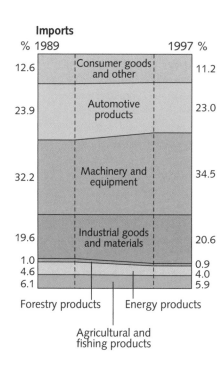

Imports

% 1989		1997 %
12.6	Consumer goods and other	11.2
23.9	Automotive products	23.0
32.2	Machinery and equipment	34.5
19.6	Industrial goods and materials	20.6
1.0		0.9
4.6		4.0
6.1		5.9

Forestry products   Energy products

Agricultural and
fishing products

> *" ...nowhere in Asia are we a major economic presence. Canada's strength in raw materials and components (which lack popular brand names or national identity) means we are, in Asia, the Unknown Country.... Although occasional sales of Candu nuclear reactors to China, aircraft to Taiwan and a rapid-transit system to Malaysia get attention and generate big returns to specific sectors, most Canadian merchandise exports are not so exclusive or lucrative in Asian markets. "*

Reported in a study by the
Asia Pacific Foundation of
Canada, 1997

Exports

% 1989	Consumer goods and other	1997 %
4.7		3.7
25.1	Automotive products	24.1
16.7	Machinery and equipment	23.2
21.3	Industrial goods and materials	19.0
15.4	Forestry products	12.0
8.7	Energy products	9.6
8.1		8.5

Agricultural and
fishing products

Figure 7.6.c Imports and exports for Canada by commodity groupings, 1989 and 1997

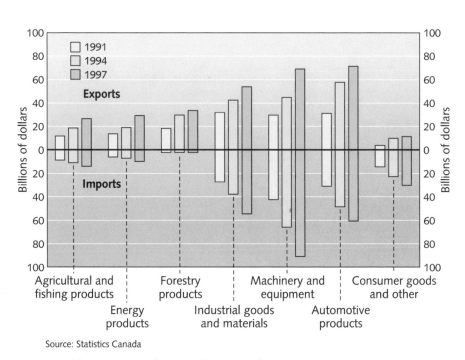

Source: Statistics Canada

Figure 7.6.b Imports and exports by commodity groupings, 1991-1997

	1993	1994	1995	1996	1997
Machinery and other equipment	24.9	30.6	34.7	35.0	39.7
Motor vehicle parts	23.7	28.3	30.3	30.5	34.4
Industrial and agricultural machinery	13.9	18.1	20.6	20.0	25.5
Miscellaneous consumer goods	17.0	18.8	20.4	21.0	23.8
Industrial goods and materials	13.0	15.3	17.0	17.4	20.5
Chemicals and plastics	11.1	13.8	16.3	17.4	19.5
Passenger autos and chassis	11.7	13.4	13.1	13.5	17.7
Office machines and equipment	9.3	11.4	12.9	13.4	15.1
Metals and metal ores	8.1	10.1	12.2	11.8	14.4
Agricultural and fishing products (except fruits and vegetables)	7.5	8.9	9.5	10.1	11.2
Aircraft and other transportation equipment	5.1	5.6	7.6	8.2	10.9
Trucks and other motor vehicles	4.6	6.1	6.8	7.1	8.6
Crude petroleum	4.7	4.6	4.8	6.7	7.2

Figure 7.6.d   Top Canadian imports, 1993-1997 (billions of dollars)

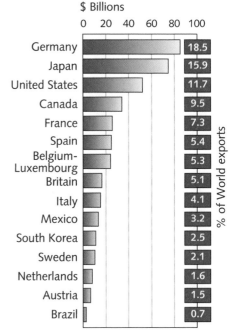

Source: World Trade Organization

Figure 7.6.f   Exports of automative products, 1996 (percentage of world exports)

	1993	1994	1995	1996	1997
Machinery and other equipment	21.4	27.2	33.1	36.2	40.3
Passenger autos and chassis	24.1	30.3	34.1	33.7	36.6
Metals and alloys	15.0	17.5	19.4	19.7	20.0
Agricultural and fishing products (except wheat)	13.2	15.3	16.5	18.5	19.6
Motor vehicle parts	13.0	15.3	15.9	17.2	19.0
Chemicals, plastics and fertilizers	9.3	11.9	15.1	15.3	17.0
Lumber and sawmill products	11.5	14.0	14.0	15.8	16.8
Industrial and agricultural machinery	7.8	9.8	12.2	13.2	14.7
Trucks and other motor vehicles	11.5	12.1	12.9	12.5	14.5
Aircraft and other transportation equipment	7.6	8.7	10.7	12.5	12.9
Other industrial goods and materials	7.0	8.7	10.4	11.3	12.8
Newsprint and other paper products	7.7	9.3	13.1	12.2	11.7
Crude petroleum	6.2	6.5	8.2	10.4	10.0

Figure 7.6.e   Top Canadian exports, 1993–1997 (billions of dollars)

Figure 7.6.g Container terminals, such as the one at Halifax, are a vital link in the transportation of Canada's imports and exports.

QUESTIONS & ACTIVITIES

1. **a)** Define "competitive advantage."
   b) Using the idea of competitive advantage, explain why Canada exports some products and imports others.
2. Here are some items that may have an impact on Canada's international trade. Group the items into three lists: those that encourage exports, those that encourage imports, and those that seem unrelated to foreign trade. For each item, explain why you put it in the list you did.
   a) Canada's high standard of health care
   b) Canada's stable democratic government
   c) Canada's high level of education
   d) the military's well-known peacekeeping role
   e) the NAFTA trade agreement with Mexico and the US
   f) the high level of foreign ownership of Canadian industries
   g) Canada's wish to see human rights improved in other countries.
3. **a)** As Figure 7.6.b shows, Canada has high levels of both imports and exports in such commodity groups as automotive products and machinery and equipment. Explain why it is that we can be both big buyers and big sellers of products in the same categories.
   b) Relate goods imported or exported to physical geography factors, e.g., climate, mineral resources, landforms, transportation, population distribution.

4. **a)** According to Figures 7.6.b and 7.6.c, which import groupings have changed the most? Which have changed the least?
   b) Which export groupings have changed the most? Which have changed the least?
   c) On the basis of these graphs, what two predictions can you make about the future of Canada's international trade?
5. Calculate the rate of change for the imports given in Figure 7.6.d, from 1993 to 1997. To do this, for each category subtract the 1993 value from the 1997 value, then divide the difference by the 1993 value. Multiple the result by 100 to get the rate of change as a percent. (For example, for Machinery and other equipment: a) 1997... 3.9.7 (billion) minus 1993... 24.9 (billion) = 15.3 billion; b) 15.3 divided by 24.9 times 100 = 61.420.) Construct a bar graph to show the rates of change, ranking the items from the greatest change to the least change.
6. Organize the export categories listed in Figure 7.6.e into three smaller lists: those that are based on natural resources, those that utilize high levels of technology, and those that spring from Canadians' need to overcome distance. Explain what your lists tell about Canada's international trade picture.
7. Figure 7.6.f identifies Canada as the fourth largest exporter of automotive products in the world. Suggest three ways that this trade improves the lives of Canadians and the Canadian economy.

TRADING BLOCS

Major Concepts

- Tariffs and free trade
- General Agreement on Tariffs and Trade (GATT)
- World Trade Organization (WTO)
- Trading blocs

DEFINITIONS

Tariffs are taxes imposed by a government on imports. The purpose of a tariff is to make imported goods more expensive so that consumers will be more likely to buy products made locally, or will be discouraged from buying foreign goods altogether.

Free trade occurs when no tariffs are applied to all goods and services. In some trade agreements there may be exceptions to completely free trade, such as when countries negotiate to protect cultural industries—book publishing, the music industry, theatres, etc.—in order to safeguard their culture.

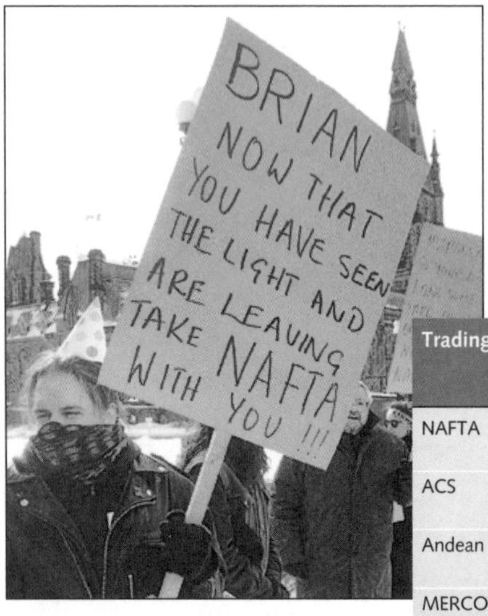

The great destruction of the Second World War meant that large parts of Europe and Asia needed to be rebuilt. The process of rebuilding resulted in new thinking about international trade. Countries began to see real advantages to free trade between countries, where tariffs were not used to keep out foreign competition. Goods and equipment would be produced in the countries where it could be done most efficiently and moved to the places that needed them. Many people thought that when the rebuilding was done, everyone would benefit. In 1946, a number of nations established the General Agreement on Tariffs and Trade (GATT). GATT set in motion the mechanisms to bring about freer global trade. The member nations signed various agreements to govern this trade. These agreements removed or reduced tariffs, established standards for trade practices, and provided ways that trade disputes could be resolved. In 1994, many of these agreements were taken over and expanded by the World Trade Organization (WTO). By the year 2000, the WTO will have more than 130 member countries who together account for 95% of world trade.

But, even as world trade was becoming freer, some countries sought still greater benefits by linking their economies to others at a level that had not been considered before. In Europe, in 1993, the 12 members of the European Community agreed to sweeping reforms in trade. They also agreed to work towards creating a central bank, a common currency, and a common European parliament. This new European Union, now up to 15 members, today functions as a **trading bloc**. The bloc allows free flow of goods, services, capital, and labour within member countries. But duties, tariffs, taxes, and inspections—according to GATT and WTO rules—are applied on goods from elsewhere. Not wanting to be put at a trade disadvantage, other groups of countries set up their own trading blocs. For example, Mexico, United States and Canada signed the North American Free Trade Agreement (NAFTA) in 1993. NAFTA eliminated immediately or phased out tariffs on almost all goods originating in the three countries. Other regional trading blocs have been established in different parts of the world.

![Protester holding a sign reading "BRIAN NOW THAT YOU HAVE SEEN THE LIGHT AND ARE LEAVING TAKE NAFTA WITH YOU !!!"]

Figure 7.7.a Not everyone wanted the NAFTA treaty to be signed by Canada, claiming it would result in job losses for Canadians.

Trading Bloc	Full Name of Block	Number of Members	Total Population (millions)	Gross Domestic Product/Capita (dollars)
NAFTA	North American Free Trade Agreement	3	396	34 280
ACS	Association of Caribbean States	25	199	3 555
Andean Pact	Andean Pact (South America)	5	105	7 916
MERCOSUR	Southern Common Market (South America)	4	209	9 700
EU	European Union	15	372	28 853
APEC	Asia Pacific Economic Cooperation	21	2 476	11 811

Figure 7.7.b Important trading blocs in the world in 1998

- To eliminate barriers to trade, and to facilitate the cross-border movement of goods and services between the member countries
- To promote conditions of fair competition in the free trade area
- To increase investment opportunities
- To provide effective protection of intellectual property rights in each country
- To create procedures to implement the agreement and resolve disputes when they arise
- To search for ways to expand the benefits of the agreement by extending it to other areas of cooperation among the three countries, looking at regional expansion, or working on multilateral aspects

Figure 7.7.c   Objectives of NAFTA

Antigua
Bahamas
Barbados
Belize
Colombia
Costa Rica
Cuba
Dominica
Dominican Republic
El Salvador
Grenada
Guatemala
Guyana

Haiti
Honduras
Jamaica
Mexico
Nicaragua
Panama
St. Kitts and Nevis
St. Lucia
St. Vincent and the Grenadines
Surinam
Trinidad and Tobago
Venezuela

▲

Figure 7.7.d   Members of the Association of Caribbean States, 1998

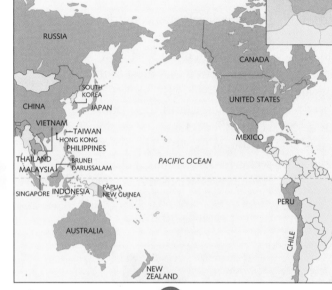

Figure 7.7.e   Countries that make up the European Union, 1998

Figure 7.7.f   Countries that are members of the Asia Pacific Economic Cooperation, 1998

QUESTIONS & ACTIVITIES ?

1. Define the term tariff and explain how tariffs are barriers to international trade.
2. **a)** Speculate on why most countries used tariffs before the idea of free trade became popular?
   b) In what ways does free trade between countries improve people's access to foreign goods and services?
   c) Why might some people and businesses oppose free trade?
3. Define the term "trading bloc."
4. **a)** Using an outline map of the Caribbean region, label and shade the members of the Association of Caribbean States listed in Figure 7.7.d.
   b) Why do you think these countries set up a trading bloc?
5. Compare the patterns of locations shown in Figures 7.7.e and 7.7.f. Which trading bloc seems to have the better reason to exist geographically? Explain your answer.
6. Suppose you were asked to create trading blocs around the world (imagine for this exercise that none exist yet). Using an outline map of the world, show where your trading blocs would be.
   a) Give reasons for creating the trading blocs you have.
   b) With which countries should Canada trade? Justify your trading bloc decisions for Canada.
   c) Which countries in the world don't seem to fit naturally into trading blocs? Why?
7. Using classroom, library resources, or electronic databases, compare the three countries that make up NAFTA. Make up a comparison chart in which you record the following characteristics: population, population density, birth rate, life expectancy, gross national product per capita, and percentage of the labour force in agriculture. In addition, find and record three statistics that show something about the quality of life of the people. Write a one-paragraph analysis of your data comparing the three countries.
8. Research who "Brian" is in Figure 7.7.a.

INTERNATIONAL TRAVEL AND TOURISM

Major Concepts

- Tourism
- Tourist arrivals
- Tourist destinations

International travel and tourism is one of the fastest-growing economic sectors in the world. In the last quarter of the twentieth century, the number of tourists and the amount of money they spent rose dramatically. This growth is largely maintained by two trends. People in developed countries continue to see relatively short trips of up to three weeks as desirable vacations and demand for foreign travel to developing countries is starting to grow.

The pattern of international tourism shows that most tourists want to travel to the same places. The top ten tourist destinations account for 53% of the world volume of tourists. This pattern seems to be changing a little. In recent years, tourism has expanded in East Asia and the Pacific regions. Many people are travelling to places like Hong Kong, China, Japan, or other Asian destinations. Traditional European destinations are being challenged by tourist choices in other parts of the world.

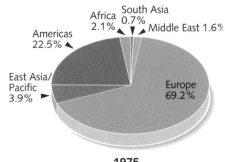

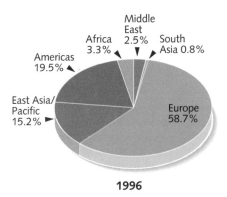

Figure 7.8.c   Percentage share of world arrivals, 1975 and 1996

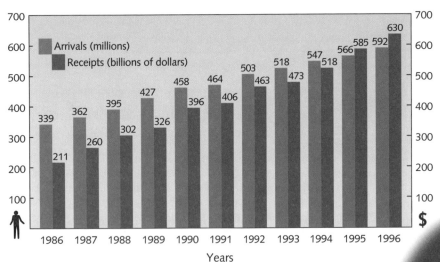

Source: World Tourism Organization (WTO)

Figure 7.8.a   Global tourism arrivals and receipts, 1986-1996

	1995 (millions)	1996 (millions)	% Change 95/96
World	566.4	591.9	4.5
Africa	19.0	19.6	2.9
Americas	110.8	115.6	4.3
East Asia/Pacific	83.2	89.8	7.9
South Asia	4.3	4.5	4.0
Middle East	13.7	15.1	10.3
Europe	335.4	347.3	3.6

Figure 7.8.b   Tourist arrivals by region, 1995-1996

Figure 7.8.d
People travel for a variety of reasons, including to experience stimulating locations and activities.

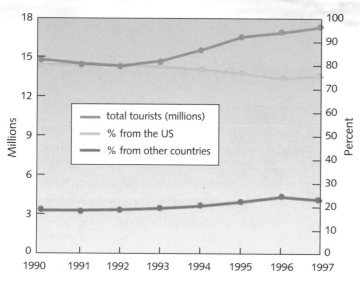

Figure 7.8.e   International tourists arriving in Canada, 1990-1997

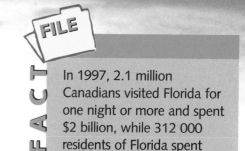
Destination	Tourists (thousands)	Average # of nights
United States	14 663	7.2
Border States	12 287	2.7
Mid-range states	3 895	3.3
Southern states	4 420	13.4
Europe	2 527	12.7
France	418	12.7
Germany	223	11.5
Italy	151	12.3
Netherlands	165	9.4
Switzerland	126	5.9
United Kingdom	714	14.4
Asia	537	18.7
Hong Kong	115	21.4
Japan	57	17.4
Caribbean	732	9.4
Cuba	184	9.4
Dominican Republic	126	9.7
Mexico	406	10.6
Australia	65	36.0
Total Overseas	3 543	18.3

Figure 7.8.g   Destinations for Canadian tourists, 1995

Rank 1990	Rank 1996	Country	Arrivals (millions) 1990	Arrivals (millions) 1996	% Market Share 1990	% Market Share 1996
1	1	France	52.5	61.5	11.5	10.4
2	2	United States	39.4	44.8	8.6	7.6
3	3	Spain	34.1	41.3	7.4	7.0
4	4	Italy	26.7	35.5	5.8	6.0
12	5	China	10.5	26.1	2.3	4.4
7	6	United Kingdom	18.0	25.8	3.9	4.4
8	7	Mexico	17.2	21.7	3.7	3.7
5	8	Hungary	20.5	20.7	4.5	3.5
28	9	Poland	3.4	19.4	0.7	3.3
10	10	Canada	15.2	17.3	3.3	2.9

Figure 7.8.f   World's top 10 tourist destinations, 1990 and 1996

QUESTIONS & ACTIVITIES

1. Here are five reasons why people travel as tourists: for pleasure or recreation; for business; to visit friends or relatives; for religious reasons; and to shop. Based on your own knowledge about why people travel, put these in order of importance for typical Canadians. Explain your order.

2. Brainstorm a list of at least five reasons that might explain the rapid growth in tourism that is indicated in Figure 7.8.a.

3. Examine Figure 7.8.b and use the percentage change information to study the patterns of growth in world tourism. Draw a bar graph to give the percentage change for each region of the world. Shade those bars that are above the world average in green and those that are below in red. What pattern does your graph suggest?

4. With a partner, name at least three features for each country that would attract tourists to the ten coun-

tries listed in Figure 7.8.f. (If you have difficulty identifying features, do some quick research on the Internet if available, using the name of the country and "tourism" as search terms.)

5. a) Suggest reasons why tourists from the United States generally make up over three-quarters of all the tourists to Canada.

   b) Make a small poster that displays 7 to 10 locations that foreign tourists visit in Canada. Attach pictures to your poster or make up small sketches to illustrate the destinations. Label your illustrations.

6. Does your circle of acquaintances have similar tourist travel patterns as typical Canadians? Survey at least 20 friends and record their tourist destinations for the past three years. Organize your findings in a table and prepare a short report comparing their travel to that of typical Canadians.

CANADA AND INTERNATIONAL SPORTS

Major Concepts

- International competition
- Organizational structure
- Friendly competition

An important way that Canadians connect with other people around the world is through international sports. This interaction is most obvious during the Olympics or Commonwealth Games, when the attention of the nation is focused on the athletes who wear Canada's colours. These competitions, however, are just the tip of the sports "iceberg." International sporting events take place all year round, pitting Canadians against people from other countries in a wide variety of sports.

While it seems that sports and international politics don't have much in common, in fact, there are many examples of how sports and sporting events have paved the way for improving international political situations. A good example is that the People's Republic of China and Taiwan, considered by China as a country in its possession, have been recognized by international sporting organizations as separate nations. Athletes from these two countries meet and compete when few opportunities like this exist for them. International sports provide

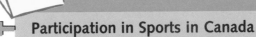

FACT FILE

Participation in Sports in Canada
- Forty-five percent of Canadians 15 years or older participate regularly in one or more sports.
- Fifteen percent of Canadians participate regularly in competition or tournament sports.
- More men (52%) than women (38%) are regular sport participants.
- British Columbia (53%) has the highest rate of amateur sports participation for adults, while Newfoundland (36%) has the lowest.

Figure 7.9.a Canadians get an opportunity to learn about people from other countries at international sporting events. Here Mark McKay of Canada and Colin Jackon of Wales hug after an event.

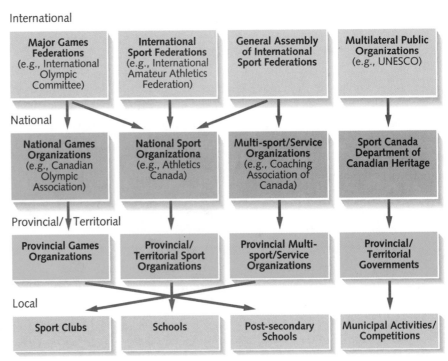

Figure 7.9.b The sports community in Canada

a setting by which people from around the world come into contact with other races, nations, and cultures.

Figure 7.9.c The headpull, a traditional Inuit game

CASE STUDY   The Arctic Winter Games

The Arctic Winter Games were created when it was recognized that the people of the Arctic needed an opportunity to compete in games that reflected their own culture. Sports competitions in the south included games that were different from the traditional sports of the Arctic. Also, the small population of the three northern territories meant that in national sporting events the athletes from the Arctic were at a real disadvantage. Developing skills for the southern games through training and competing was much more difficult for northerners because of the great distances and small communities in the north.

The goal of the Arctic Winter Games is to bring together as many people of the region as possible for athletic competition, cultural exhibition, and social interaction. These three objectives are symbolized by the three interlocking rings in the Games' logo. In keeping with the philosophy of the Games, the only trophy that is awarded goes to the team that best displays the spirit and values of the Games. Some of the competitions in the Games include such sports as the headpull, the two-legged high kick, and the face pull. Many of the traditional sports of the people of the Arctic are activities that developed skills that were needed for survival.

At the beginning, only teams from the Northwest Territories, Yukon and Alaska attended the Arctic Winter games. Now, teams also represent Greenland, two provinces in Russia, northern Alberta, and Nunavut. Every two years, over 1600 athletes, coaches, officials, and cultural performers come together in friendly competition and social communication to make the Games possible.

QUESTIONS & ACTIVITIES

1. a) In groups of two or three people, make up a list of ten international sporting events at which Canada is represented.
   b) Suggest three ways that participating in international sports benefits a nation such as Canada. Explain your ideas.

2. Using Figure 7.9.b, explain the connections that each of the following organizations have within the sport community of Canada and of the world:
   a) Canadian Olympic Association
   b) Sport Canada
   c) Canadian Figure Skating Association
   d) your school's teams

3. According to the Fact File, provincial participation in sports varies across the country. Suggest five factors that might influence participation rates.

4. What are some advantages for an athlete in preparing for and competing in international sporting events?

5. In what ways are the Arctic Winter Games different from other international sporting events? In what ways are they similar?

6. Suppose you are part of a committee organized to set up an international sporting event that is designed to bring together a specific group of people for competitions in activities that are considered essential for survival in their environment. The athletes you are targeting are people who live in large urban areas. Design the Large Cities Games, naming 10 events that will be run. Identify three possible locations for the Games, and suggest what groups of people within urban areas should be invited to compete. Make up a logo and a poster to promote your Games.

CANADA AND INTERNATIONAL PEACEKEEPING

Major Concepts

- Peacekeeping
- United Nations' operations
- Land mines

For many Canadians, peacekeeping is a part of our national heritage. Peacekeeping, under United Nations operations, came into being in 1956 during a conflict between Egypt and Israel in the Middle East. To help keep peace between the two warring countries, Canada's Secretary of State for External Affairs, Lester B. Pearson, proposed placing an international force under the UN flag between the two countries. For his accomplishments, he was awarded the Nobel Peace Prize. Canadian forces were involved in that peacekeeping operation, and in over 40 other situations since that time. Over the years, Canada has regularly provided troops and other resources for UN peacekeeping and is routinely called on for advice and contributions.

The nature of peacekeeping changed in the early 1990s after the break-up of the Soviet Union and the end of the Cold War. During this time, the threat of international war was much reduced. At the same time, however, regional and local conflicts flared into open violence. The UN began to see a need to take responsibility for peacekeeping

Figure 7.10.b Canadian peacekeepers patrol the Green Line—the line separating Greek and Turkish Cypriots—in Nicosia, Cyprus, as part of the UN force stationed there to keep peace.

FACT FILE

- Over 100 000 Canadians have served in UN peacekeeping missions.
- In over 40 years, 107 Canadian military personnel have lost their lives while performing peacekeeping duties.

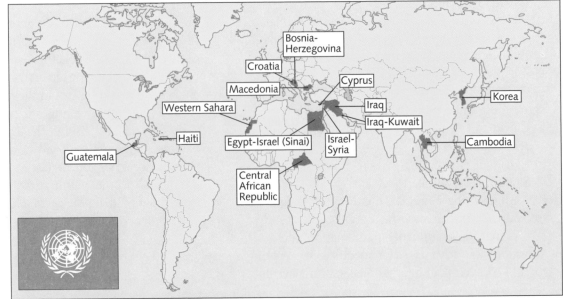

Bosnia-Herzegovina
Croatia
Macedonia
Cyprus
Korea
Western Sahara
Iraq
Iraq-Kuwait
Haiti
Egypt-Israel (Sinai)
Israel-Syria
Cambodia
Guatemala
Central African Republic

Figure 7.10.a Canadian peacekeeping operations as of June 1998

within countries, rather than just *between* countries. **Peacekeeping** thus in many cases became peacemaking. This new mandate took UN peacekeepers into places such as the former Yugoslavia in eastern Europe, Haiti in the Caribbean, and Somalia in eastern Africa. Canadians have responded to this new type of peacekeeping by establishing the Lester B. Pearson Canadian International Peacekeeping Training Centre in Cornwallis, Nova Scotia, and in conducting an innovative study on how the UN can respond most effectively to help resolve internal conflicts. One interesting aspect of the new role is the variety of human resources thought to be necessary to achieve and maintain peace in such situations. Canadian peacekeepers now include the Royal Canadian Mounted Police, Elections Canada personnel, and the Canadian Red Cross. It is likely that peacekeeping and peacemaking will continue to involve Canadians in a variety of roles for many years to come.

Location	Year	Mission
Afghanistan, Pakistan	1990–92	Military advisory unit
Haiti	1990–91	Observe 1990 elections
Persian Gulf	1990–91	Help to secure liberation of Kuwait
Iraq-Kuwait	1991–	Monitor boundary after Gulf War
Iraq	1991–	Assist in supervision of destruction of nuclear, biological, and chemical weapons
Western Sahara	1991–94	Monitor ceasefire; supervise referendum
Angola	1991–93	Monitor ceasefire
El Salvador	1991–95	Investigate human rights, violations and monitor military reforms and elections
Cambodia	1991–93	Monitor ceasefire; establish mine awareness program; monitor disarmament
Former Yugoslavia and neighbouring states	1991–94	Monitor ceasefire
Red Sea	1992	Naval participation in embargo of Iraq
Yugoslavia	1992–95	Observation patrols, mine clearance, construction of shelters; enforce no-fly zone
Somalia	1992–93	Headquarters personnel
Somalia, Kenya	1992–93	Distribution of relief supplies
Mozambique	1993–95	Security; monitor demining operations
Cambodia	1993–	Assist in demining the country
Somalia	1993–95	Assist in provision of relief, economic rehabilitation, political reconciliation
Uganda, Rwanda	1993–94	Monitor border to enforce military embargo
Haiti	1993–94	Embargo enforcement
Rwanda	1993–96	Provide protection for refugees and civilians; distribution of relief supplies
Dominican Republic	1994	Monitor Dominican Republic-Haitian border
Haiti	1994–	Training of military and police for elections; ongoing training of police
Bosnia-Herzegovina	1995–	Participate in stabilization force to consolidate peace
Guatemala	1997–	Verify implementation of human rights agreement
Central African Republic	1998–	Maintain and improve security and stability following civil and military unrest

Figure 7.10.c UN Peacekeeping Missions with Canadian Involvement, from 1990

Figure 7.10.d Canadian peacekeeper passes rocks to local Haitians as part of a school-building program in Haiti.

CASE STUDY   The Campaign to Eliminate Land Mines

Canadians were leaders in the campaign to establish a treaty to ban the use of land mines.

Land mines are military weapons that have been used by most countries of the world. They are inexpensive and effective military tools. Once in place, they don't need any further attention, remaining destructive for years. Most anti-personnel land mines are not designed to kill people, just to maim them, because an injured soldier needs to be cared for and uses up some of the enemy's medical resources. In civil wars, civilians have sometimes made and used land mines to protect themselves from approaching armies. During some conflicts, millions of land mines were buried, often with no records kept about where they were installed.

Unfortunately, a land mine cannot distinguish a soldier's footstep from a civilian's footstep. Long after a conflict is over, land mines that have not been removed remain capable of destroying the limbs of men, women, and children, and animals. Experts estimate that 20 000 people a year, mostly civilians, are injured or killed every year by land mines. While it might only cost a few dollars to lay a land mine, it costs many times that money to painstakingly locate and deactivate buried land mines. Most developing countries, trying to rebuild after civil or international conflict, simply cannot afford this incredible expense, or the expense of caring for people seriously injured by land mines.

As part of their peacekeeping efforts, the Canadian military takes on demining duties, to seek out and deactivate land mines in a variety of countries around the world.

FACT FILE

- Worldwide, land mines kill or maim two persons every hour.
- The largest producers of land mines, countries such as China, Russia, and the United States, did not sign the treaty to ban land mines.
- There are an estimated 9 million land mines buried in the African country of Angola, which has a population of 10.5 million people.

Figure 7.10.f Land mines damage non-military targets as well as soldiers.

Bosnia-Herzegovina & Croatia
2 million

Iraq
5–10 million

Kuwait
5 million

Afghanistan
9–10 million

Sudan
1 million

Cambodia
4–7 million

Nicaragua
100 000+

Rwanda
50 000

Ethiopia
1 million

Angola
9 million

Mozambique
1–2 million

Falkland Islands
15 000+

Figure 7.10.e Millions of land mines remain buried in countries around the world.

Figure 7.10.g Canadian soldiers are experienced in removing land mines.

China — Iraq — Russia
Cuba — Israel — Saudi Arabia
Egypt — Libya — Serbia
India — Nigeria — Turkey
Iran — Pakistan — United States

Figure 7.10.h Some countries that did not sign the 1997 treaty to ban land mines

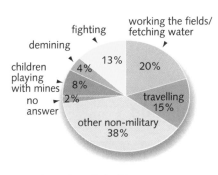

fighting
working the fields/fetching water
demining
children playing with mines
no answer
13%
4%
8%
2%
20%
travelling 15%
other non-military 38%

Source: ICRC Peshawar Study 1993

Figure 7.10.i What people were doing at the time of injury

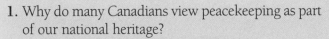

Leftover land mine from Gulf War kills 2 children

Two Iraqi children were killed during the weekend by a land mine left over from the Persian Gulf war eight years ago, the official news agency INA said yesterday. The mine exploded in a region west of Baghdad, killing a six-year-old and an 11-year-old.

So far, 56,000 explosive devices have been cleared from the region, including mines, cluster bombs and shells, the agency said. *AFP*

Figure 7.10.j From *The Globe and Mail*, Dec. 2, 1998

QUESTIONS & ACTIVITIES

1. Why do many Canadians view peacekeeping as part of our national heritage?

2. Before 1990, UN peacekeeping was mostly designed to keep the peace between two or more countries. In what ways has peacekeeping changed since then? Why?

3. According to the map in Figure 7.10.a and the countries listed in Figure 7.10.c, in which parts of the world have peacekeeping efforts largely been focused in the 1990s?

4. Using dictionaries and other resources, define these terms used in Figure 7.10.c:
   - monitor - human rights - disarmament
   - embargo - relief   - political reconciliation

5. a) In what ways would Canadian peacekeeping efforts benefit the countries in which they take place?
   b) In what ways would Canadian peacekeeping efforts benefit Canada?

6. While the United Nations reimburses some of the expenses of peacekeeping, a part of the cost of peacekeeping is borne by the country sending the peacekeepers. Over the years, Canada has spent a considerable amount of money on peacekeeping in

other parts of the world. Do you think that Canada should continue to support peacekeeping in view of these costs? Write a one-page essay in which you give reasons for your answer.

7. a) In a few sentences, explain what a land mine is and what it is designed to accomplish.
   b) Offer at least three reasons to explain why land mines are popular weapons.
   c) Why are most of the victims of land mines civilians, not soldiers?

8. With a partner or small group, research why the United States or the Republic of China refused to sign the treaty to ban land mines. Prepare a brief point-form report of your findings.

9. Choose one of the countries shown in Figure 7.10.e. Using classroom and library resources, identify the time period when the land mines were probably laid and briefly summarize the reasons for the mines being used.

10. Canadians risk their lives when trying to disarm land mines, which is a slow process of detecting, uncovering and deactivating the mines, one by one. Brainstorm other ways that land mines might be destroyed.

COMPARING QUALITIES OF LIFE

Major Concepts

- Quality of life
- Development
- Ecological footprint

Quality of life is an indication of how happy and economically and personally secure people are with their situation in life. The term takes into account a whole variety of aspects, including state of health, freedom from need, material wealth, the level of threats from people around them and from the environment, access to human rights, and so on.

Population

Countries	Population Density (persons/km²)	Growth Rate (percent)	Net Migration (per 1000 people)	Ages 0–14 (% of population)
Brazil	19.3	1.10	0.0	30
Bulgaria	74.7	−0.63	−0.9	17
Canada	3.0	1.13	6.1	20
France	107.1	0.35	0.6	19
India	294.1	1.72	−0.1	35
Kenya	49.4	2.13	−0.3	44
Papua New Guinea	9.7	2.28	0.0	40
Syria	87.2	3.30	0.0	46
Vietnam	228.0	1.51	−0.4	36

Figure 7.11.a Population comparisons for selected countries, 1997

Health Care Indicators

Life Expectancies **Infant Mortality**

Brazil
Bulgaria
Canada
France
India
Kenya
Papua New Guinea
Syria
Vietnam

■ Male
□ Female

85 80 75 70 65 60 55 50
Years

0 10 20 30 40 50 60 70
Per 1000 live births

Figure 7.11.b A comparison of life expectancies and infant mortality

Ecological Footprint

An **ecological footprint** is the impact that a person's way of life has on natural systems. This impact includes use of resources, degradation of ecosystems, amount of waste produced, and the like (see section 5.1).

Material Wealth

Gross National Product (GNP) is the value of all the goods and services produced and sold in a country during a year. To make comparisons among countries easier, GNP is often expressed as GNP per capita, stating the average dollar value per person in the country.

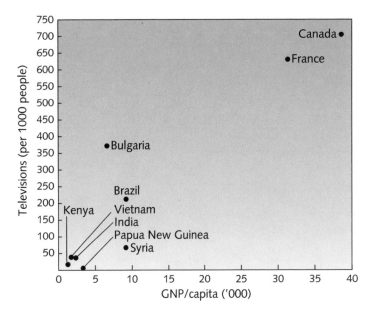

Figure 7.11.c   A scattergraph comparing GNP/capita and televisions

---

Economic Development

Literacy (percent)

Primary Employment (percent)

Urban Population (percent)

Brazil   Bulgaria   Canada   France   India   Kenya   Papua New Guinea   Syria   Vietnam

- Literacy rate
- Primary employment
- Urban population

Figure 7.11.d   Economic development measures for selected countries

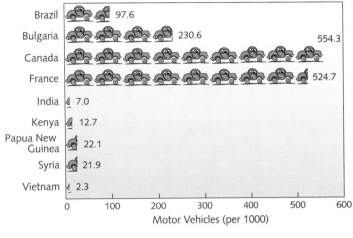

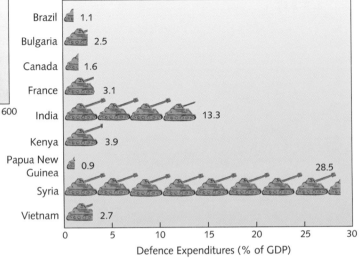

◀ **Figure 7.11.e** Motor vehicles per 1000 people for selected countries

Figure 7.11.f Defence expenditures for selected countries

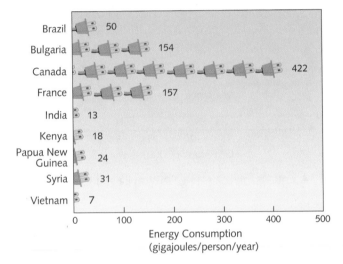

◀ **Figure 7.11.g** Energy consumption for selected countries. Note: a **joule** is a measure of work; a **gigajoule** is a million joules.

QUESTIONS & ACTIVITIES

1. On an outline map of the world, locate and shade in the nine countries that have been used as sample countries for this topic. Label the general area of the world that each country represents.

2. **a)** Rate your quality of life. Draw seven lines on your notepage and label them like this:

   very poor |-------|-------|-------|-------| very good
              0   1   2   3   4

   Label each line with one of the headings below. After careful consideration, put an "X" to indicate where you think you fall on the scale.
   - material wealth
   - protection of human rights
   - safety and security
   - optimism for the future
   - career and job aspirations
   - ability to practise faith or religion
   - freedom from illness

   b) According to your rating scales, do you have a high quality of life? Explain.

   c) Suppose you lived in Kenya or India. Complete the rating scales again based on how you would have answered if you had been born in one of these countries.

   d) Rank the nine countries used in these two pages in order of quality of life. Write a paragraph in which you justify your ranking.

3. **a)** What are five factors that determine the ecological footprint of a person? Review section 5.1.

   b) Based on the evidence that is given in Figures 7.11.e, 7.11.f, and 7.11.g, in which country does a typical person have the "lightest" or best footprint? In which country does a person have the "heaviest" or worst footprint? Explain your answers.

4. Make up a poster in which you show the best and the worst qualities of life in Canada.

CANADA'S FOREIGN ASSISTANCE

Major Concepts

- Non-governmental organizations
- Official development assistance
- Emergency assistance

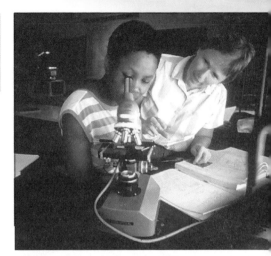

Figure 7.12.a Canadian official development assistance at work in Botswana.

There are wide gaps in the quality of life people enjoy throughtout the world. In some countries, like Canada, people generally have food, housing, and material wealth. Many people in developing countries are hungry, homeless, and poor.

Many Canadians work to try to improve the living conditions of less fortunate people. Organizations such as World Vision, Red Cross, and Save the Children ask Canadians for donations of money or goods to improve other people's quality of life. These **non-governmental organizations (NGOs)** often involve high school students in their efforts, through events like World Vision's 30-Hour Famine, for example.

The government of Canada also gives help to developing countries as **official development assistance (ODA)** through the Canadian International Development Agency (CIDA). A small portion of the tax dollars that the federal government collects, equal to less than half of one percent of Canada's Gross National Product, is used for ODA. ODA assistance includes:

- providing people with access to clean water and sanitation
- helping to build or improve essential services, such as power grids
- working to make governments more democratic so human rights are better protected

- protecting the environment.

These activities help more than one billion people worldwide.

Critics of Canada's ODA often argue that we should not be giving our tax dollars away when there are still needy people in this country. But development assistance benefits Canadians too. Most programs use Canadian goods and services, so that 70% of ODA contributes to the

CASE STUDY Canadian Assistance to Hurricane Mitch Victims

In November 1998, a massive hurricane formed in the Atlantic Ocean and tracked westward. After battering Caribbean island nations, Hurricane Mitch slammed into Central America, focusing its might on the tiny countries of Nicaragua, El Salvador, Guatemala, and Honduras. When the skies cleared, approximately 11 500 people were dead, about 14 000 were missing, and some 3.5 million people were homeless. Damage to the region's infrastructure—roads, bridges, power lines, water treatment plants, and the like—was enormous. Coffee and banana plantations were completely destroyed. Estimates put the total damage at about $4 billion.

The international community responded quickly and generously to the victims of this natural disaster. For its part, Canada allocated over $9 million in emergency assistance, including $2 million in food aid. Non-governmental organizations received about $1.5 million of this money to support their relief activities. A Canadian military mobile hospital, complete with its own water purification plant, was sent to the area. Taking a longer view, Canada pledged $100 million over four years to help rebuild the region. These funds were focused on rebuilding farms and plantations, restoring health care facilities, and helping to reconstruct the infrastructure. Canada also helped out by setting aside debt repayments for Honduras so that the Honduran government could use its resources to meet the needs of the people. While Canada's donations were tiny compared to the costs of rebuilding, Canadian contributions were important in signaling the concerns of this country for its battered neighbours.

Canadian economy. An estimated 35 000 jobs exist in Canada because of ODA. In addition, Canadian businesses in supplying the goods and services are making connections in some of the fastest-growing markets in the world. In the end, Canadian official development assistance to other parts of the world makes good business sense.

> 66 *Noble sentiments are fundamental to foreign aid, but charity is too slender a reed on which to rest a complex development-assistance program. The most potent justification for helping the development of other countries should be economic self-interest.* 99

Roy Culpeper,
The Globe and Mail

Foreign Aid

- Over 70% of Canada's ODA goes to Africa and Asia.
- Fifty Canadian universities and 60 colleges are involved in projects in developing countries partly funded through partnerships by CIDA.
- Canada has a target of giving 0.7% of the country's Gross National Product as development assistance. We have never reached this target and currently give about 0.4% in aid.

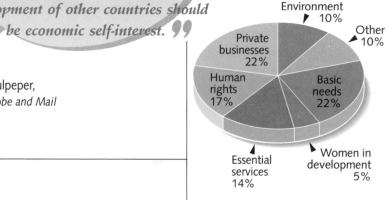

Figure 7.12.b The Canadian International Development Agency has concentrated its ODA efforts in six areas:
- basic human needs
- women in development
- essential **infrastructure** services
- human rights, democracy, and good government
- development of private businesses
- the environment

In a typical year, the assistance given directly to other countries is in the proportions shown in the pie graph.

Pie graph labels: Environment 10%, Other 10%, Basic needs 22%, Women in development 5%, Essential services 14%, Human rights 17%, Private businesses 22%

Figure 7.12.c Some of the destruction left behind by Hurricane Mitch in 1998

Figure 7.12.d Canadian relief workers help the local people to rebuild after Hurricane Mitch.

QUESTIONS & ACTIVITIES

1. Canadians help people in other countries in two different ways, by contributing to NGOs and through CIDA. Suggest three ways action could be taken to prevent the same problems in the future.

2. Make a chart to compare arguments for and against foreign assistance. Discuss with your classmates.

3. Under what circumstances do you think emergency assistance should be given? Here are several circumstances that might be considered as reasons to give emergency assistance to a country. Decide which you feel qualify as real emergencies. Give reasons for your decisions.

   a) devastating earthquake in a large city

   b) the end of a civil war brought about by a revolution started by a minority group

   c) famine caused by poor government decisions on agriculture

   d) economic collapse as a result of the bankruptcy of several large companies

   e) tidal wave sweeps over a heavily populated coastal area

4. Examine the six priorities for CIDA in Figure 7.12.b. Rank these six items according to your views about foreign assistance by listing them in order from most important to least important. Give reasons for your ranking.

5. a) How much of a person's income, as a percentage, should be given to help other people? Give reasons for your answer.

   b) Should a country give the same percentage of income as a person does? Explain.

   c) According to your views about helping other people, does Canada give too little or too much help to others? Discuss your answer with other people in the class.

6. List the ways that Canada helped Central American countries respond to the Hurricane Mitch natural disaster. Suggest three other actions that we might have taken.

7. Using Internet and library resources, research one other situation when Canada responded with emergency assistance. Find out where and when this situation occurred, what caused the emergency, how Canada responded, and the outcome of the emergency response. A good place to start looking would be CIDA's Internet site at http://w3.acdi-cida.gc.ca/.

CHANGING PERSPECTIVES

Organize a debate on the following: "Be it resolved that Canadians should always take their vacation within Canada."

Perspectives on Research: Presentations

How you present your information to people will be important all your life. Here are some presentation methods:

- written–reports, essays, résumés, descriptions
- spoken–seminars, debates, public speaking
- posters and display boards–collages, drawings, signs
- maps and graphs (all types of visual information patterns, GIS)
- computer software, diskettes, CDs, websites, hypermedia

The method of presentation that you decide will be most effective for your purposes will depend on the purpose for your presentation and the audience for whom you are preparing the material.

UNIT 8 OPPORTUNITIES FOR THE FUTURE

Change is a part of reality. Many changes provide countries with opportunities to grow, both nationally and internationally. This unit looks at issues in Canada's future.

NUNAVUT

Major Concepts

- Cultural homogeneity
- Government-Aboriginal negotiations
- Tourism advertising

Nunavut came into being on April 1, 1999. It is made up of the eastern two-thirds of the former Northwest Territories. The territory covers 2 242 000 km², about 24% of Canada's land mass, and covers three time zones. Close to 45% of Nunavut is on the mainland part of Canada, with the rest of the territory being made up of hundreds of islands in Canada's Arctic and one island in Hudson Bay.

Nunavut's population is quite distinctive in Canada, with a high degree of **cultural homogeneity**. About 84% of the population describes themselves as either partially or entirely of Inuit descent. In addition, 74% of the people report Inuktitut—the language of the Inuit—as their mother tongue. The territory is home to 63% of all the Canadians who reported speaking Inuktitut in the 1991 census. **Birth rates** in Nunavut are keeping **population growth rates** in this area much higher than in other parts of the country.

The creation of Nunavut came about through a long period of negotiation between the government of Canada and the Inuit people. Initially, the people of the Northwest Territories were asked if they supported the idea of dividing the NWT and then if they approved of the plan that was developed to achieve the division. In 1993 the Canadian parliament passed the *Nunavut Act*, bringing the new territory into legal exis-

tence in 1999. Nunavut elects one member to the federal House of Commons. It has its own elected legislative assembly and will be governed largely by Inuit who make up the majority of the assembly.

The new territory faces some tremendous opportunities as well as serious challenges. The negotiations that brought about Nunavut included land claim settlements that gave the Inuit authority over the development of the territory's natural resources. These resources will help the people of Nunavut build a unique Aboriginal society. Important tools in building this society also include control over the territory's education and justice systems, use of the Inuktitut

FACT FILE

- In Inuktitut, Nunavut means "our land."
- Population per square kilometre in Nunavut is 0.01 (in Canada as a whole it is 2.9).
- Nunavut has 25 000 people compared with the Ontario population of 10 million.
- In Nunavut, a litre of milk costs $2.89; in Toronto, a litre sells for $1.89.
- 59% of Nunavut households are dependent on hunting and fishing.

Figure 8.1.a The territory of Nunavut. Note: The remainder of the former Northwest Territories (sometimes called the Western Territory) may be renamed in 2000 during territorial elections there.

language in government and media, and the ability to make laws that concern wildlife and the environment. But there are significant problems that must be resolved. Only a few Inuit have the training and skills to take on the jobs of running the new territory. Family ties are strong in Inuit communities and many people resent having to move away from their homes to other centres in order to take government jobs. Substance abuse has become a concern and suicide and welfare rates are currently high. These are all challenges that will have to be addressed before the Inuit of Nunavut can truly be in charge of their own futures.

Nunavut is proof that the nation as a whole, represented by the federal government, and Aboriginal groups can work together to develop new relationships that benefit the country and all Canadians.

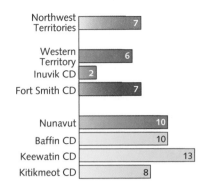

Figure 8.1.b Population growth rates in the Northwest Territories, 1995

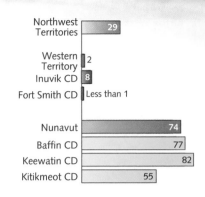

Figure 8.1.c Percentage of the population with Inuktitut as mother tongue, 1991

Figure 8.1.e Census divisions of Nunavut and the Northwest Territories

	Milestones in the creation of Nunavut
1982	A vote was taken in the NWT to measure public support for dividing the territory into two parts. Fifty-six percent voted "yes."
1992	In May, a majority of voters in the NWT approved the proposed boundary for Nunavut. Later that year, Inuit voters within the proposed territory accepted a land claims agreement with the Government of Canada.
1993	The Canadian parliament passed the *Nunavut Act.*
1999	April 1, Nunavut Territory came into legal and political existence.

Figure 8.1.d Milestones in the creation of Nunavut

QUESTIONS & ACTIVITIES

1. Based on the information given here, what seems to have been the reason for the creation of Nunavut?

2. a) Make up an "opportunities" and "challenges" chart for Nunavut. Brainstorm at least seven items for each heading of your chart.

   b) If you had been a voter in the Northwest Territories in 1982, would you have voted to divide the territory into two separate areas? Write a paragraph in which you explain your answer.

3. Looking at Figures 8.1.b and 8.1.c, what geographical justification is there for Nunavut?

4. a) If you were to design a tourism ad for Nunavut, what are three features of the area that you might highlight in your ad?

   b) Sketch out a tourism advertisement for Nunavut. If available, use pictures or sketches to make your ad more finished. Write a short paragraph in which you explain your choice of wording, the images you used, and any other significant aspects of your ad.

THE PROMISE OF SUSTAINABLE DEVELOPMENT

Major Concepts

- Sustainable development
- Environmental protection
- Global agreements

While Canada and the world face extremely complex environmental problems, there do seem to be some new ideas about how the natural environment should be protected. One of the most promising is the notion of **sustainable development**.

In 1992, at the United Nations Conference on Environment and Development in Rio de Janeiro, the global community committed itself to the goal of sustainable development. This commitment means that leaders will work together to encourage development that meets the needs of—that sustains—the present but that does not lessen the ability of future generations to meet their own needs. In forestry, for example, sustainable development would mean that for every tree that is cut, steps would be taken to ensure that another tree reaches maturity. In this way, the forest stock would be sustained—it would never decrease—for future generations. Sustainable development provides a framework for linking economic development and environmental protection with human well-being and quality of life. It implies that Canadians' health and economic prospects are directly linked to the health of the environment.

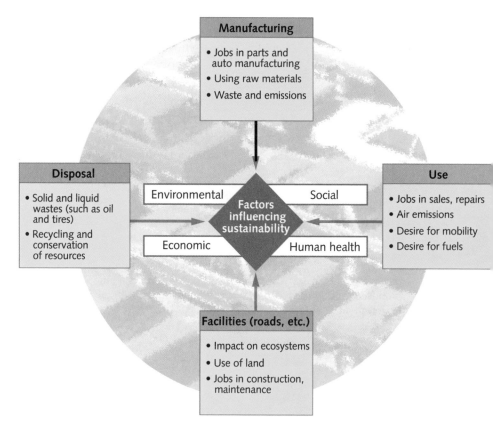

Figure 8.2.a The automobile industry illustrates the complexity of factors and interactions that need to be considered when an industry tries to bring its production in line with sustainable development.

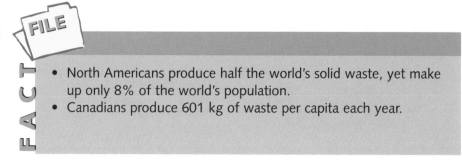

FILE

FACTS

- North Americans produce half the world's solid waste, yet make up only 8% of the world's population.
- Canadians produce 601 kg of waste per capita each year.

As Figure 8.2.a suggests, achieving sustainable development is an extremely complex process and will not be easy. On the international level, the Canadian government has been helping to clarify the meaning of sustainable development through the negotiation of global agreements on the use of chemicals, climate change, protecting the oceans, and combating desertification (the expansion of desert areas). Nationally, the federal government has developed new policies, strategies, and regulations that are consistent with sustainable development.

Other players, too, have accepted the challenge of achieving sustainable development. Industries have made important strides towards protecting the environment. For example, by 1998, companies representing 91% of Canada's base metal production had joined a program of non-regulatory measures to reduce pollution. The key to sustainable development, however, is its acceptance by all Canadians—by society as a whole. There is growing evidence that such acceptance is happening. For example, a recent survey reported that 86% of Canadians think that maintaining abundant wildlife is important and 83% agreed that it is necessary to protect endangered species. It is the commitment to sustainable development in all areas of our society that will produce real results in dealing with environmental problems.

> " We realized one cannot 'save the environment' without profoundly changing some basic human activities: the way people govern themselves; the way those governments cooperate; the way people trade and do business; the ways in which energy, food and timber are produced; and the rates at which our species reproduces itself. We found many aspects of human progress ecologically and economically unsustainable. So we called for 'sustainable development.'... "

Gro Harlem Brundtland,
Chair, UN World Commission on
Environment and Development, 1992

Social Benefits	Economic Benefits	Environmental Benefits
1.75 million direct and indirect jobs	Represents 38% of all Canadian exports	Canada has 12% of the world's protected areas
500 communities depend on resource industries	$91.6 billion contributed to Canada's economy	An estimated 300 000 species will be less threatened
30 million people visit national and provincial parks annually	Represents 24% of all capital investment	Almost 10% of the world's fresh water will be managed for the future
Aboriginal cultural and spiritual values are tied to the natural environment	Backdrop for Canada's $26 billion tourist industry	20% of the world's remaining wilderness areas are included

Figure 8.2.b Sustainable development of Canada's natural resources results in many benefits for present-day Canadians as well as for future Canadians.

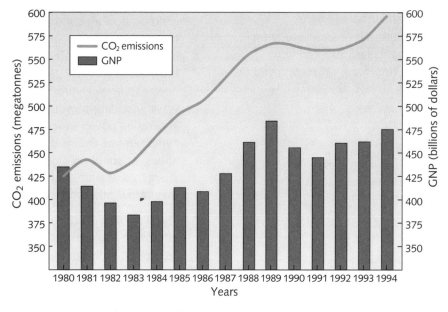

Figure 8.2.c Trends in carbon dioxide emissions and Gross National Product, 1980–1994

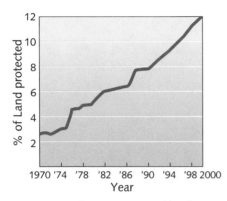

Figure 8.2.d   Percentage of land protected in Canada, 1970–2000

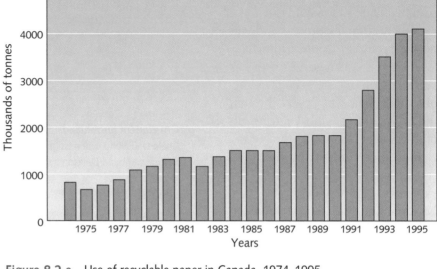

Figure 8.2.e   Use of recyclable paper in Canada, 1974–1995

FACT FILE

- Hydrogen will become competitive with oil as a fuel in the first decade of the twenty-first century.
- Experimental vehicles powered by hydrogen fuel cells have demonstrated high fuel efficiency and reduced emissions compared to vehicles using conventional energy sources (see Case Study on the Ballard fuel cell and Figure 5.3.g on page 183.)

CASE STUDY   Hydrogen fuel cells

Much experimentation is going on to figure out how to extract energy directly from water. Molecules of water (H_2O) can be split into two atoms of hydrogen and one atom of oxygen. In this process, the oxygen is given off as waste. It is the electrochemical process between hydrogen and oxygen within a **fuel cell** that produces electric power. One side of a fuel cell circulates hydrogen, which is separated into electrons and protons. On the other side of the cell, oxygen ions join hydrogen ions at a cathode/electrolyte interface to form water, the waste product. The electrical energy that is produced is much cleaner than that produced by conventional power sources. Hydrogen fuel cells can be applied in a variety of ways, including powering space vehicles, transportation on land, and generating power in remote Arctic locations. Another advantage of hydrogen fuel cells is that they generate power at quite low temperatures, at about 85°C, which is much lower than most other forms of energy generation, including the internal combustion engine. Thus they throw off much less heat into the atmosphere.

The stumbling block to this energy source is the cost of developing affordable applications. For example, for a hydrogen-fuelled car to be economically competitive, it will have to be priced about the same price as automobiles equipped with internal combustion engines. To create such automobiles involves solving problems related to size, weight, and performance of the fuel cells.

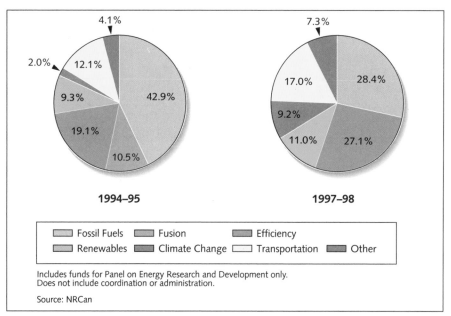

1994–95   1997–98

Legend: Fossil Fuels, Fusion, Efficiency, Renewables, Climate Change, Transportation, Other

Includes funds for Panel on Energy Research and Development only.
Does not include coordination or administration.

Source: NRCan

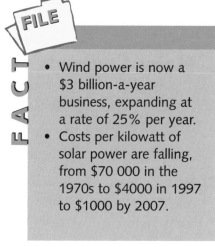

FACT FILE

- Wind power is now a $3 billion-a-year business, expanding at a rate of 25% per year.
- Costs per kilowatt of solar power are falling, from $70 000 in the 1970s to $4000 in 1997 to $1000 by 2007.

Figure 8.2.f Changing priorities in energy research (percent of research funds available)

QUESTIONS & ACTIVITIES

1. **a)** Review your definitions of "sustainable development."

   b) Give an example of a behaviour or action that you might do that would contribute to sustainable development.

2. **a)** Why are governments seen as leaders in the campaign to achieve sustainable development?

   b) Identify roles that each of these groups might play in achieving sustainable development:
   - the federal government
   - industry groups
   - the Canadian public

3. Figure 8.2.a shows the relationship between the automobile industry and sustainability. This diagram shows the complex factors that the industry must consider if automobile development is to achieve sustainability. Create a web diagram to show the relationship between housing and sustainability.

4. Using Figure 8.2.b, identify three ways that a typical Canadian will benefit from sustainable development.

5. Explain how protecting more land in Canada (see Figure 8.2.d) is an example of sustainable development.

6. Explain how Figures 8.2.b and 8.2.e show that there may be some progress towards achieving a sustainable future.

7. Why is the hydrogen fuel cell seen as a real advance in the generation of useful electrical energy?

8. Based on the information about the hydrogen fuel cell, explain why it is difficult to develop and produce new products in the automobile industry, or any other major industry. In your answer, consider such things as the cost of research and consumers' acceptance.

9. **a)** Suppose you were the manager of a large municipal transit fleet. What factors might make you consider buying buses powered by hydrogen fuel cells? What factors might discourage you (see Figure 2.12.c)?

   b) Based on what you have read here about hydrogen fuel cells, would you agree to buy buses with this fuel source? Give reasons for your answer.

10. What might be some problems that will make it difficult to put sustainable development in place in Canada? Carefully consider this question and write a one-page report in which you discuss the following topics:
    - who might oppose sustainable development
    - what might prove to be difficult to change
    - how long will it take to achieve
    - what are the costs of achieving sustainable development

    Prepare a rough draft with a partner.

    Do you support the idea of sustainable development? Support your answer with good ideas and evidence. Write your final copy.

ADVOCATING FOR THE ENVIRONMENT

Major Concepts

- Protecting natural systems
- Advocating for the environment
- Lobby groups

actively trying to change people's attitudes and behaviour towards the environment. Greenpeace and the World Wildlife Fund are two well-known advocacy organizations or **lobby groups** that advocate for the

There are times when it seems that environmental destruction is simply a part of human existence. Everywhere we see the ways our modern way of life has harmed the natural environment—from global warming, to pollution of the Great Lakes, to disruption of local streams because of urbanization. It would be easy to see human abuses of our **natural systems** as an unfortunate part of life. But not everyone accepts such abuses as inevitable or necessary. Some individuals and groups argue that we should do everything we can to protect and enhance natural systems. They **advocate for the environment**.

Advocating, or lobbying, for the environment goes beyond just doing your part in day-to-day living— recycling materials, conserving energy, and so on. It involves

The most effective letters **advocating for the environment** are:

a) brief
b) focused on just one environmental topic or issue
c) clear about views and positions on the issue
d) not overly emotional
e) ask for a reply, such as in justifying an action that has taken place

Figure 8.3.a Writing letters to decision makers

CASE STUDY — The World Wildlife Fund and "The Gully"

Slicing through the continental shelf off the East Coast of Canada is a deep canyon known as the "The Gully." Just 260 km from Nova Scotia, a little east of Sable Island, The Gully is a huge underwater gorge, deeper and wider than the Grand Canyon. The steep walls of the canyon force water currents into giant swirls called "gyres," similar to twisters in the water. The circling and upward movements of the water carry nutrients from the depths up towards the surface of the ocean. These nutrients are food for dense schools of plankton, which feed many species of fish, seabirds, and marine mammals. Some of the interesting species in The Gully are the Northern Bottlenose whale, Purple Sunstarfish, Red Deepsea crabs, and corals. The Gully is truly a unique **ecological area**.

The Gully is threatened by offshore oil and gas development in the area. Six oil fields are currently under production in the region and dozens of oil and gas fields have been identified by petroleum companies as "significant."

The World Wildlife Fund decided that The Gully is too valuable a natural system to be disturbed by energy developments in the area and pledged to advocate on its behalf. The organization launched a campaign in 1996 to have the area declared Canada's first offshore marine protected area. Their campaign included:

- participating in environmental assessment hearings on energy projects;
- funding scientific work in the area;
- monitoring effects of the developments;
- cooperating with fishers whose livelihoods are tied to the ecological health of The Gully;
- mounting a national letter-writing campaign to inform government officials.

In December 1997, the federal government announced plans to protect 7700 km² of The Gully.

The actions of the World Wildlife Fund, and other groups advocating for the environment, play an important role in keeping environmental issues before the public and in pressuring decision makers to change the way things are done in Canada and around the world.

protection of the environment on an international basis. The most effective environmental groups run campaigns around high-profile issues, lobbying to convince decision makers to put in place positive changes for the environment. In many cases these campaigns are designed to get the public's support in putting pressure on elected officials to pass appropriate laws.

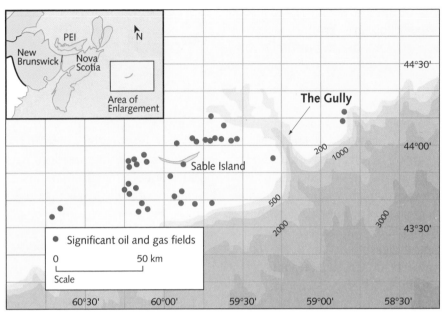

Figure 8.3.c The location of The Gully

Changes in individual attitudes about the environment	54%
More effective action at the national level, including new legislation	42%
International agreements and bilateral cooperation	33%
More effective action by local governments along with the help of local citizens' groups	31%
More effective corporate action	18%
Support for nongovernmental organizations and their activities	16%

◀ **Figure 8.3.b** A survey of attitudes about how Canadians want to protect the environment

QUESTIONS & ACTIVITIES

1. Make up a definition for the phrase "advocating for the environment."
2. Make a list of some actions that people and groups undertake that would be considered to be advocating for the environment.
3. Figure 8.3.b shows that many Canadians think that changing people's attitudes is the key to making real progress on the environment. Explain why this is the case.
4. Members of Greenpeace are famous for their dramatic actions on behalf of the environment, such as hanging banners on bridges and smokestacks or racing along in small boats between whales and whalers.
   a) Of what purpose are these actions?
   b) In your opinion, do these actions have any impact in bringing about positive environmental change? Explain your opinion.

5. Summarize the strategy of the World Wildlife Fund in trying to protect The Gully.
6. Access the World Wildlife Fund on the Internet at http://www.wwfcanada.org/ to see what other campaigns currently are being run by this advocacy organization. Record your findings in chart form.
7. There are likely some environmental issues in or near your community that are receiving some attention from environmentalists. Using ideas about advocating for the environment, plan a campaign for bringing about change on an issue. Your plan should identify the groups or individuals that should be targeted and the reasons for targeting them. Include your ideas in a one-page written report.

GLOBALIZATION AND OUR TRADE FUTURE

Major Concepts

- Globalization
- Dependence on foreign trade
- International communications

Canada's future as a trading nation is tied to our ability to compete in a world market. Over the past decades our dependence on international trade has grown. A good way of seeing this growth in dependence is to look at what percentage exports are of the total value of the **Gross National Product**. Between 1970 and 1995, global exports rose from 10% to 23%. For developing countries the percentage in 1995 was 30%. For Canada, the percentage jumped to 40% of our GNP. This trend means that Canada is, and will continue to be, dependent on foreign trade for our economic well-being. This increasing interdependence on other countries is referred to as **globalization**.

Of the factors that are encouraging globalization of business, technological change, particularly in communication technologies, is the most prominent. Using the new technologies, corporations are able to think and plan on a global scale. They can shift their resources and production rapidly to places where they will gain the most advantage. If conditions become unfavourable for business in one country, assets can be transferred to another location where the business environment is more likely to result in higher profits. This ability to move assets quickly gives large multinational corporations a good deal of influence over countries, as the corporations' decisions to move to or from a country can have an immediate positive or negative effect on the economies of many smaller nations.

Not everyone agrees that globalization of business is a good thing. Critics argue that globalization leads to unemployment and reduced wages because businesses will move to where labour costs are cheapest. They also point out that globalization of business encourages the movement of corporations to places where overall costs are lower, often because little attention is paid to

---

Globalization of business is most successful in countries where:

- the state does little to interfere with business, which includes acting to protect the culture and the environment
- labour costs are low, something that is often accomplished by keeping wages low and reducing to a minimum related costs, such as benefits and health and safety provisions
- the power of labour unions is reduced or eliminated
- taxes on corporations are low
- the cost of social programs – such as unemployment insurance and health care – are as low as possible
- there are few government services, so that the private sector provides the services that might at one time have been done by government agencies

Figure 8.4.a Conditions that promote globalization of business

---

"
Globalization has some real value for Canadians. First of all, because we are a trading nation, we will earn greater wealth from the international trade that will take place. Second, our access to foreign suppliers means that there will be much greater choice of goods and services for Canadian consumers. And third, the increased global competition will create pressures on suppliers to lower prices, so all Canadians will benefit from cheaper goods and services.
"

"
Globalization will destroy the things that make Canada such a great place to live. First, because we are a trading nation, we have to compete with producers from all around the world. This means that businesses will have to compete with places where wage rates are much lower than they are in Canada and we may lose business to foreign companies. In the second place, Canadian businesses may close their operations here to move to other countries where the cost of doing business is not so high. This creates unemployment. Third, even though prices might fall, the downward pressure on wages means that some Canadians won't benefit anyway.
"

Figure 8.4.b Differing opinions on globalization

protecting the environment, promoting human rights, and improving the quality of life of workers. In the end, critics of the globalization of business argue, societies become deeply divided into two groups—those who benefit from globalization of business and become more wealthy, and those who are hurt by globalization of business and become poorer.

International Communications
- Between 1970 and 1990, the cost of an international telephone call fell by more than 90%.
- Since the 1980s, telecommunications traffic has been expanding by an average of 20% per year.
- The number of people who use the Internet is doubling every year.

66 *The reality of globalization is not that new frontiers—new lines to be pushed back or pierced—have suddenly appeared. What is happening is precisely the reverse: the lines are disappearing. Globalization is not so much our going out into the world; it is the world coming in and enveloping us. We are not dealing with new frontiers; we are dealing with no frontiers.* 99

Helen Sinclair, president, Canadian Bankers Association, 1989

Country or corporation	GDP or corporate sales 1997/98
General Motors	265.5
Turkey	264.4
Denmark	251.6
Ford	228.9
South Africa	197.4
Toyota	141.7
Exxon	182.4
Shell	190.9
Norway	225.3
Poland	185.8
Portugal	150.3
IBM	116.9
Malaysia	133.8
Venezuela	100.2
Pakistan	94.7
Unilever	72.6
Nestle	71.9
Sony	81.9
Egypt	95.8
Canada	920.8
Mexico	600.4
Wal-Mart	177.7
General Electric	135.3
Philip Morris	83.6
Vietnam	38.7

Figure 8.4.c The state and corporate power: selected countries and top multinational corporations, 1994 (billions of dollars)

QUESTIONS & ACTIVITIES

1. In what ways does the percentage that exports are of our Gross National Product show that globalization of business is affecting Canada?

2. Explain why globalization of business works best in places where governments and labour unions have little influence over economic conditions.

3. The Fact File gives statistics that demonstrate some of the technological changes that have taken place in international communications (review also sections 3.7, 3.8, and 3.9).

   a) List three ways that your own life has been changed by technological innovations in international communications.

   b) Think of at least three ways that businesses use international communications in their operations.

   c) Explain why improvements in international communications were necessary before globalization of business could become widespread.

4. a) Make up an advantage/disadvantage chart for globalization of business for Canada. Record at least five items in each side of your chart.

   b) Using your chart, Figure 8.4.b, and other information on these pages, give your opinion about the value of globalization of business. Write a one-page argumentative essay to present your views. State clearly the evidence that supports your case.

5. What message does the table in Figure 8.4.c give about globalization of business?

6. Think about what your life will be like over the next five or ten years and then brainstorm some ways that you are likely to be affected by globalization. Some topics you might want to consider are: education, jobs, entertainment, travel, fashion, and consumer products. Communicate your ideas as a display poster, a hypermedia show, or written as a journal article for a futuristic magazine.

INFORMATION TECHNOLOGY AND GIS

Major Concepts

- Information technology
- Innovation
- Geographic Information Systems (GIS)

Product	Year Invented	Years to Spread
Electricity	1873	46
Telephone	1876	35
Automobile	1886	55
Airplane	1903	64
Radio	1906	22
Television	1926	26
VCR	1952	34
Microwave oven	1953	30
Personal computer	1975	16
Cellular phone	1983	13
Internet	1991	7

Figure 8.5.a Length of time for a new technology to spread to a quarter of the world's population

Geography is dead! This is a view commonly held by people who work with information technology. Using telecommunications, information can be just as easily transmitted half way around the world as it can be next door. When it comes to modern economies, the availability of a sophisticated **information technology infrastructure** is among the top critical factors for success in business. Today, **innovations** in home electronics, information packaging and distributing, telecommunications, traditional media, and the computer industry are coming together to provide a smooth, immediate system for the delivery of information.

The expansion of information technology is a good example of how technology often drives growth. For example, the development of computers, followed by the widespread use of personal computers, spurred the development of the Internet, which is having a profound impact on people and businesses. The drive to keep pace with technological change means that scientists and businesses must work faster all the time to develop new products. One estimate suggests that the number of scientists and researchers have doubled since the early 1970s, and that the number of new products put on the market annually has tripled since 1980. The faster the

pace of invention and innovation, the faster the pace of economic growth.

An area of technological innovation that has experienced rapid growth in recent years is **Geographic Information Systems (GIS)**.

FILE

FACT

- There is a 25% chance that any international call anywhere in the world will be switched by a piece of equipment built in Ontario.
- In North America a new computer is switched on for the first time every two seconds.

Some countries adopt technological changes easily, while other countries seem to resist change. What are the factors that encourage change?

- the level of the technology already existing within a country
- the extent of the uses of the new technology
- the number of ways that the innovation links to other technologies to create new products
- the time it takes for new products to spread throughout society
- the overall market size for the new products

Figure 8.5.b Factors that influence the rate of technological change

> *It is far from coincidental that Canada and Canadians have been at the cutting edge of virtually every major technological innovation in this domain [communications] in the modern era. From the earlier inventions of Bell and Marconi to the more recent innovations in broadcast and satellite communications, Canadians have been at the centre of most of the breathtaking breakthroughs that have taken place in communications in the twentieth century.*

D. Paul Schafer, director, World Culture Project, 1990

CASE STUDY — Geographic Information Systems (GIS)

Geographic Information Systems (GIS) is a term that refers to sophisticated software that contains several components that work together. First, there is a database management system that sorts and stores statistics and other data arranged in rows and columns. Second, there is a statistical analysis system for manipulating the stored data, performing mathematical calculations, etc. Third, a GIS system has an image-processing system so that the data can be displayed as graphs and other visuals. Fourth, a map digitizing process is added so that maps can be used with the data. Fifth, there is a geographic analysis system in which the stored data can be arranged with the maps as organizers. Using this powerful tool, information about places can be analyzed in a multitude of ways. Information can be sorted and added to maps as layers that will help solve specific problems (see Figure 8.5.c).

The global market for GIS products and services is growing at 20% per year and exceeded the $10 billion mark by the late 1990s. One important use for GIS is in protecting the environment. Data can be collected and analyzed to identify areas of environmental **degradation** or to help manage resources to avoid problems in the future.

Canadian companies are leaders in the use and development of GIS. As a country, we rank second in the world in the development of GIS technology, surpassed only by the United States, and ahead of France, Germany, and the United Kingdom. Businesses in Canada supply about 15% of the world's GIS equipment and technology, including satellite to ground receiving stations. Innovations have spurred the growth of the industry to take advantage of the expanding markets, largely in North America and Europe.

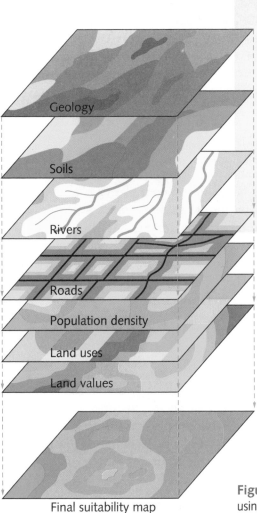

Geology

Soils

Rivers

Roads

Population density

Land uses

Land values

Final suitability map

Figure 8.5.c An example of layering using GIS to solve a problem

Figure 8.5.d Geographic Information Systems have wide applications in planning communities and businesses.

Figure 8.5.e GIS mapping allows "911" emergency systems to work. Every home and business is linked to the digital maps used by emergency services.

QUESTIONS & ACTIVITIES

1. Brainstorm a list of seven examples of how information technologies affect your life and day-to-day living.
2. In a flow diagram or other illustration, explain how innovations lead to economic growth.
3. **a)** Refer to Figure 8.5.a. For what reason do you suppose that it took much longer for automobiles to reach one-quarter of the world's population than it did for radios?
   b) Why do you suppose it has taken such a short time for the Internet to reach the same number of people?
4. **a)** Think about your own experiences. What are some of the characteristics of a person who adapts easily to new ideas and technology? What are some of the characteristics of a person who does not look for or adapt easily to technological change?
   b) Are you the type of person who likes to see innovation and change in your life? Give examples of your behaviour to support your answer.
5. A Geographic Information System has five components. Make up a symbol to represent each of these components, making sure your symbol is visually related to what goes on in each component.
6. Suppose you were asked to use a GIS program to find the best location in your community for a new convenience store. What layers of information would you consider in your analysis? Give reasons for your choices.
7. Conduct a short research study to find five jobs that use GIS as part of their activities. Survey your friends and neighbours, use the Internet, or contact organizations such as the planning department of your municipality or school board. Display your information in a visual way.

JOBS AND CAREERS IN A CHANGING CANADA

Major Concepts

- Changing technologies
- Technological waves
- Aging work force

Changing technologies, combined with globalization, are having profound impacts on the work that Canadians do. Frank Feather, a Canadian futurist, has examined the technological past of this country and argues that Canada has had and will experience six waves of innovation, taking us up to the middle of the twenty-first century. Each of these **technological waves** emphasizes a certain set of jobs and a specific range of skills. Workers trained for a previous wave will be less valued in each of the following waves.

1. *The natural resources wave*, where jobs were connected to extracting and processing raw materials taken from the land, forests, and waters. Strong backs and arms were originally required in workers. Few workers had formal education or training. (Example: miner)

2. *The industrial wave*, during which time manufacturing grew in Canada and workers found jobs in factories and machine shops. A basic level of literacy was needed so that workers could read instructions and follow procedures. (Example: factory worker)

Education Required	1985	1995	2005
8 years or less	6	3	2
Some high school	12	8	6
High school diploma	40	28	20
Some college	20	22	18
College or university	15	24	32
Advanced degree	7	15	22

Figure 8.6.b Education requirements for job openings (percentages)

Figure 8.6.a Percentage of labour force during stages of Canada's six-wave economy

Figure 8.6.c A healthy, dynamic workplace has a balance of mature and young workers.

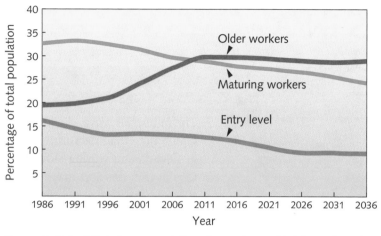

Figure 8.6.d Work force populations (percentage of total population)

Figure 8.6.e Jobs of the future: Space Industry, Ecologist, Satellite Technician, Flight Attendant.

3. *The service wave*, in which the focus for economic activity shifted from making things to providing services. Workers needed to be trained in specific service occupations. (Example: bank teller)

4. *The information wave*, a time when economic activities centre on computers and the processing of information. Workers need a high level of training in using technology to make decisions and solve problems. (Example: engineer)

5. *The leisure wave*, which will occur because automation and computerization have given workers more time for non-work activities and they are looking for things to occupy their free time. Workers will be trained for specific leisure services. (Example: restaurateur)

6. *The outer space wave*, during which time activities will focus on exploring and exploiting outer space. Workers will need extensive training in very technological fields. (Example: communications specialist)

Canada will be experiencing these latter waves of technological change over the coming decades. At the same time, we will also be dealing with an aging work force as baby boomers approach retirement. This aging of the population is changing the balance of mature and youthful workers in the work force.

QUESTIONS & ACTIVITIES

1. In your opinion, what is the most important factor influencing the demand for people with specific job skills? What are two other important factors affecting jobs?

2. Develop a visual way of showing the six waves of technological change described here. You might, for example, create a flow diagram, a cartoon, or a set of symbols to represent each stage. Be prepared to explain your illustration to others in your class.

3. Suppose you were a bank teller during the service wave and recognized the technological changes that would affect your job. How would you feel about those changes? Write your thoughts in a one-paragraph diary entry.

4. a) Examine Figure 8.6.a. Why is it that each old wave remains even though the new waves have come along?

   b) What observations can you make about the early beginning of a wave, the middle of a wave, and the later periods of a wave, based on the patterns in the graph?

   c) Is the outer-space technological wave the last one? Explain your answer.

5. a) What patterns are shown in Figure 8.6.b?

   b) What are the implications of the patterns for you as a young person?

6. Figure 8.6.d shows that the percentage of maturing workers is declining throughout the time period shown in the graph. Describe some ways that this trend might affect:

   a) work-force productivity

   b) workplace attitudes

   c) chances for promotion

7. Conduct research using the Internet or library resources about future jobs like those shown in Figure 8.6.e. Record information about the amount of education required, the length of training needed, types of work done on the job, and prospects for the future.

CANADA'S AGING POPULATION

Major Concepts

- Median age
- Baby boomers
- Population pyramid

Figure 8.7.a Canada's aging population has created both challenges and opportunities.

Canadians are getting older, statistically speaking. In 1921, the **median age** of Canadians was 23.9 years. In other words, half the population was older than this age and half was younger. By the early 1990s, the median age had crept up to 33.8 years. It is expected to be greater than 40 years by 2036. Another way of seeing this trend is to look at the proportion of people over 65 years old in the population. In 1996, senior citizens made up just over 12% of the population. This figure will increase to 16% in 20 years and to 23% by 2041. This increasing average age has been called "the greying of Canada."

Many people are worried about the financial burden of an increasingly older population. As they retire, senior citizens begin to withdraw their pensions, both from private plans and the Canada Pension Plan. Because of their numbers, **baby boomers** will make larger than normal demands on pension plans. Some analysts are concerned that the plans will not have large enough reserves to cover the demand. In addition, as a group, seniors use health care and social services to a greater extent than other age groups. One estimate is that the health care costs for an average person over 65 years of age are three times higher than for those below that age. Our increasingly older population means that there will be more seniors relying on fewer workers to pay for the benefits.

However, the aging population also provides opportunities. Older Canadians are consumers and their growing consumer choices are creating new markets. Travel companies are beginning to target seniors, offering a greater variety of leisure packages. The fashion industry has expanded their range of lines for more mature tastes and sizes, while the financial sector has adjusted its services to better meet the needs of clients who are no longer part of the workforce. Home builders are developing smaller homes and apartments with special features that older people want. However, the greatest expansion of services for seniors is in health care and related products and services. More and more Canadian businesses will be started to meet the growing needs of Canada's aging population.

The condition:	Longer life expectancies	Lower fertility rates	The baby boom
Is produced by:	Improved nutrition, health care and hygiene	Family planning and lifestyle choice; careers for women	High post-Second World War birth rate (1947-1965)
which results in:	More older people in society	Fewer younger people in society	Large numbers of people now older than the median age

and leads to: → **A Greying Canada!** ←

Figure 8.7.b Reasons for Canada's aging population

FACT FILE

In order to make room for younger workers, some employers have implemented early retirement plans in which workers are encouraged to retire as early as 55 years old. Today, the rate of retirement of workers under age 60 is twice what it was in 1980. One-quarter of all new retirees are between 55 and 59 years old.

Year	% under 5	% 5–19	% 20–44	% 45–64	% over 65
1941	9.14	28.39	37.19	18.61	6.67
1951	12.29	25.60	36.63	17.74	7.75
1961	12.37	29.44	33.19	17.37	7.63
1971	8.42	30.97	33.87	18.66	8.09
1981	7.32	24.70	39.14	19.13	9.70
1991	6.99	20.42	41.33	19.66	11.61
1996	6.65	20.60	39.03	21.49	12.23
2001	6.04	19.85	37.97	23.50	12.64
2006	5.71	19.05	35.88	26.29	13.03
2011	5.59	18.12	34.14	28.09	14.04
2016	5.53	17.42	32.27	30.60	15.88

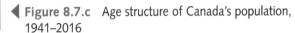

Figure 8.7.c Age structure of Canada's population, 1941–2016

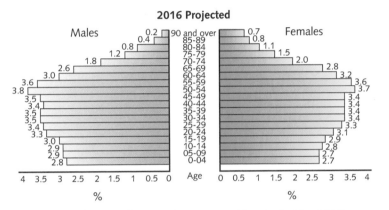

Figure 8.7.d Canada's population pyramid projected for 2016

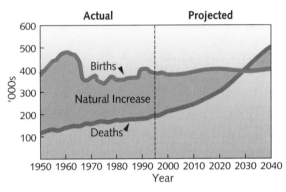

Source: Statistics Canada

Figure 8.7.e Birth and death rates for Canada, 1950–2040

QUESTIONS & ACTIVITIES

1. Identify five ways that it might be important to you that the average age of Canadians is getting older.

2. In a two-column chart, list the "challenges" and "opportunities" of a greying population in Canada.

3. In one paragraph, summarize the factors that are causing the greying of Canada's population.

4. **a)** Illustrate the changes in the age structure of Canada by drawing divided bar graphs for 1951, 1981, 2001 and 2016, using the data in Figure 8.7.c. Start by drawing four bar graphs each 100 mm high x 10 mm wide. Label each of the bars one of the years in our analysis. Divide the bars according to the percentages in the table (see Figure 8.6.a on page 275 for an example of a divided bar graph). In this graph, each percentage equals 1 mm, so 12.29% equals a little more than 12 mm in height.

   b) In one paragraph, describe the patterns shown in your graph.

5. Explain how early retirement incentives might benefit the work force as a whole. How might it be harmful to a work force?

6. **a)** Describe the shape of the population pyramid that is shown in Figure 8.7.d.

   b) In what ways is this pyramid different than the one that would show the current Canadian population? (Hint: refer to Figure 3.3.c for information.)

   c) What are two things that the changes in shape of the pyramid tell us about the population of Canada?

7. In Figure 8.7.e we see that the death rate line, for the most part, is lower than the birth rate line. The space between the lines represents the **natural increase** for the country.

   a) About what year are the birth and death rates expected to be equal?

   b) Why is it that death rates will increase, when for many decades they have been low?

   c) Predict what will happen to birth and death rates between 2041 and 2071. Explain your answer.

TRENDS IN A CHANGING SOCIETY

Major Concepts

- Consumer Price Index
- Inflation rate
- Trends

Over a number of years many things change in a country as large and dynamic as Canada. Some changes, some people would suggest, are not helping to create a better future for the country. These negative changes include higher rates of poverty among single-parent families and children, rising rates of personal bankruptcies, climbing rates of energy consumption, and the like. These negative changes remain challenges for the future. But many changes do point to a better future. These pages contain information on positive trends that look hopeful for the future.

Year	College Diplomas	University Degrees
1988	80 096	143 232
1989	82 190	146 109
1990	82 506	152 795
1991	83 824	159 806
1992	85 949	168 872
1993	92 515	173 850
1994	95 296	178 074
1995	na	178 066

Figure 8.8.d Diplomas and degrees awarded in Canada, 1988–1995

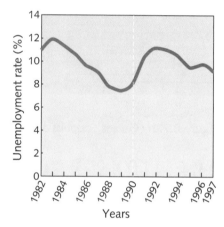

Figure 8.8.e While unemployment rates remain high, the 1990s pointed to a downward trend.

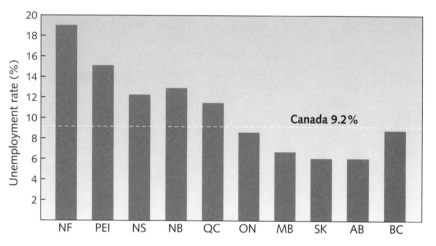

Figure 8.8.a Provincial unemployment rates, 1997

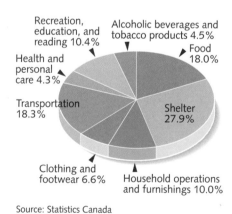

Source: Statistics Canada

Figure 8.8.b The "basket" of goods and services used to calculate the **Consumer Price Index** and the **Inflation rate**

Year	Inflation (%)	Year	Inflation (%)
1981	12.4	1990	4.8
1982	10.9	1991	5.6
1983	5.8	1992	1.5
1984	4.3	1993	1.8
1985	4.0	1994	0.2
1986	4.1	1995	2.2
1987	4.4	1996	1.6
1988	4.0	1997	1.6
1989	5.0	1998	1.0

Figure 8.8.c Canada's inflation rate

Year	Percent	Year	Percent
1971	46.9	1984	57.5
1972	46.1	1985	56.3
1973	46.3	1986	57.5
1974	47.4	1987	57.8
1975	48.1	1988	57.5
1976	46.7	1989	59.1
1977	50.8	1990	59.8
1978	50.8	1991	61.5
1979	51.6	1992	63.9
1980	51.7	1993	64.3
1981	53.6	1994	62.3
1982	55.1	1995	65.1
1983	55.2	1996	64.8

Figure 8.8.f Women's earnings as a percentage of men's earnings, 1971–1996

Country	Education spending as a percentage of total public spending	Secondary school graduation rate (percentage)
Canada	13.8	72
United States	13.6	76
France	10.8	87
United Kingdom	11.6	na
Germany	9.4	88
Italy	8.8	67
Japan	10.8	94

Figure 8.8.g Education comparisons, Canada to selected other countries, 1995

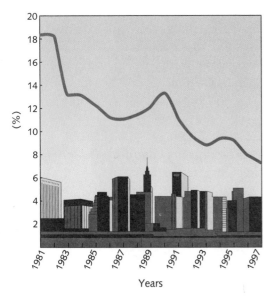

Figure 8.8.h Mortgage interest rates on a five-year term, 1981–1997

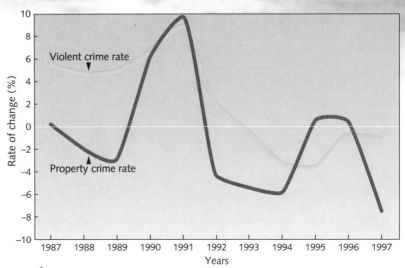

Figure 8.8.i Percentage change in the violent crime rate and the property crime rate in Canada, 1987–1997

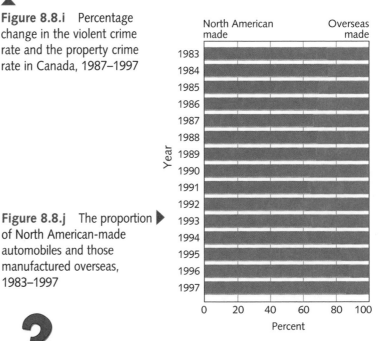

Figure 8.8.j The proportion ▶ of North American-made automobiles and those manufactured overseas, 1983–1997

QUESTIONS & ACTIVITIES ?

1. These pages contain a variety of topics pointing out trends in Canada—unemployment, inflation, the wage gap between males and females, mortgage interest rates, higher education, crime rates, and buying trends in the auto industry. For each of the topics, identify three reasons why the trends might show improvements. List three reasons why the trends might show negative changes. It might be helpful to organize your answers in a chart form.

2. For each of the trends identified on these pages, explain how the changes can be seen as being positive or helpful for the future of Canada.

3. Using Internet and library resources, identify one other trend that is positive for the future of Canada. (Hint: Think of new developments in technology or the economy, or in social trends.) Record some data that shows the trend and explain why you think it is good for the country.

4. From what you have learned about the country of Canada, how positive are you about its future? Rate your feelings about the future of Canada from 1 to 10, with 10 being very optimistic. Write a paragraph in which you justify your rating.

5. What do you see as your future in Canada? Write a one-page prediction of what your life will be like twenty years from now. Be as realistic as possible, thinking about where you will likely be living, the kinds of work you will be doing, and what you see as your hobbies and pastimes.

CHANGING PERSPECTIVES

In a group, brainstorm a list of reasons why Canada is usually listed in the top 10 places to live in the world. Circle the five reasons you consider most important. Compare your five choices with those of a partner and agree upon a new list of five. Make a class summary of the top 5 reasons from each pair. As a class, reach a consensus on the five reasons that the class as a whole agrees best represents why Canada is one of the top 10 places to live. As a complementary activity make a list of five negative factors regarding quality of life in Canada.

Perspectives on Research: Evaluation

When you evaluate something, you want to arrive at a judgment, a choice or conclusion that will be based on good reasoning. Here are some simple criteria to make an evaluation:

- plus–minus (e.g., buying a car)
- pro–con (e.g., choosing a movie)
- pass–fail (e.g., driving licence)
- approve–reject (e.g., quality control)
- cost-benefit (e.g., driving your car)
- advantage-disadvantage (e.g., moving your room to the basement)

APPENDIX

Appendices are used to explain more about items from the text, or to provide additional information or materials.

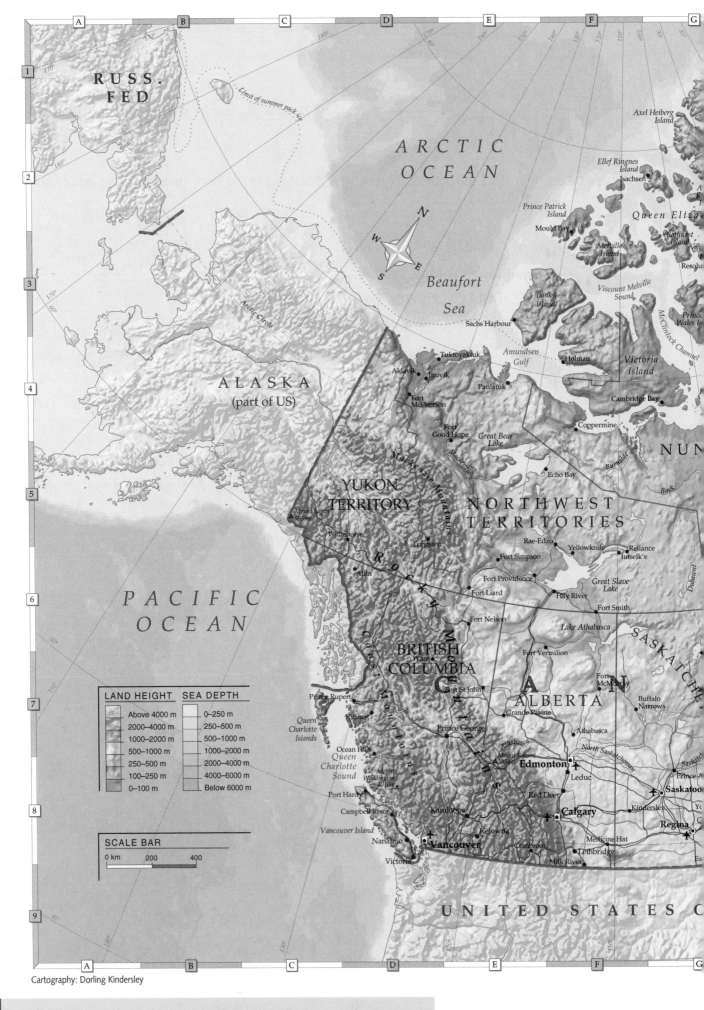

RUSS.
FED

ARCTIC
OCEAN

Limit of summer pack ice

Beaufort
Sea

N
W E
S

Axel Heiberg
Island

Ellef Ringnes
Island
Isachsen

Prince Patrick
Island
Mould Bay

Queen Eliza

Melville
Island

Bathurst
Island

Resolu

Arctic Circle

ALASKA
(part of US)

Sachs Harbour

Banks
Island

Viscount Melville
Sound

McClintock Channel

Prince
Wales Is

Tuktoyaktuk

Amundsen
Gulf

Holman

Victoria
Island

Aklavik   Inuvik
Fort
McPherson

Paulatuk

Cambridge Bay

YUKON
TERRITORY

Fort
Good Hope

Mackenzie Mountains

Great Bear
Lake

Mackenzie

Coppermine

Burnside

NUN

Mount Logan
5959m

Whitehorse

Tungsten

Echo Bay

Back

NORTHWEST
TERRITORIES

Rae-Edzo
Yellowknife
Reliance
Tutselk'e

Fort Simpson

Dubawnt

PACIFIC
OCEAN

Atlin

Rocky

Fort Providence
Fort Liard

Great Slave
Lake

Hay River

Fort Nelson

Fort Smith

Lake Athabasca

SASKATCHE

BRITISH
COLUMBIA

Ware

Mountains

Fort St John

Fort Vermilion

Fort
McMurray

Buffalo
Narrows

Prince Rupert

Kitimat

Grande Prairie

ALBERTA

Athabasca

Queen
Charlotte
Islands

Prince George

Athabasca

North Saskatchewan

Saskat

Prince A

LAND HEIGHT   SEA DEPTH

Above 4000 m   0–250 m
2000–4000 m   250–500 m
1000–2000 m   500–1000 m
500–1000 m   1000–2000 m
250–500 m   2000–4000 m
100–250 m   4000–6000 m
0–100 m   Below 6000 m

Ocean Falls
Queen
Charlotte
Sound

Mount
Waddington
4016m

Mount Robson
3954m

Edmonton

Leduc

Saskatoo

Red Deer

Kindersley

Yo

Port Hardy

Campbell River

Kamloops

Calgary

Regina

Vancouver Island

Nanaimo

Kelowna

Medicine Hat

SCALE BAR

0 km   200   400

Vancouver

Cranbrook

Lethbridge

Victoria

Milk River

UNITED STATES O

Cartography: Dorling Kindersley

GREENLAND
(Danish external
territory)

Baffin Bay

Davis Strait

Knud Rasmussen Land

Arctic Circle

Limit of summer pack ice

Baffin Island

ATLANTIC
OCEAN

Igloolik

Nettilling Lake

Amadjuak Lake

Iqaluit

Cumberland Sound

Resolution Island

Melville Peninsula

Foxe Basin

Repulse Bay

Hudson Strait

Charles Island

Akpatok Island

Button Islands

Labrador Sea

Cape Harrison

Brodeur Peninsula

Southampton Island Coral Harbour

Ivujivik

Péninsule d' Ungava

Ungava Bay

Nain

Makkovik

Cartwright

Rankin Inlet

Whale Cove

Coats Island

Ottawa Islands

Mansel Island

Inukjuak

Kuujjuaq

Rivière à la Baleine

Hopedale

Lake Melville

St Anthony

Arviat

Hudson Bay

Koksoak

Schefferville

Smallwood Reservoir

NEWFOUNDLAND
and LABRADOR

Churchill

Gander

Churchill

Lac Minto

Réservoir de Caniapiscau

Grand Falls

St John's

Corner Brook

Newfoundland

Cape Race

Belcher Islands

Lac Bienville

Labrador City

Q U E B E C

Laurentian Mountains

Fort Severn

Winisk

James Bay

Nelson

Réservoir Manicouagan

Île d'Anticosti

STRAIT OF BELLE ISLE

Channel-Port aux Basques

ST PIERRE
& MIQUELON
(French territorial
collectivity)

Southern Indian Lake

Thompson

Canadian Shield

Winisk

Akimiski Island

Fort Albany

Attawapiskat

Eastmain

Rivière de Rupert

Gulf of St. Lawrence

Îles de la Madeleine

Sydney

Glace Bay

Cape Breton Island

MANITOBA

Albany

O N T A R I O

Moosonee

Lac Mistassini

Chibougamau

Harricana

Sept-Îles

Havre-St-Pierre

Péninsule de Gaspé

Gaspé

Matane

Baie-Comeau

Rimouski

Sable Island

Lake Winnipeg

Sandy Lake

Attawapiskat

Réservoir Gouin

Lac St-Jean

Rivière-du-Loup

Bathurst

New Glasgow

Charlottetown

PRINCE
EDWARD
ISLAND

St. Lawrence

NEW
BRUNSWICK

Moncton

NOVA SCOTIA

Truro

Lac Seul

Armstrong

Kapuskasing

Cochrane

Amos

Val-d'Or

La Tuque

Chicoutimi

Jonquière

Edmundston

Fredericton

Oromocto

Dartmouth

Halifax

Lake Nipigon

Longlac

Hearst

Timmins

Rouyn-Noranda

Charlesbourg

Bay of Fundy

Liverpool

Dryden

Marathon

Foleyet

Kirkland Lake

Drummondville

Québec

St-Georges

Saint John

Kenora

Nipigon

▲Tip Top Mountain
640m

Wawa

Sudbury

North Bay

Pembroke

Gatineau
Hull

Laval

Sherbrooke

Trois-Rivières

Montréal

Yarmouth

Winnipeg

Lake of the Woods

Rainy Lake

Atikokan

Thunder Bay

Lake Superior

Sault Ste Marie

Georgian Bay

OTTAWA

Nepean

Kingston

ATLANTIC
OCEAN

Fort Frances

Lake Huron

Midland

Peterborough

Oshawa

Brampton

Toronto

Lake Ontario

Kitchener

St. Catharines

M E R I C A

Lake Michigan

Sarnia

Hamilton

Niagara Falls

London

Windsor

Leamington

Lake Erie

CITIES AND TOWNS
▣ Over 500,000 people
◉ 100,000–500,000
● 50,000–100,000
• Less than 50,000

APPENDIX

Topographical Map Symbols

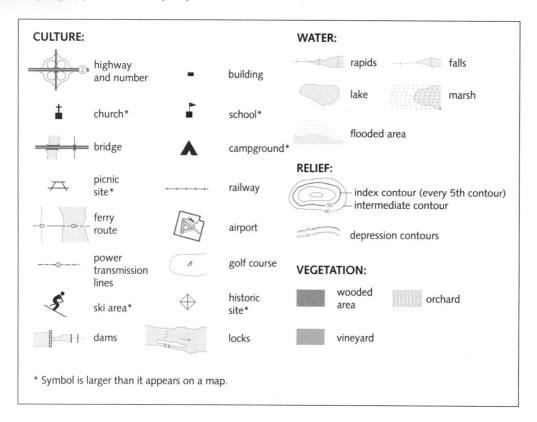

CULTURE:

- highway and number
- church*
- bridge
- picnic site*
- ferry route
- power transmission lines
- ski area*
- dams

- building
- school*
- campground*
- railway
- airport
- golf course
- historic site*
- locks

WATER:

- rapids
- falls
- lake
- marsh
- flooded area

RELIEF:

- index contour (every 5th contour)
- intermediate contour
- depression contours

VEGETATION:

- wooded area
- orchard
- vineyard

* Symbol is larger than it appears on a map.

CHARACTERISTICS OF ECOZONES

Areas of Ecozones

Ecozones	Total Area (% Canada)	Land Area (sq. km)	Land Area (% Canada)	Water Area (sq. km)	Water Area (% Canada)
Arctic Cordillera	2.5	230 873	2.3	19 717	0.2
Northern Arctic	15.2	1 361 433	13.7	149 447	1.5
Southern Arctic	8.3	773 041	7.8	59 349	0.6
Taiga Plains	6.5	580 139	5.8	66 861	0.7
Taiga Shield	13.7	1 253 887	12.6	112 513	1.1
Boreal Shield	19.5	1 782 252	17.9	164 118	1.6
Atlantic Maritime	2.0	183 978	1.8	19 772	0.2
Mixed-wood Plains	2.0	138 421	1.4	56 009	0.6
Boreal Plains	7.4	679 969	6.8	57 831	0.6
Taiga Cordillera	2.7	264 480	2.7	360	<0.1
Prairie	4.8	469 681	4.7	8 429	0.1
Boreal Cordillera	4.7	459 680	4.6	4 920	<0.1
Pacific Maritime	2.2	205 175	2.1	13 805	0.1
Montane Cordillera	4.9	479 057	4.8	13 053	0.1
Hudson Plains	3.6	353 364	3.5	8 996	0.1
Canada	**100.0**	**9 215 430**	**92.4**	**755 180**	**7.5**

Population Characteristics of Ecozones				
Ecozones	Population 1996 Census	Percent of Canada	Urban Pop (%)	Rural Pop. (%)
Arctic Cordillera	1 196	0.004	0.0	100.0
Northern Arctic	18 881	0.065	21.1	78.9
Southern Arctic	11 729	0.041	0.0	100.0
Taiga Plains	23 986	0.083	45.0	55.0
Taiga Shield	36 889	0.128	35.3	64.7
Boreal Shield	2 895 437	10.037	59.8	40.2
Atlantic Maritime	2 549 061	8.836	49.2	50.8
Mixed-wood Plains	14 840 411	51.446	84.8	15.2
Boreal Plains	744 631	2.581	42.2	57.8
Taiga Cordillera	358	0.001	0.0	100.0
Prairie	3 979 522	13.795	81.0	19.0
Boreal Cordillera	32 904	0.113	53.0	47.0
Pacific Maritime	2 848 289	9.874	86.8	13.2
Montane Cordillera	851 656	2.952	60.2	39.8
Hudson Plains	11 811	0.041	10.1	89.9
Canada	**28 846 761**	**100.000**		

Canada's Ecozones

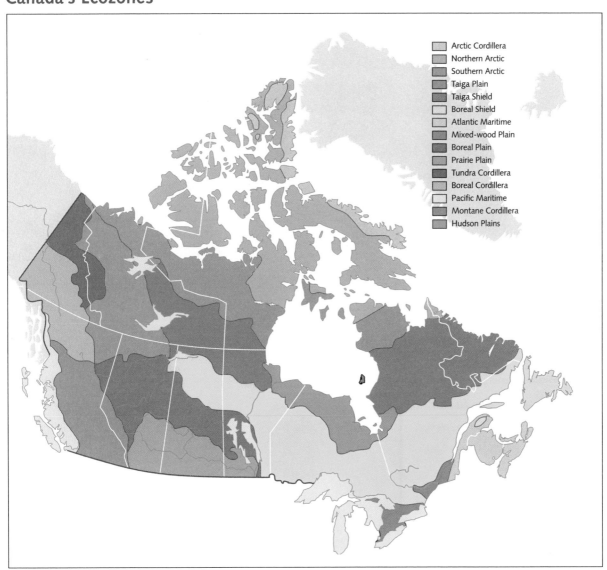

Arctic Cordillera
Northern Arctic
Southern Arctic
Taiga Plain
Taiga Shield
Boreal Shield
Atlantic Maritime
Mixed-wood Plain
Boreal Plain
Prairie Plain
Tundra Cordillera
Boreal Cordillera
Pacific Maritime
Montane Cordillera
Hudson Plains

Farming in Ecozones

Ecozones	Number of Farms	Total Farm Area (ha)	Av. Farm Size (ha)
Arctic Cordillera	0	0	0.0
Northern Arctic	0	0	0.0
Southern Arctic	0	0	0.0
Taiga Plains	46	14 736	320.3
Taiga Shield	0	0	0.0
Boreal Shield	12 393	1 574 695	127.1
Atlantic Maritime	20 567	2 140 679	104.1
Mixed-wood Plains	84 793	6 389 985	75.4
Boreal Plains	43 627	13 476 202	308.9
Taiga Cordillera	0	0	0.0
Prairie	100 659	42 290 752	420.1
Boreal Cordillera	0	0	0.0
Pacific Maritime	8 468	161 611	19.1
Montane Cordillera	9 421	1 698 842	180.3
Hudson Plains	0	0	0.0
Canada	**279974**	**67 747 502**	**242.0**

Housing Characteristics of Ecozones

Ecozones Dwellings	Movable Houses	Detached Apartments	Total 4+ Stories	Apartments
Arctic Cordillera	0	184	0	0
Northern Arctic	6	2 470	300	146
Southern Arctic	17	1 565	167	1
Taiga Plains	547	4 162	872	59
Taiga Shield	406	5 471	1 841	317
Boreal Shield	20 466	667 441	156 270	21 021
Atlantic Maritime	31 408	615 082	154 439	18 122
Mixed-wood Plains	23 940	2 568 428	1 849 070	710 222
Boreal Plains	24 733	179 008	21 481	1 699
Taiga Cordillera	0	104	1	0
Prairie	30 738	879 314	291 666	89 461
Boreal Cordillera	1 269	6 830	1 327	4
Pacific Maritime	22 774	527 184	273 406	66 578
Montane Cordillera	24 055	194 595	33 320	2 287
Hudson Plains	194	1 676	59	0

Provincial/Territorial Share of Ecozones

(square kilometres)

Ecozone	British Columbia	Alberta	Saskatchewan	Manitoba	Ontario	Quebec
Tundra Cordillera						
Boreal Cordillera	207 535					
Pacific Maritime	197 040					
Montane Cordillera	419 445	43 855				
Boreal Plain	93 895	375 850	258 765	129 685		
Taiga Plain	29 885	68 090				
Prairie		166 975	253 645	70 515		
Taiga Shield		6 420	39 890	122 630		490 095
Boreal Shield[1]			100 030	248 455	652 180	693 705
Hudson Plains				78 665	278 380	8 625
Mixed-wood Plains[2]					138 020	56 935
Atlantic Maritime[3]						54 710
Southern Arctic						157 360
Northern Arctic						79 250
Arctic Cordillera						
TOTAL	947 800	661 190	652 330	649 950	1 068 580	1 540 680

Ecozone	New Brunswick	Nova Scotia	Prince Edward Island	Newfoundland	Yukon	Northwest Territories	Total
Tundra Cordillera					227 745	149 215	376 960
Boreal Cordillera					218 235		425 770
Pacific Maritime							197 040
Montane Cordillera							463 300
Boreal Plain					23 975	425	882 595
Taiga Plain					5 495	453 780	557 240
Prairie							491 135
Taiga Shield				226 515		415 740	1 301 290
Boreal Shield[1]	490			122 985			1 817 845
Hudson Plains						5 150	370 820
Mixed-wood Plains[2]							194 955
Atlantic Maritime[3]	72 950	55 490	5 660				188 810
Southern Arctic				56 220	8 010	771 005	992 595
Northern Arctic						1 329 340	1 408 590
Arctic Cordillera						301 665	302 665
TOTAL	73 440	55 490	5 660	405 720	483 450	3 426 320[5]	9 970 610

[1]The figure for the Boreal Shield includes portions of the Great Lakes. If the Great Lakes are not included, the total for the Boreal Shield would be 1 780 095 km^2. The figure for the Ontario part of the Boreal Shield would be 614 430 km^2, without the Great Lakes.

[2]The figure for the Mixed-wood Plains includes a portion of the Great Lakes. If the Great Lakes are not included, the total for the Mixed-wood Plains would be 144 440 km^2. The total for the Ontario part of the Mixed-wood Plains would be 87 505 km^2 if the Great Lakes are not included.

[3]The figure for the Atlantic Maritime ecozone includes the St. Lawrence River estuary. If the St. Lawrence River estuary is not included, the total for the Atlantic Maritime would be 154 480 km^2. The total for the Quebec part of the Atlantic Maritime would be 20 380 km^2 if the St. Lawrence estuary is not included. The St. Lawrence River estuary is defined as the portion of the river between Île d'Orléans and Anticosti Island.

Population by Ecozone, 1986 and 1996

Provincial/Territorial ecozone	Area square kilometers	Population 1986	Population 1996	Change 1986–1996	Density 1986 persons per square km	Density 1996 persons per square km	Change 1986–1996 percent
Newfoundland							
Taiga Shield	219 766.2	4 540	4,168	-372	0.02	0.02	-8.19
Boreal Shield	161 859.1	563 809	547 624	-16 185	3.48	3.38	-2.87
Arctic Cordillera	19 382.1	-	-	-	-	-	-
Total	**401 007.3**	**568 349**	**551 792**	**-16 557**	**1.42**	**1.38**	**-2.91**
Prince Edward Island							
Atlantic Maritime	5 712.3	126 646	134 557	7 911	22.17	23.56	6.25
Total	**5 712.3**	**126 646**	**134 557**	**7 911**	**22.17**	**23.56**	**6.25**
Nova Scotia							
Atlantic Maritime	56 352.0	873 176	909 282	36 106	15.50	16.14	4.14
Total	**56 352.0**	**873 176**	**909 282**	**36 106**	**15.50**	**16.14**	**4.14**
New Brunswick							
Atlantic Maritime	73 318.1	709 442	738 133	28 691	9.68	10.07	4.04
Total	**73 318.1**	**709 442**	**738 133**	**28 691**	**9.68**	**10.07**	**4.04**
Quebec							
Taiga Shield	530 005.8	7 302	10 193	2 891	0.01	0.02	39.59
Boreal Shield	642 880.4	1 154 683	1 285 777	131 094	1.80	2.00	11.35
Hudson Plains	37 376.8	1 540	2 075	535	0.04	0.06	34.74
Mixed-wood Plains	28 357.4	4 605 131	5 068 405	463 274	162.40	178.73	10.06
Atlantic Maritime	67 236.6	760 011	767 089	7 078	11.30	11.41	0.93
Southern Arctic	154 080.6	2 586	3 642	1 056	0.02	0.02	40.84
Northern Arctic	36 734.5	1 208	1 614	406	0.03	0.04	33.61
Arctic Cordillera	13 496.7	-	-	-	-	-	-
Total	**1 510 168.7**	**6 532 461**	**7 138 795**	**606 334**	**4.33**	**4.73**	**9.28**
Ontario							
Boreal Shield	640 636.6	926 174	973 823	47 649	1.45	1.52	5.14
Hudson Bay Plains	263 077.5	2 390	7 744	5 354	0.00	0.03	224.02
Mixed-wood Plains	85 613.4	8 173 130	9 772 006	1 598 876	95.47	114.14	19.56
Total	**989 327.5**	**9 101 694**	**10 753 573**	**1 651 879**	**9.20**	**10.87**	**18.15**
Manitoba							
Boreal Plains	90 539.5	104 960	116 087	11 127	1.16	1.28	10.60
Prairie	67 071.8	886 828	922 199	35 371	13.22	13.75	3.99
Taiga Shield	130 373.4	1 217	1 445	228	0.01	0.01	18.73
Boreal Shield	250 040.5	67 583	72 175	4 592	0.27	0.29	6.79
Hudson Plains	70 246.1	2 428	1 992	-436	0.03	0.03	-17.96
Southern Arctic	1 491.9	-	-	-	-	-	-
Total	**609 763.2**	**1 063 016**	**1 113 898**	**50 882**	**1.74**	**1.83**	**4.79**
Saskatchewan							
Boreal Plains	177 644.3	162 431	159 468	-2 963	0.91	0.90	-1.82
Prairie	240 977.9	832 975	813 480	-19 495	3.46	3.38	-2.34
Taiga Shield	46 656.8	1 214	1 254	40	0.03	0.03	3.29
Boreal Shield	176 185.3	12 993	16 035	3 042	0.07	0.09	23.41
Total	**641 464.2**	**1 009 613**	**990 237**	**-19 376**	**1.57**	**1.54**	**-1.92**
Alberta							
Montane Cordillera	47 394.3	28 003	36 498	8 495	0.59	0.77	30.34
Boreal Plains	381 673.9	373 651	413 329	39 678	0.98	1.08	10.62
Taiga Plains	62 517.7	2 048	3 153	1 105	0.03	0.05	53.96
Prairie	156 020.8	1 962 123	2 243 843	281 720	12.58	14.38	14.36
Taiga Shield	8 920.7	-	-	-	-	-	-
Boreal Shield	4 540.0	-	3	3	-	0.00	-
Total	**661 067.3**	**2 365 825**	**2 696 826**	**331 001**	**3.58**	**4.08**	**13.99**
British Columbia							
Boreal Cordillera	192 095.3	3 273	2 496	-777	0.02	0.01	-23.74
Pacific Maritime	208 804.8	2 158 515	2 848 289	689 774	10.34	13.64	31.96
Montane Cordillera	442 839.9	670 740	815 158	144 418	1.51	1.84	21.53
Boreal Plains	39 355.3	45 813	52 759	6 946	1.16	1.34	15.16
Taiga Plains	67 592.7	5 026	5 798	772	0.07	0.09	15.36
Total	**950 688.1**	**2 883 367**	**3 724 500**	**841 133**	**3.03**	**3.92**	**29.17**
Yukon							
Southern Arctic	4 563.1	-	-	-	-	-	-
Taiga Cordillera	182 824.4	294	358	64	0.00	0.00	21.77
Boreal Cordillera	273 711.2	23 210	30 408	7 198	0.08	0.11	31.01
Taiga Plains	18 357.4	-	-	-	-	-	-
Pacific Maritime	4 195.6	-	-	-	-	-	-
Total	**483 651.6**	**23 504**	**30 766**	**7 262**	**0.05**	**0.06**	**30.90**
Northwest Territories							
Taiga Cordillera	84 459.1	238	-	-238	0.00	-	-100.00
Boreal Plains	15 506.3	4 479	2 988	-1 491	-	-	-
Taiga Plains	462 073.7	13 324	15 035	1 711	0.03	0.03	12.84
Taiga Shield	431 999.6	13 531	19 829	6 298	0.03	0.05	46.54
Hudson Plains	3 569.6	-	-	-	-	-	-
Southern Arctic	691 537.4	6 768	8 087	1 319	0.01	0.01	19.49
Northern Arctic	1 493 092.7	12 973	17 267	4 294	0.01	0.01	33.10
Boreal Cordillera	4 669.6	-	-	-	-	-	-
Arctic Cordillera	211 704.9	925	1 196	271	0.01	0.01	29.30
Total	**3 398 612.9**	**52 238**	**64 402**	**12 164**	**0.02**	**0.02**	**23.29**
Canada total	**9 781 133.2**	**25 309 331**	**28 846 761**	**3 537 430**	**2.59**	**2.95**	**13.98**

Population by Ecozone 1986 and 1996

Provincial/Territorial ecozone	Area square kilometers	Population 1986 persons	Population 1996 persons	Change 1986–1996	Density 1986 persons per square km	Density 1996 persons per square km	Change 1986–1996 percent
Ecozone							
Atlantic Maritime	202 619.0	2 469 275	2 549 061	79 786	12.19	12.58	3.23
Mixed-wood Plains	113 970.8	12 778 261	14 840 411	2 062 150	112.12	130.21	16.14
Boreal Shield	1 876 141.8	2 725 242	2 895 437	170 195	1.45	1.54	6.25
Prairie	464 070.4	3 681 926	3 979 522	297 596	7.93	8.58	8.08
Boreal Plains	704 719.3	691 334	744 631	53 297	0.98	1.06	7.71
Montane Cordillera	490 234.2	698 743	851 656	152 913	1.43	1.74	21.88
Pacific Maritime	213 000.4	2 158 515	2 848 289	689 774	10.13	13.37	31.96
Boreal Cordillera	470 476.1	26 483	32 904	6 421	0.06	0.07	24.25
Taiga Cordillera	267 283.5	532	358	-174	0.00	0.00	32.71
Taiga Plains	610 541.5	20 398	23 986	3 588	0.03	0.04	17.59
Taiga Shield	1 367 722.4	27 804	36 889	9 085	0.02	0.03	32.68
Hudson Plains	374 270.0	6 358	11 811	5 453	0.02	0.03	85.77
Southern Arctic	851 673.0	9 354	11 729	2 375	0.01	0.01	25.39
Northern Arctic	1 529 827.2	14 181	18 881	4 700	0.00	0.01	33.14
Arctic Cordillera	244 583.7	925	1 196	271	0.00	0.00	29.30
Canada total	**9 781 133.2**	**25 309 331**	**28 846 761**	**3 537 430**	**2.59**	**2.95**	**13.98**

Notes:
The area figures for ecozones and the Canada total do not include the areas of a number of large freshwater bodies located on ecosystem boundaries.
Ecozone boundaries are the 1996 set produced by the Ecological Stratification Working Group and in some instances differ from previously released compilations.
The population figures presented here are not adjusted for net undercoverage and non-permanent residents.

Sources:
Statistics Canada Environment Accounts and Statistics Division; Statistics Canada Census of Population; Ecological Stratification Working Group 1996
A National Ecological Framework for Canada Agriculture and Agri-Food Canada and Environment Canada.

GLOSSARY

A

aboriginal: existing in a land before recorded history or before colonists arrived

Aboriginal peoples: descendants of the original inhabitants of a land or territory. In Canada, they are Indians, Inuit, and Metis.

Aboriginal rights: consist of land, fishing and hunting rights, and other cultural traditions before treaties were signed

abyssal plain: flat areas at the lowest depths of the ocean floor

advocate for the environment: spokesperson defending the environment

aggregate: mixture of sand, gravel, and crushed rock that sometimes hardens into a rock formation

aggregate industry: the business of supplying sand, gravel, crushed stone, or quarried rock

agribusiness: a group of industries dealing with farm produce and services

airborne toxic cycle: the movement of harmful materials through the air

air mass: large body of air that has the same moisture and temperature conditions throughout and that influences the weather by carrying its distinct characteristics to other areas

alternative energy sources: alternatives to "conventional" energy sources such as hydroelectric and nuclear power. Common alternative energy sources include solar, wind, hydrogen, and tidal power.

altitude: height above sea level

analogy chart: a graphic organizer intended to show similarities

Anik: Inuktitut word for brother, and the name of Canada's second series of satellites

animal rights activists: person or group defending animals

Antarctica: continent that surrounds the South Pole

anti-fur campaign: protests over using furs or hide products in the fashion industry

appendix: supplementary information put into a section at the end of a book

aquaculture: farming (growing and nuturing in captivity) fresh water and marine plants and animals

archipelago: a group of many islands

Arctic: the north polar regions

at-risk species: an animal or plant species that could soon become extinct

autotrophs: living organisms that create their own food from inorganic material, and are the green plants

avalanche: a rapid slide of a mass of snow, mud, ice, rock, and other debris in alpine or escarpment areas

B

baby boomers: people born after the Second World War (between 1946 and 1964)

Ballard fuel cell: Canadian invention to improve fuel efficiency in cars by producing energy from a chemical reaction between hydrogen and oxygen

band: group of Aboriginal people for whom the Canadian government sets aside money and land (reserves) for use by the band. There are over 600 bands in Canada. Today, the term "First Nation" is replacing the term "band."

bandwidth: carrying capacity of an electronic communications system

Banff: urban centre of Banff National Park in Alberta

Barnardo children: orphaned or poor children brought by Dr. Thomas Barnardo as immigrants from Great Britain to Canada

basic activities: goods and services created within a community to generate income outside of it (e.g., a mine that exports its output)

bilingualism: a government policy that supports having two languages with equal status; in Canada, English and French

biodiversity: the variety of life found within any given area

biomagnification: a process whereby toxins (like PCBs) accumulate and increase in the food chain.

biome: an area with a characteristic geographic and climatic pattern that supports certain animal and plant populations (e.g., boreal forest)

bioregion: a region defined by its natural and human characteristics. It constitutes a natural ecological community.

birth rate: the total number of births in a year for every 1000 people

bog: an area of soft, wet spongy ground by a shallow lake or pond, filled with decaying vegetation, and often covered with sphagnum moss

boom and bust cycles: in many resource-based industries the price of the resource (such as oil, gold, agricultural products) may rise and fall on a regular basis. When the price is high, many jobs are created and there are good economic times (boom). When the price is low, many jobs are lost and there are poor economic times (bust).

boreal forest: a coniferous forest dominated by spruce, fir, and pine trees that stretches from east to west across Canada

bylaw: a law or rule passed by a municipal council that applies only to that municipality

C

CBD: see "Central Business District"

CFCs: see "chlorofluorocarbons"

CIDA: see "Canadian International Development Agency"

CITIES: see "Convention in International Trade in Endangered Species"

CMA: see "Census Metropolitan Area"

CRTC: see "Canadian Radio-television and Telecommunications Commission"

Canadian Heritage River Systems: rivers designated by the federal government to have historical significance in Canada

Canadian International Development Agency (CIDA): an agency in the federal government responsible for foreign aid projects

Canadian Radio-television and Telecommunications Commission (CRTC): federal agency that regulates broadcast signals, licences, and program content for radio and television

Canadian Shield: a geologic region in central Canada that consists of Precambrian rock and is the oldest rock formation on Earth

carnivores: flesh-eating animals and plants

Census Metropolitan Area (CMA): city and surrounding area with 100 000 people or more

Central Business District (CBD): the downtown area of a town or city that contains most of the commercial activities

chemical waste: chemicals that are surplus to a use and that could become potential environmental problems

chlorofluorocarbons (CFCs): refrigerants that can escape into the atmosphere and damage the ozone layer

Convention in International Trade in Endangered Species (CITIES): Canada is one of a number of countries that have joined together to fight the illegal trade in endangered species.

citizenship: the condition of having the rights, duties, and responsibilities as a member of a state or nation

clear-cutting: all trees in an forest area are cut at the same time

climate: the daily weather conditions of a place averaged over a long period of time

clustering: when similar or complementary functions locate near one another.

coastal marsh: wetlands at the edge of oceans, often mixing salt and fresh water, sometimes affected by tides

coaxial cable: cable used in telecommunications systems to deliver electronic signals, e.g., most cable television and radio broadcasts

commodity: goods or services purchased or used by consumers

communication systems: networks that allow information to be passed in a variety of forms, voice or digital

commuter travel: daily movement of people to and from, e.g., work or school. This pattern influences transportation planning and policies.

compaction: air spaces or lack of them; sometimes applied to soils and sometimes to garbage handling (see "soil compaction")

competitive advantage: a better price or service than other competitors, often used in business and commerce

comprehensive land claims: in Canada, claims based on Aboriginal rights in regions where no treaties were signed. This includes northern Quebec, the Atlantic provinces, and parts of British Columbia, the Yukon, Northwest Territories, and Nunavut.

concept map or web: a diagram that shows various relationships between ideas, and can also contain references to events, laws, themes, or other items related to the concept

condensation: occurs when water vapour is reduced from a gas to a liquid by cooling. Condensed water vapour forms clouds.

coniferous forest: cone-bearing trees with needle-like leaves that are widespread north of 50°N (Canada, Europe, and Asia). Dominant species are spruce, fir, and pine.

consumer price index: a measure used by Statistics Canada to gauge the relative cost of living; a measure of the change in the cost of living relative to a particular period in the past

container port: a port city specializing in container facilities

containers: metal boxes of standard size used for moving freight. The containers are loaded at the point of shipment and remain sealed until they reach their destination. They may be moved by truck, train, plane, or ship.

continental drift: a theory that claims that in the last 200 million years the continents have moved by great distances; they are still moving today; see also "plate tectonics"

continental shelves: gently sloping seabed (shelf) of a continent that extends to a point of steeper descent to the ocean floor. They average 200 m in depth.

continental slope: the sharp angle of a seabed that drops off quickly from the continental shelf to the ocean depths of the abyssal plain

contour interval: the stated interval or rise between contour lines, usually in metres

contour lines: lines on topographic maps that join places of the same elevation above sea level, usually in metres

contour ploughing: cultivating farmland by ploughing around landforms to prevent loss of soil from runoff

convectional storms: heavy rainfall created by the rapid rising, cooling and condensing of hot air. This rapid movement of air often causes thunderstorms or hailstorms.

convection currents (flows): flows of energy from the transfer of heat inside the Earth that move upwards and outwards as they approach the Earth's surface

cordillera: a group of mountain systems, each one containing several ranges, e.g., the Western Cordillera of Canada

core: the hot molten centre of the Earth

correlation: a casual, complementary, parallel, or reciprocal relationship between two things

cost-benefit situation: an examination of the costs or expenses of a project versus the benefits or rewards of it

cost of living: average price paid by a person, family, etc., for food, housing, clothing, transportation, etc., within a given period

crop farming: seeding and growing plants on a farm

crop rotation: a plan to move selected crops from field to field on a farm to help maintain or improve soil conditions

cross-section: a diagram of an object or landform that has been sliced in half and sketched from that perspective

Crown corporation: company owned by the federal or provincial governments that are set up like a private business (e.g., Canada Post)

Crown lands: lands owned by the government

crystals: clear transparent mineral formations

cultural homogeneity: a group of people with the same way of life; e.g., customs, beliefs, or language

culture: the beliefs, traditions, attitudes, and way of life shared by a people

cyclonic storms: heavy precipitation caused when warm moist air rises over heavier cooler air masses, creating areas of low pressure or depressions

D

dairy farming: raising breeds of cows to produce milk and milk products

death rate: the number of deaths in a year for every 1000 people

decentralizing technology: a process whereby a transfer of economic activity from large to smaller urban centres is made possible by information technology

deciduous forest: consists of trees with broad-leaves that shed leaves in the autumn or at times of great environmental stress; examples are maple, birch, oak

deforestation: the destruction and removal of a forest and its undergrowth by natural or human agents

demographic explosion: a rapid increase in the population

density: the number of people living in a given area of land, usually measured in people per square kilometres

desert: an almost barren tract of land caused by the lack of rainfall

desertification: expansion of desert areas due to processes such as climatic change, global warming, deforestation, over-grazing, and wildfires

digital information: information produced and transmitted electronically

direct communication: methods of communication between people that require personal contact (e.g., talking, Internet)

drainage: the ability of water to flow through soil; the removal of water from an area by streams, rivers, and lakes

drainage basins: areas drained by a river and its tributaries

drainage divides: a high point of land or ridge from which water runs in two or more directions

drainage system: network of streams and rivers that drain the runoff from the land into a river system

drift-net fishing: a method of catching fish by dragging a huge open-mouthed net through the ocean and hauling in all species trapped in the net

drought: a prolonged shortage of precipitation that may reduce water supplies, soil fertility and plant growth

dumping: trade practice whereby a country tries to sell its surplus products below production costs in another country

E

e-mail: the exchange of messages (letters, notes, and other materials) through the Internet

e-zines: electronic magazines that are available on the Internet

earth tremors: shock waves created by moving tectonic plates in the Earth's crust

ecodistricts: subdivisions of an ecoregion. There are 5395 ecodistricts in Canada.

ecology: the study of all interactions that occur within the biosphere, the portion of the planet that supports life and living organisms within it

ecological area: an area with a distinct set of plant and animal conditions

ecological footprint: the total human impact on an ecosystem

ecological restoration: the process of returning an ecosystem to its original, natural condition

economic activities: all functions that create wealth, income, and employment within a community

economic indicator: a statistical measure that gives an indication of the overall performance of an economy

economy: the system of how people produce and consume various commodities and services within a society

ecoprovinces: one of 47 subdivisions of the ecozones in Canada

ecoregions: one of 177 subdivisions of of the ecoprovinces in Canada

ecosystem: a group of living organisms that, along with their environment, form a self-regulating system through which energy and materials are transferred

ecotourism: travel for the purpose of observing ecosystems

ecozone framework: an ecological land classification system developed for use by Environment Canada and Statistics Canada.

ecozones: an ecological classification system developed for use by Environment Canada and Statistics Canada. Canada has 15 distinct terrestrial ecozones, based on the particular combinations of natural features (landforms, climate characteristics, vegetation and soils, and wildlife) and human activities that are distinct for each ecozone. It also has 5 marine ecozones.

emigrants: people who leave their country to live in another country

emigration: the movement of people out of a region, territory, or nation

Employment Equity Act: laws to create fair and equal pay for jobs of equal value

environment: everything, both natural and synthetic, that surrounds us; surroundings, particularly the factors that affect the growth and development of organisms

environmental accord: mutual agreement on environmental issues

environmental assessment: estimating the state and value of a specific environmental area

environmental conservation and stewardship program: a plan to care for an environmental area

environmental hazards: natural events that are harmful to humans, plants, and animals

environmental harmony: limiting the impact of human activities upon an ecosystem

environmental protection: steps or plans to prevent damage to the environment

erosion: the process by which exposed land surfaces are broken down into smaller particles or worn away by water, wind, or ice; transportation of weathered materials by running water, waves, wind, ice

eskers: narrow, winding gravel ridges deposited by a sub-glacial stream

ethnic groups: people sharing a social or cultural identity based on a particular language, religion, homeland, and/or set of customs

ethnic origins: coming from a specific country and/or cultural, linguistic group

exports: commodities produced in one country for sale in another country

F

fair trade: a movement to prevent trading partners from exploiting both human labour and the environment

family farms: farms owned by a single family unit

fault line: a line where the Earth's crust has fractured or broken

federal government: a system of central or national government in which several political jurisdictions form a unity but retain autonomy in defined areas; the people who decide upon and enforce the national laws and policies for Canada

fibre-optic cables: glass-based transmission lines capable of carrying tens of thousands more electrical pulses than traditional copper lines

First Nation: a term created in the 1970s to replace the word Indian band or Indian reserve

fish meal: a powdered protein product made from fish

fish stocks: the estimated numbers of a family or breed of fish

floating factory ships: ships that can catch and process fish at sea, as well as serve a fleet of trawlers for the same purpose

flood: when a river or lake rises and overflows its banks or shorelines

fodder crops: plants grown for feeding animals

food chain: the linkages between life that allow the transfer of energy throughout an ecosystem, usually describing food sources for various species that depend on one another for survival

food pyramid: see "food chain"

food web: complex pattern of interlocking food chains

footprint: a term expressing the impact of human activity upon an ecosystem

foresters: officers in charge of a forest or of growing timber

forests: large tracts of land covered with trees

fossil fuels: minerals formed from the remains of ancient plants and animals that produce energy. These include coal, natural gas, and petroleum.

fossil records: remains of the form of a plant or animal, which have been preserved in the rocks of the Earth. These rock layers can be used to analyze the geologic history of the Earth.

free trade: the exchange of goods between countries without the payment of duties or tariffs

frost-free period: total number of days between the last expected frost in the spring and the first expected frost in the fall

fuel cell: a power source produced by an electromechanical reaction between hydrogen and oxygen

future wheel: a diagram, consisting of boxes connected by lines, used to develop and show future relationships based on predictions

G

GDP: see "Gross Domestic Product"

GIS: see "Geographical Information Systems"

GNP: see "Gross National Product"

GPS: see "Global Positioning Systems"

gazetteer: an index of geographical names, commonly used in atlases

Geographical Information Systems (GIS): an integrated software package for the input, management, analysis, and display of spatial information

geographic inquiry: the process of collecting, organizing, analyzing, and communicating geographic information

geologic time: history of the Earth from its formation to the present. The Earth's history may be divided into several major time periods, called eras: Cenozoic Era (most recent), Mesozoic Era, Paleozoic Era, Precambrian Era (oldest).

geological regions: areas where the composition and structure of rocks are similar

geotechnologies: technologies used to carry out geographic studies (e.g., GIS)

geothermal energy: uses heat and steam from the Earth to generate power and direct heat to buildings; the heat of the Earth's interior, sometimes in the form of hot springs or geysers

gigajoule: a huge unit measure (one billion joules, see "joule") of energy and work used to measure the production and consumption of energy of countries

glacial moraine: rock and soil debris deposited by a glacier

glaciation: accumulation of snow to form a mass of ice and the movement of the ice

glaciers: large ice masses that flow slowly; glaciers may be either sheets or rivers of ice

globalization: the process in which many regions of the world have become increasingly interconnected in terms of economics, culture, and financial services as a result of modern communications technology

Global Positioning Systems (GPS): a satellite navigation system that is used to compute location on the Earth

global warming: the apparent rise in the average annual temperature of the Earth caused by human activity resulting in an unnatural increase in the amount of greenhouse gases (e.g., water vapour, carbon dioxide, methane) in the atmosphere

glossary: an alphabetical list of words with explanations relating to a specific text or book

gold rushes: boom cycles of prospectors seeking gold

Grand Banks: area of the continental shelf off the east coast of Newfoundland

graphic organizer: a visual tool used to organize and present relationships between ideas and information

grain elevator: a tall, box-like or cylindrical structure with an elevating or lifting device inside, used to clean, sort, and store grain for shipment

Great Circle: any circle on the Earth's surface that has the Earth's centre as its centre. An arc of a Great Circle is the shortest distance between two points on the surface of the Earth.

Great Lakes airshed: the location of air masses and their flow patterns over the Great Lakes

Green Plan (Canada): the environmental master plan of the Canadian government

greenhouse effect: warming of Earth's atmosphere that occurs when outgoing long-wave radiation is absorbed by water vapour and carbon dioxide. It began billions of years ago. Recently, the burning of fossil fuels has added 30% more carbon dioxide to the atmosphere, adding to the greenhouse effect.

greenhouse gases: gases such as carbon dioxide and ozone that contribute to the greenhouse effect

grid pattern: a survey system based on squares and rectangles; a road system pattern

grid square farm pattern: a survey system of farms based on squares and rectangles.

Gross Domestic Product (GDP): the total monetary value of goods and services produced and consumed within a country by nationals and outsiders in a given period

Gross National Product (GNP): the value of all the goods and services produced in a country in one year (including imports and exports)

growing season: the period during which crops can grow. In Canada, it is the number of days when the average temperature is over 5.6 degrees.

H

habitat: the natural home of plants or animals

Healing Rock: rocks covered with over 100 paintings and symbols by Natalie Rostad, a Metis artist

herbivores: animals that feed on plants

herbicides: substance toxic to plants, used to destroy unwanted vegetation

heterotrophs: living organisms that either eat plants (herbivores), other heterotrophs (carnivores), or the dead tissue of other organisms (decomposers and scavengers)

high-density housing: housing with a large number of people per square unit of measurement

high-order services: services requiring a large population in order to be functional (e.g., specialized hospitals, universities, provincial art galleries)

hospital waste: dangerous refuse such as out-of-date drugs, contaminated fluids, and diseased flesh from hospital operations

House of Commons: the name of the elected assembly of Parliament, and the place where the elected members of the national legislature meet in the Parliament Buildings in Ottawa

human rights: rights belonging to all people as defined in the Universal Declaration of Human Rights which was adopted by the United Nations in 1948

human waste: usually sewage, but can be litter or landfill sites

humane societies: shelters for unwanted or neglected animals

hurricanes: tropical cyclones or storms formed by warm, moist air rapidly rising and spinning. High winds revolve around a central area of rising air, which feels calm and is called the "eye." Most storms occur in the Fall as they move westward across the warm, moist

Atlantic waters off the coast of Africa and then northward from the Caribbean along the coastline of the US.

hydrograph: graph that shows flow patterns of a river

hydrologic cycle: continuous circulation or pathway of all water in the atmosphere, water bodies, and land

hypermedia: electronic text, sound, video, and graphics information sources, such as websites and CD-ROMs

hythergraph: a grid that shows temperature and precipitation. It is useful for comparing the climates of two or more places.

I

IJC: see "International Joint Commission"

igneous rock: rock formed from the cooling of molten rock (magma or lava)

immigrants: people who move to a new country with the intention of settling there

immigration: the movement of people into a region, territory, or nation

import: products and services that are brought into a country from another country

in-migration: movement of people into an area

index: the alphabetical list of names and subjects at the end of a book listing the page numbers on which the name/subject can be found

Indian: all Aboriginal peoples in Canada who are not Inuit or Metis

Indian Act: first passed in 1876 and revised in 1982 and 1985, giving the federal government jurisdiction over "Indians and lands reserved for Indians"

indigenous: people, flora, and fauna belonging naturally to a region

indirect communication: methods of communication that do not require personal contact (e.g., radio, television)

inflation rate: the rise in the cost of living measured by Statistics Canada

information highway: pathways of rapid information exchange in the global communication network

information technology infrastructure: the framework of people and equipment to manage information in all its forms

infrastructure: the networks of transportation, communications, education, and other public services that are required to sustain economic and societal activities

innovation: new method or idea brought about by change

inorganic material: things of mineral origin; not organic substances

internal migration: movement of people within a city, province, or country

International Joint Commission (IJC): organization with members from Canada and the US responsible for the Great Lakes

Internet: international computer communication network

interrupted projections: techniques for mapping the spherical shape of the Earth onto flat paper

Inuit: Aboriginal peoples who are located largely in the Arctic regions

Inuk: the name given to one Inuit

isolines: lines on a map connecting points of equal value

isotherms: lines on a map that join points with the same atmospheric temperature

J

joule: a unit that measures energy and work. One joule is done when a force of one newton moves an object one metre in the direction of the force.

K

Kyoto Protocol: an international agreement signed in Kyoto, Japan, in an effort to reduce air pollution and to protect the environment from such things as CFCs and global warming

L

land claims: the formal demands presented by Aboriginal peoples for ownership and control of lands on which they live or have traditionally lived

land reclamation: the process of restoring land or transforming it for other uses

land use conflicts: points of disagreement over land-use planning and implementation

land use study: an analysis of how urban, suburban, or rural land is and can be best used (e.g., parks, housing, industry, commercial)

landforms: natural features of the Earth's surface such as mountains, valleys, or plains

latitude: distance north or south of the equator, measured in degrees

leaching: removal of soluble substances from rock or topsoil by water

leeward: side of a mountain or mountain range facing away from the prevailing winds, often creating an area of low precipitation or a rain shadow

legacy: material or immaterial things handed down from one person or group to another

Leonids: the largest recurring meteor shower, intersecting Earth's orbit every 33 years

lichen: plants like fungi and algae, usually found growing on and colouring rocks and tree trunks

lichen heath: open flat tract of land covered with lichen, usually found in the Arctic or on mountainous slopes

lithosphere: the solid layer of the Earth's crust, the rock layer

livestock: animals raised on a farm or in captivity

lobby groups: person or persons acting to try to influence public officials in favour of their cause

location costs: the expense of locating a business or a house in an area

low-income families: families living with an income lower than the average income in their area

low-order services: services available in a large number of places (e.g., variety stores, gas stations)

M

magma: molten rock beneath the Earth's surface

mantle: massive, concentric layer of the Earth, about 2900 km thick, consisting of relatively dense, molten rock between the crust and the core

map scale: the ratio used to reduce the Earth's surface to the map page

marine waste: discharges of oily ballast from ships, garbage dumped from cities, chemicals washed into oceans are examples of this ocean pollution

maritime: living or found near the sea; also a region in Canada

market garden: vegetables produced for sale

marsh: a tract of soft, wet land in low-lying areas; has poor drainage caused by soils like clay

mass media communication: means of getting information to a large audience, e.g., television, radio, newspaper

mechanization: the replacement of human and animal labour with machinery

mega projects: very large and expensive projects, often for the development

of land or natural resources, such as the James Bay hydroelectric plant; very large undertakings, usually involving the extraction or exploitation of natural resources

median age: the age at which half of the population is older and half of the population is younger

Metis: person of European and Aboriginal descent

middle-order services: services that are available in towns and cities (e.g., grocery stores, banks)

migration: the movement of people from one region to another for economic, political, religious, or other reasons; the movement of animals with the seasons

milk quotas: government limitations on milk production

mind map: a graphic representation showing relationships between ideas and/or information

mineral: a naturally formed, solid, inorganic substance with a characteristic chemical composition and often a particular crystalline shape

minority rights: the privileges of full legal, economic, and social equality accorded to particular groups in society that do not comprise the majority of the society

mixed livestock: a variety of animals on a farm

montane: referring to mountainous country

Montreal Protocol: signed in 1987. The agreement restricts the use of chlorofluorocarbons (CFCs). These refrigerants adversely affect the ozone layer.

morality: conduct according to the ethics and practices of a group of people

moratorium: the temporary suspension of an activity

mosaic: an arrangement of a group of pictures or symbols, sometimes applied to a group of people

mother ship: a floating factory ship that has a fleet of trawlers working with it

mother tongue: the language a person first learns

mountain: a large natural elevation on the Earth's surface

multi-faceted: having many sides

multicultural: a number of distinct cultural groups existing side by side within the same country, as in Canada

municipality: a town, city, county, district, or other area having local self-government

muskeg: swamp or bog, usually refers to northern Canada

N

NAFTA: see "North American Free Trade Agreement "

NGOs: see "non-governmental organizations"

national government: see "federal government"

National Parks Act: a federal government law passed in 1930 to set aside areas of land for the benefit, education, and enjoyment of the Canadian people

natural gas: fossil fuel formed under conditions similar to those that produce oil; natural gas is found in porous sedimentary rock

natural hazards: major natural disasters such as floods, wildfires, and earthquakes

natural increase: the rate of increase in a population when the death rate is subtracted from the birth rate

natural systems: interwoven parts of the natural environment

net immigration rate: the number of immigrants (people coming into the country) compared to the number of emigrants (people leaving the country)

net migration: the difference between immigration and emigration

night soil: human waste used to plough into the soil to keep it fertile

nomadic: roaming from place to place for pasture or hunting

non-basic activities: services (e.g., grocery stores) that cater only to residents but do not generate income outside of a community

non-conforming land use: a piece of land that does not conform to the official land use plan

non-governmental organizations (NGOs): organizations not belonging to or associated with a government (e.g., Oxfam, Amnesty International, Greenpeace)

non-renewable resources: resources that are limited and cannot be replaced once they are used up (e.g., coal, oil, natural gas)

North American Free Trade Agreement (NAFTA): a trade agreement signed by Canada, the United States, and Mexico to remove trade barriers between the three countries over a ten-year period. The treaty came into effect in January 1994.

northern cod: a species of cod fish

nuclear energy: energy produced by using the heat from nuclear fission (the splitting of atoms), usually to generate electricity

nuclear waste: radioactive materials that are produced by the nuclear industry

Nunavut: Canada's newest territory established on April 1, 1999; formerly eastern part of the Northwest Territories

O

ODA: see "official development assistance"

official development assistance (ODA): government foreign-aid program that helps developing countries and is administered by the Canadian International Development Agency (CIDA).

official plans: land-use plans adopted by municipal governments to create zoning regulations and other matters related to land development

offshore limit: a maritime boundary line, important in establishing claims to resources like fish and oil, and for national defence. In Canada, it is 200 nautical miles or 370 kilometres from the shoreline.

oil sands: mixture of heavy crude oil, sand, and water

old-growth forests: forests in their natural state that have never been logged

open-pit method: digging a large hole to mine ore found near the Earth's surface

ore: a mixture of valuable and worthless minerals from which at least one of the minerals can be extracted at a profit

ore deposits: a concentration of ore found in rock layers in the Earth

organic food production: the production of food without the use of chemical fertilizers, pesticides, and herbicides

orographic precipitation: see "relief rainfall"

ozone layer: a region of the Earth's upper atmosphere containing a high concentration of ozone, which absorbs solar, ultraviolet radiation

P

PCBs: see "polychlorinated biphenyls"

Pacific Ring of Fire: the area around the edge of Pacific Ocean in which tectonic activity is greatest. The area is named for its large number of volcanoes.

parent rock: the original rock from which sediments were derived to form later rocks, or the rock from which soils are formed

parliament: an elected assembly responsible for passing legislation and granting the right to levy taxes. In Canada, the federal legislature consists of the Governor General, the Senate, and the House of Commons.

polychlorinated biphenyls (PCBs): toxic wastes from many industrial sources that have polluted air and water

peacekeeping: to prevent or refrain from conflict

peak demand: period of time of the maximum need for power in a day or in a year

peatlands: land where vegetation has broken down in water and turned partly to carbon which can be used for fuel

periphery: the edge or bounding line of a region

permafrost: permanently frozen soil typical of tundra and high alpine regions

pesticide: substance for destroying pests, especially insects or rodents

petrochemical industry: produces fuels, oils, lubricants and other chemicals extracted from petroleum

photosynthesis: change of light energy into stored chemical energy by plants and algae

pits: excavations producing sand, gravel, and crushed stone for the aggregate industry

plain: a level tract of land

pluralism: a form of society in which members of minority groups maintain their traditions

poachers: people who capture fish or game in an illegal way

polar: climate zones north of the Arctic Circle (66.5°N) and south of the

Antarctic Circe (66.5°S). These areas have cool or cold temperatures all year.

pollutants: something that causes pollution (e.g., by-products from manufacturing, candy wrappers)

pollution: the destruction of the purity of the environment

population density: the average number of people occupying an area, calculated by dividing the number of people by the area they occupy

population distribution: the pattern of where people live within an area

population growth rates: the speed of population increase

population pyramid: a graph that shows the makeup of a population by age and by gender

poverty line: the minimum income level needed to get the necessities of life

poverty rate: percentage of the population with very low incomes, below the poverty line

prairie: grasslands that are found in the southern part of Alberta, Saskatchewan, and Manitoba; the natural grasses of this region have been largely replaced by wheat

prairie slough: glacial potholes scraped out by moving ice, seasonally flooded by melting snow and spring rain

Precambrian: first and oldest era in the Earth's geologic history. There were virtually no life forms at this time.

prevailing winds: winds that are most commonly found in an area; for example, over most of Canada the prevailing winds are Westerlies, which blow from west to east

primary production: the production of primary products such as minerals that are mined or quarried, or an agricultural product that is harvested in its raw state

primary sectors: industries that extract and process natural resources (e.g., mining, forestry, fishing, and agriculture)

provinces and territories: political divisions of Canada

pull factors: conditions that attract people to a place, especially a country

push factors: factors, such as the lack of freedom of speech or unemployment, that make people want to leave their country and move to another one

Q

quality of life: factors that measure how comfortable life is in a country

quarry: an open excavation for the extraction of building stone or rock

quaternary: a fourth level of service in an economic system

quota: a share that an individual or corporation is entitled to take or contribute–fish quotas, milk quotas, etc.

R

rain shadow: area on the leeward side of mountains with little precipitation

recreational activities: free time spent in relaxation, playing sports, or taking holidays

redevelopment: new use of land to upgrade its potential

Registered Indian: a person who according to the *Indian Act* is registered as an Indian or is entitled to be registered as an Indian

relief: the difference in elevation on any part of the Earth's surface

relief rainfall: precipitation on the windward side of the mountains caused by the cooling of the air as it rises in elevation

remote sensing: images of Earth taken from satellites and aircraft

renewable resource: a resource that can be replaced, e.g., when trees are cut down for lumber, new trees can be planted in their place

renewable energy sources: energy supplies that can be replenished after they are consumed, e.g., solar or wind power

reserve: areas of land set aside for the use of Aboriginal peoples; now referred to as a "First Nation community"

Rio Summit Conference: a United Nations conference on the environment held in 1992 in Rio de Janeiro. The nations of the world made a commitment to the goal of sustainable development.

river flood plain: flat land bordering a river that is subject to flooding. Flood waters create wetland conditions.

runoff: the amount of water from rainfall or melting snow that flows over the Earth's surface instead of sinking into the ground

runoff rates: the speed or the amount of runoff in a given time period

rural: pastoral or agricultural areas outside towns and cities

S

salination: the process whereby land or water becomes saturated with salts

satellites: unmanned spacecraft placed in orbit around the Earth. Satellites are used for telecommunications, to study the Earth's resources, and to aid the military.

satellite signals: data transmitted between satellites and Earth

secondary production: producing manufactured goods from raw materials

secondary sector: consist of industries that manufacture finished goods from the raw materials processed by primary sector industries, e.g., automobile plants

sedimentary rocks: rocks that have been formed by sediments under water, deposited in layers. They are one of the

three main types of rock that make up the Earth's crust.

seigneurial long-lot: a unit of land in the seigneurial system; the lots ran from the shore of a river to the interior highlands

seigneurial system: method of assigning parcels of land in Quebec. The seigneur was the main holder and tenants were granted long-lots.

seismic waves: shock waves produced by earthquakes

semantic web: a graphic organizing tool that allows the user to develop and demonstrate the links between ideas and/or information

semi-nomadic: groups of people or tribes moving from place to place for pasture or hunting on a seasonal basis

service sector: the sector of the economy that provides a service for customers, e.g., hair cutting or banking

settlement patterns: distribution of homes, farms, villages, towns, and cities in an area

shield: large area of Precambrian rock that forms the core of a continent, e.g., Canadian Shield, Baltic Shield

shock waves: tremors created by the movement of plates within the Earth's crust

silting: sediments deposited by water, e.g., lake beds, or stream sandbars

silviculture: a branch of forestry that is devoted to growing and tending trees

site: the physical location where something is located

situation: the general economic circumstances that are associated with a location

slope: an area of rising or falling ground

soil: a complex mixture of particles that have come from weathered rocks, living and dead organisms, water and air

soil compaction: a process that occurs when layers of soil are pressed or squashed together, preventing plant growth

soil conservation: efforts to prevent the loss of soil by erosion

soil depletion: the process by which usable soil loses its nutrients or is removed faster than it can be replenished (e.g., by erosion)

soil erosion: the loss of soil by natural forces such as wind and water

soil formation: the development of a soil profile from the natural or parent rock

soil profile: the different horizons (layers) in the soil and the rock layer (bedrock) below the soil. Each horizon has different physical, biological, and chemical composition

soil type: a term used to classify soils. It is the unit used in soil mapping and soil studies.

solar energy: energy produced from the sun

solar radiation: electromagnetic energy from the sun

spawning runs: the return of fish such as salmon to the headwaters of a river to lay their eggs

species: groups of plants or animals that are similar in make-up and can interbreed

specific land claims: the restoration of lands and rights where Aboriginal groups believe that the meaning and intent of original treaties are not being met, or that parts of the Indian Act are not being carried out fairly

spiritual: concerned with sacred or religious things

split-run magazines: American magazines that produce a version for Canada by inserting minor editorial and structural changes

stable population base: occurs when the population of a country is not likely to change significantly

state: a political organization that has control or sovereignty over the population within a geographic area

Status Indian: see "Registerd Indian"

stream flow: the volume of water flowing past a point in a set amount of time

strip mining: mining of minerals located on the Earth's surface by stripping off the layers of the deposit, e.g., the Alberta Tar Sands

structure: in soils; the air, mineral and plant particle combinations in a soil type

subduction zone: the area of the crust where one plate slides beneath another, creating volcanoes on the Earth's surface

suburban: the land in transition between urban and rural, usually residential

succession of vegetation: the order of appearance that plants follow when an ecosystem is renewed. Some plants disappear or die off in the process, e.g., trees replace bulrushes as marshes evolve to drier land.

sunrise crop: a crop whose popularity is growing with farmers and consumers

sunset crop: a crop whose popularity is declining with farmers and consumers

sustainable: something that can be prolonged or renewed

sustainable energy: see "renewable energy sources"

sustainable development: goal of development that meets the needs of the present generation without compromising the ability of future generations to meet their needs

swamp: low-lying wetland that is overgrown with vegetation, usually caused by poor or slow drainage

T

table of contents: list found at the beginning of a book with page numbers and chapter headings and sub-headings

taiga: coniferous forest land of Siberia. The name is often used for all coniferous forests in the northern hemisphere.

tar sands: mixture of heavy crude oil, sand, and water

tariffs: taxes paid to the federal government on goods entering the country

technological change: new developments in technology

technological waves: a theory of six waves of innovation that Frank Feather, a Canadian futurist, has applied to the development of Canada

technology: scientific knowledge that is applied to practical purposes

tectonic forces: the processes that mold the Earth's surface by breaking, bending and warping the Earth's crust

tectonic plates: large jigsaw-like pieces of the Earth's crust that float on the molten mantle

telecommunications: communication over long distances by cable, short wave or other forms of transmission

temperate: the mid-latitudes between the Tropic of Cancer and the Arctic Circle with distinct warm and cool seasons

tertiary industries: services that are supplied directly to consumers, e.g., banking, transport, education, health care, and retailing

tertiary sector: industries including services, e.g., banking, transport, education, health care, and retailing

texture: the arrangement of small individual parts of rock, soil, or tissue

"The greying of Canada": a reference to the average age of the Canadian population, which is getting older

thematic map: a map showing a particular topic or theme such as climate

tidal wave: see "tsunami"

toll highway: a fee charged for the use of the highway, also for toll bridges

topographic map: a detailed large-scale map representing the surface features of a place or region, and their relative positions and elevations

tornado: an extremely violent whirlwind caused when hot, damp air from the Gulf of Mexico meets cool, dry air from the north. High wind velocities near the centre cause great destruction along its narrow track.

toxins: harmful or poisonous substances that get into the ecosystem

trade: the exchange of commodities for money or other commodities

trade patterns: the history of business activity conducted by a nation

trade protection: efforts made by a nation to help businesses conduct their activities

trading blocs: groups of nations that join together for improved business conditions

trade mission: the efforts by the Canadian government and members of the business community to create more trade opportunities for Canada

tradition: opinions, beliefs, or customs handed down orally or by practice from elders and ancestors

traditional status: rank or social position gained from historical factors

Trans-boundary Movement of Hazardous Waste: an agreement signed in 1986 between Canada and the US to insure that the movement of hazardous wastes across boundaries is done safely

transborder pollution: pollution that crosses national borders

transition zone: an area where one region gradually blends into the next. The area contains a mixture of natural vegetation, soils, and wildlife found in the two neighbouring regions.

transpiration: emissions of watery vapour from the leaves of plants

transponders: devices to communicate with and assess fees to cars using modern toll highways

transportation links: the interconnections between methods of moving people and goods

transportation systems: networks of transportation modes that complement one another

Treaty Indian: a Status Indian who belongs to an Aboriginal group that signed a treaty with the Canadian Government

tree line: marks an area where climate factors restrict the growth of trees to shrub height; boundary between the tundra and boreal forest zone

tropical: hot climate zone between the Tropic of Cancer (23.5°N) and the Tropic of Capricorn (23°S), where no distinctive winter season occurs

tundra: the treeless plains of northern North America, principally along the Arctic Circle. The summers are short, the winters are cold and windy, making tree growth impossible.

tsunami: a huge ocean wave caused by a submarine earthquake or volcanic eruption

twisters: see "tornado"

U

underground mining: carried out below the ground, often at great depth, using shafts and tunnels

unit trains: trains that carry only one cargo from one location to one destination

urban: having to do with cities or towns

urban functions: activities that occur in an urban place and allow it to exist; for example, manufacturing, retail trade, and government

urban hierarchies: the ranking of communities by size, from a hamlet (the smallest) to a village, a town, and a city (the largest)

urbanization: the process by which an area becomes urban

V

Venn diagram: consists of two or more circles, each representing sets of things. The overlap of the circles indicates the common elements between the sets.

vertical development: high-density housing such as apartment buildings

virtual wilderness: experiencing wilderness through sensory perceptions generated by computers

visible minority: an ethnic group whose members are clearly racially distinct from those of the predominant race in a society

W

WAPPRIITA: see "Wild Animal and Plant Protection and Regulation of International and Inter-provincial Trade Act"

waste: garbage; thing or substance no longer serving a purpose, or left over after use

water cycle: the flow of water through the Earth and through the atmosphere (see "hydrologic cycle")

watershed: an area drained by a lake or a river and its tributaries

water spout: a tornado occurring over a body of water

weather: condition of the atmosphere at any given time. Weather includes temperature, precipitation, air pressure, humidity, cloud cover, and winds.

weathering: breakdown of rocks and minerals into small particles by physical disintegration and/or chemical decomposition

wetlands: areas where the water table occurs at or near the surface most of the year

wheat: a highly nutritious cereal plant

Wild Animal and Plant Protection and Regulation of International and Inter-provincial Trade Act (WAPPRIITA): a law protecting Canadian and foreign species from illegal trade. It also protects Canadian ecosystems from the introduction of harmful species.

wilderness: an uncultivated and uninhabited tract of land where humans have not taken over

wildlife: collective term for wild animals

windward: side of a landform exposed to the wind

win-win situation: solution that benefits all parties

wind erosion: loss of soil or destruction of landforms caused by wind

World Heritage Site: selected places on the Earth that are protected for the benefit of humans for all times

world reserve: the amount of a material found in the Earth, usually applied to natural resources

Z

zone of ablation: the area where a combination of processes cause a glacier to shrink or melt

zone of accumulation: area of a glacier where snow builds up and turns into ice. The glacier moves outward from this area.

zoning by-laws: laws usually passed by community governments, that control the type and amount of development in an area

ACKNOWLEDGMENTS

The authors and publisher would like to thank the people and organizations listed for providing the illustrative material for this book. Every effort has been made to acknowledge correctly the source of illustrations reproduced in this book. The publisher welcomes any information that will enable him to rectify, in subsequent printings, any errors or omissions that may have been made in giving a credit line.

UNIT 1

1.3.e: 31D/8 © 1985, 6 edition, Produced under licence from Her Majesty the Queen in Right of Canada, with permission of Natural Resources Canada; 1.3.g: Nova Scotia Department of Housing & Municipal Affairs; 1.3.i: 82N/8 © 1996, 7 edition, Produced under licence from Her Majesty the Queen in Right of Canada, with permission of Natural Resources Canada; 1.5.b Courtesy of the Canada Centre for Remote Sensing, Natural Resources Canada; 1.6.h Ernst Haas/Tony Stone Images; 1.10.b Nunavut Tourism; 1.13.c Photographer: Tim Hagen; 1.15.a Collected and edited by Edith Fowke, first published in *The Penguin Book of Canadian Folk Songs*, Fowke, Edith ed. Penguin Books Canada 1973, permission granted by The Writers' Union of Canada; 1.15.b Gift of Dr. and Mrs. J. Murray Speirs, McMichael Canadian Art Collection, 1969.20; 1.15.c Published with permission of the Hugh MacLennan Estate from *Two Solitudes*, published by Macmillan Company of Canada, 1978. First published in 1945; 1.15.d "Not just a platform for my dance" by Marilyn Dumont, published in *A Really Good Brown Girl*, London, ON: Brick Books, 1996; 1.15.e Reprinted with the permission of House of Anansi Press, Toronto, Ontario; 1.15.f Roy Henry Vickers.

UNIT 2

2.1.a Courtesy of EMI Music Canada, photo credit: Jim Allen; 2.1.b Courtesy Ken Suzana; 2.1.d The Toronto *Star*/Russell; 2.1.e Louise Chernetz; 2.1.f Courtesy Ontario Parks—Petroglyphs Provincial Park, photographs by A.Wallace; 2.1.g Courtesy Liz Wright; 2.3.a Photograph courtesy of the Royal Ontario Museum; 2.3.c B.C. Archives, #D-07548; 2.3.d Glenbow Archives, Calgary, #NA-2507-26; 2.4.e RWED, Government of Northwest Territories; 2.5.d B.C. Ministry of Fisheries; 2.6.d Ontario Ministry of Natural Resources; 2.7.b Landsat data Copyright NOAA. Received by Canada Centre for Remote Sensing, Processed and distributed by RADARSAT International. Reproduced with permission of Space Imaging. Image courtesy P. Murtha, Department Forest Resources Management, University of British Columbia; 2.7.c Courtesy Lorraine Gilbert; 2.8.c, 2.8.d and 2.9.c Photobar Agricultural Stock; 2.11.f © 1998 Ontario Tourism; 2.11.g and 2.11.h Permission of Ontario Hydro; 2.11.i The Canadian Press; 2.11.j Ontario Hydro Corporate Archives 91.0167-11; 2.11.k B.C. Hydro Information Services; 2.12.a AXOR; 2.12.c City of Kitchener, photograph by Ovi Colavincenzo; 2.12.d Nova Scotia Power; 2.12.e Public Archives and Records Office of P.E.I., I.I.S. Collection; 2.13.c Jiri Hermann/BHP Diamonds Inc; 2.13.d Aerocamera Services Inc., Grand Valley, ON; 2.13.g Courtesy: Battle Mountain Gold Company; 2.13.h Falconbridge Limited; 2.13.i Courtesy of the Canada Centre for Remote Sensing, Natural Resources Canada; 2.13.j Aur Resources Inc.; 2.14.c *National Post*; 2.14.f. HMDC; 2.14.g Wabash Mines; 2.15.i Copyright Reuters Limited 1998; 2.15.j © 1998 Ontario Tourism.

UNIT 3

Unit opener Douglas Leighton; 3.1.a: 31H/5 © 1988, 9 edition, Produced under licence from Her Majesty the Queen in Right of Canada, with permission of Natural Resources Canada; 3.1.b Aerial photograph A31008-95- 1975. Her Majesty the Queen in Right of Canada, reproduced from the collection of the National Air Photo Library with permission of Natural Resources Canada; 3.1.d: 30M/4 © 1996, 7 edition Produced under licence from Her Majesty the Queen in Right of Canada, with permission of Natural Resources Canada; 3.1.f: 62H © 1994, 6 edition, Produced under licence from Her Majesty the Queen in Right of Canada, with permission of Natural Resources Canada; 3.4.e Gerry Boland Studio, Courtesy of St. John's Port Corporation; 3.4.f: 92G © 1995, 3 edition, Produced under licence from her Majesty the Queen in Right of Canada, with permission of Natural Resources Canada; 3.4.g: 62H/14 © 1987, 4 edition, Produced under licence from Her Majesty the Queen in Right of Canada, with permission of Natural Resources Canada; 3.5.f Bell Canada MultiVisual Productions; 3.6.a Courtesy: Ford of Canada; 3.6.f COMPASS—Ontario Ministry of Transportation; 3.7.a Canadian Broadcasting Corporation; 3.7.c Stamps reproduced courtesy of Canada Post Corporation; 3.7.d Aboriginal Youth Network and Indian and Northern Affairs Canada; 3.8.a Telesat Canada; 3.9.b CORBIS/Roger Ressmeyer; 3.9.d Copyright Reuters Limited 1999. Source: Magellan Systems/NYT Pictures; 3.11.b Douglas Leighton; 3.11.d: 31B5 © 1982 7 edition, Produced under licence from Her Majesty the Queen in Right of Canada, with permission of Natural Resources Canada; 3.11.f Courtesy of Parks and Recreation of the City of Toronto. Gera Dillon; 3.12.d Logo of World Wildlife Fund, WWF; and The Nature Conservancy of Canada, the only national charity dedicated to preserving ecologically significant natural areas, places of special beauty and educational interest, through outright purchase, donations and conservation agreements;

3.12.e Photographer: Shirley Sloat, Images of New Brunswick; 3.13.e Canada Centre for Remote Sensing, Natural Resources Canada; 3.13.g Doug Dealey; 3.13.i. J-P Dumas/PONOPRESSE.

UNIT 4

Unit opener First Light; 4.1.c. Reuters/Mike Blake/Archive Photos; 4.3.b First Light; 4.3.c National Gallery of Canada, Ottawa, Artist: Lawrence Paul Yuxweluptoun; 4.3.d Forest Alliance/COFI; 4.4.c Aerocamera Services Inc., Grand Valley, ON; 4.5.a. Tim Hagen 4.5.c First Light; 4.5.e and 4.5.f Agriculture and Agri Food Canada; 4.8.a Sidney Harris; 4.8.f V. Last, Geographical Visual Aids, Wiarton, ON; 4.9.a, Fact File, and 4.9.e Courtesy of the Aggregate Producers' Association of Ontario; 4.9.b, 4.9.c and 4.9.d Courtesy of the Butchart Gardens; 4.9.f Courtesy of the Ontario Ministry of Natural Resources (M. Browning); 4.10.a Brewster Bus Lines; 4.10.b V. Last, #12711, Geographical Visual Aids, Wiarton, ON; 4.10.c Courtesy of J.D. Taylor; 4.10.e Niagara Escarpment Commmission; 4.10.h Heineman Educational UK/Dr. Peter Furley; 4.11.c Courtesy of Parks and Natural Areas Newfoundland—Ned Pratt

UNIT 5

Unit opener CP Picture Archives/Nick Procaylo; 5.1.a Royal Tyrrell Museum of Palaeontology/Alberta Community Development; 5.1.b Courtesy of Dr. Alan V. Morgan; 5.1.d Canada Centre for Remote Sensing, Natural Resources Canada; 5.3.d CP Picture Archives/Stapelton; 5.3.g Courtesy: Ford of Canada; 5.4.a Courtesy of Frank Parkizgar; 5.4.b. Courtesy of J.D. Taylor; 5.4.c Photo by Thomas Bertelsen for the Rolex Awards; 5.5.b Courtesy of J.D.Taylor; 5.5.c RWED, Government of the Northwest Territories; 5.5.d RWED, Government of the Northwest Territories 5.5.e Photograph by Bruce Leighty; 5.6.d CP Picture Archives/Richard Drew; 5.6.e CP Picture Archives/Nick Procaylo; 5.6.f and 5.6.g Courtesy of Ray Jackson; 5.7.a Copyright Vincenzo Pietropaolo; 5.7.b CP Picture Archives/Tom Hanson; 5.7.c Courtesy of Cheryl Conlon; 5.7.f Copyright Vincenzo Pietropaolo.

UNIT 6

Unit opener Stelco Inc.; 6.2.c Photo by Ronald Maisonneuve, Courtesy of Patheon; 6.3.b Greg Fulmes/Artel Stock Images; 6.3.b Fisheries and Oceans Canada; 6.4.d Economic Development Edmonton; 6.4.e Bombardier, Inc.; 6.5.a (1) Stelco Inc., 6.5.a (2) The Greater Hamilton Photography Contest and Jeff and Mary Hales, 6.5.a (3) Hamilton Economic Development and 6.5.a (4) Victor K. Copps Trade Centre/Arena (Copps Coliseum), Photography by Dennis R. McGreal; 6.7.d (1) West Edmonton Mall; 6.7.d. (2) City of Toronto; 6.7.d. (3) City of Toronto; 6.7.g Foto Flight Surveys Ltd., Calgary, AB; 6.7.h From *The Maritime Provinces Atlas, New Updated Edition*, by Robert J. McCalla, Cartographers Dawn Allen and Peggy McCalla, Revised Edition Copyright © 1991. Contents Copyright© 1988, Maritext Publishing, Halifax 1991; 6.8.a From *Safe Seasons Calendar*, Childhood and Youth Division, Health Canada. Reproduced with permission of the Minister of Public Works and Government Services Canada 1999; 6.9.d. Courtesy of The Food Bank of Waterloo Region, Kitchener, Ontario; 6.9.f Photographer Ivaan Kotulsky; 6.10.a Union Station; 6.10.b The Toronto Harbour Commission Archives PC14/1804; 6.10.d City of Toronto Land Information Services 98/04/18.

UNIT 7

Unit opener Mary Card; 7.1.c Mary Card; 7.1.e Caribbean Cultural Committee/Caribana TM Photograph by David Griffith; 7.2.a Mary Card; 7.4.b First Light; 7.4.f Credit: Department of National Defence ILC78-209; 7.4.i Mr.Glen Carroll/Department of National Defence IEC96-659-15; 7.4.l Courtesy of the Arctic Winter Games International Committee; 7.5.k Prime Minister's Office photo; 7.6.g Jocelin d'Entremont Ship to Shore Photography; 7.7.a CP Picture Archive (Fred Chartrand); 7.8.d Whistler Resort Association; 7.9.a Canadian Olympic Association; 7.9.c Courtesy of the Arctic Winter Games International Committee; 7.10.b Department of National Defence IXC88-341; 7.10.d Department of National Defence IEC95-533-1; 7.10.f Department of National Defence ISC97-05-28; 7.10.g Department of National Defence ISC92-5873; 7.12.a CIDA Photo: Bruce Paton; 7.12.c Department of National Defence RED98-292-09; 7.12.d CIDA Photo: David Trattles.

UNIT 8

Unit opener CP Archives; 8.5.d Terra Surveys Limited; 8.6.c Health Canada; 8.6.e Cancom; 8.6.e D.W. Larson: Cliff Ecology Research Group, University of Guelph; 8.6.e Courtesy of Canadian Airlines; 8.7.a Health Canada.

INDEX